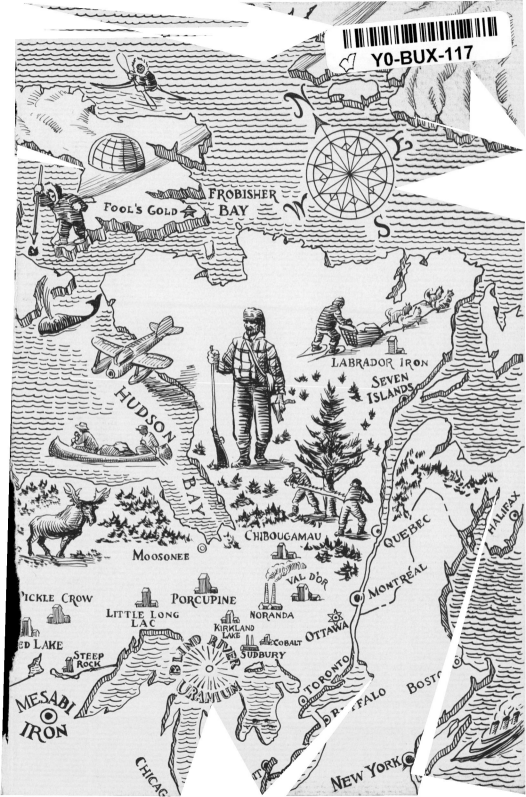

FREE GOLD

ARNOLD HOFFMAN

FREE GOLD

The Story of
Canadian Mining

by ARNOLD HOFFMAN

Illustrated by IRWIN D. HOFFMAN

ASSOCIATED BOOK SERVICE · NEW YORK

SECOND PRINTING, 1958

Foreword

To write a book on Canadian mining requires industry. To include, also, the history of the various mining camps requires no little temerity, for all of them abound with contention and controversy regarding priority of discovery. Many of the prospectors and promoters who were the chief actors in the drama of ore search and mine development are now dead, and with the passage of time versions of their activities have become hazy and moot. The traditional stories of discovery are given here, together with fresh material which has never yet been published. The reader who is interested in the large picture of the rise and growth of a mighty industry will find the principal elements in *Free Gold,* and that, I believe, is all that may be expected in a work of this scope.

The human side of mining has been stressed throughout. To my knowledge, the success of any camp has hinged upon one or more dominating personalities, without whom the northward march would have been halting and uncertain.

While I have naturally drawn heavily from my own experience, early history has necessarily been derived from the patient accumulations of Canadian scholars, the excellent and prolific Dominion and Provincial reports and bulletins, and the daily press. Old files of the *Northern Miner* have been invaluable. For current history, acknowledgments would be a formidable task indeed, since this would require listing friendships and associations embracing a quarter of a century.

I have long been convinced that we in the United States are astonishingly uninformed, even misinformed, concerning our virile northern neighbor. If this book contributes, however modestly, toward a better understanding of Canada, then I shall feel that my labors have not been in vain.

Arnold Hoffman

Cavendish, Vermont
September, 1946

TO

My Mother

The Biggest Bonanza of Them All

Table of Contents

FREE GOLD

Johnny Dillon Speakin'

Big Johnny Dillon eased into his leather swivel chair and swung his feet onto the shining desktop. Eyes half closed behind tortoise-shell glasses, he sighed voluptuously and rubbed his paunch with obvious satisfaction.

"Yeah, laddie," he smiled, showing an expanse of gold teeth, "I'm what you call a ruttin' minin' maggot now."

A bell tinkled thinly. His body otherwise unmoving, Johnny reached out with one long leg and by a series of delicate jabs nursed the telephone within reach. At the same time he rolled his cigar so that the talking end of his mouth was directed at the receiver.

"Johnny Dillon speakin'," he announced crisply, and then, with a quick wink at me, added, " 'n person."

He listened impatiently, barked, "On the nose, Twinkletoes, haff a million shares. That's right, five hun'red thousan'. . . . What's 'at? Give *you* a hun'red thous' at fifty? Why, you little, no-good, sonuva . . ." and his voice droned into a singsong of vituperation, punctuated by a final crash as he slammed the receiver in place.

"Chiseler," he gritted. "Wants a hun'red Vega at fifty when the market's sixty-five—real market, too. Gawd-damn Englishman, 'at's what he is!"

With neat accuracy, he expectorated into the wastepaper basket without removing the cigar, an accomplishment which, among others, had long ago earned him a juicy reputation in the North Country.

"Yeah—" he grinned goldenly—"the lads is all after me these

3

days for cheap stock. But all the cheap stock goes to a man by the name o' Johnny Dillon. By Gawd, I earned it!"

I nodded; he had, indeed.

"You oughter know," he said, "you've traveled the bush.[1] It's an easy game, ain't it, fightin' flies an' hummin'birds, an' windfall, an' muskeg an' takin' them long portages. Not to say snowshoein' around breakup time. Jeez!" His eyes narrowed, as if in pain. "That spring of the Rouyn rush was a nice picnic in the woods, wassen it? In nineteen and twen'y-three, March. Kin you ever forget that old stopping place, Bushee and Geneau's, where we all got lousy and doused ourself with kerosene? An' freeze an' thaw, it was, day after day, till we diden know whether to use snowshoes or water wings. Sure, yeah, an' to make life more interestin' I had to go through the rotten ice at Pelletier Creek." He winced and repeated, "Through the ice. Your big brother pulled me out, yeah; the first time a Hawva'd man rescued a broken-down Mick prospector in northern Quebec. Great lad, that. Say, what's he doin' now?" Not pausing for an answer, he rushed on. "Hope he ain't towned yet like most of 'em. Had some great talks with 'im that time goin' in from Larder Lake. An' the other lads, too, Ike Waite, Bobby Cockeram, Dan Willans— poor old Dan, he's dead now—an' Freddy Thompson; they was all in the party. That was most of the rush, just a handful of us along with the Gambles, the McDonoughs, Bert McDonald an' a few others. The papers played it up like they was an army in there. You know how it is. Well, sir, we scattered, staked our groun', prospected an' waited for the boom. You was in there the summer of 'twenty- three; you remember, doncha?"

Yes, Johnny, I remember.

"Gawd, we was broke in them days, flatter'n beer on a plate. An' them fancy ingineers diden help none, I kin tell you. Turned down Noranda cold, all of 'em. Damn fools, with their notebooks an' college degrees. Why, since then Noranda's paid a hun'red seven million in dividends an' still goin' strong, but in them days the smart money listened to the paper boys who do their minin' outer books. Sure, your brother was different, he liked Noranda, but don't forget he was one of us with lots of ground in the area. He *had* to like Noranda." Johnny waved my protests aside. "Yeah, I know he really liked it. So what? He diden have a nickel behind him—too young to cut any ice with the stuffed shirts. Y'know, laddie, money's a cowardly thing, cowardly as hell. Needs lots of urgin', like some women. One time I read a book up in Red Lake. I think it was written by Mark Twain. Anyway, I ain't ever forgot it. He says people

[1] See Glossary at end of book for this and other mining and colloquial terms.

everywhere kin never get together on what to worship—Gawd, power, whisky, women or what have you. Exceptin' one thing they all agree on"—and here Johnny finally removed his cigar and waved it for emphasis—"an' that's money. Yes, sir, money. Black, white, red or yellow, they *all* worship that. So it's a big job to separate any from 'em. Why, if it wassen for Noah Timmins, good old Noah, the Noranda'd still be moose pasture. Yeah, sure. He got the Hollinger to put up the money for the smelter after that pig rutter of an ingineer from Noo Yawk—you oughter remember, it was you lads that had 'im sent up from the American Metal Company—said he wooden spit on the Noranda, or was it somethin' else? Not enough ore, he says, to put in your hat. Well, sir," and Johnny flashed his golden smile, "old Noah comes back an' says he'd build a thousand-ton smelter; there'd be enough ore. An' the old boy did and they was —all kinds of ore. She's shovin' out five thousand tons a day, more'n them bright lads in Noo Yawk with their fat heads and bellies ever see. Thirty million tons has come out of that hole since nineteen and twenty-seven when the smelter blew in an' there's twen'y million more all blocked out with a red ribbon aroun' it waitin' to be taken out. Hell, she'll be goin' long after we're pushin' up daisies. Noo Yawk!" He spat derisively.

"Yeah," he continued, after a brief interval, "we come a long way since them days, laddie. Takes a spot o' time to learn this minin' game. It ain't like these buzzards on Bay Street thinks—I jest diden set up shop like a bartender an' rake in the dough. I worked hard, it was tough—you see—" And garrulous Johnny, wonderful to relate, was at a loss for words.

"You had to serve a long apprenticeship?" I suggested.

"Ain't nothin' like a college eddjication!" he beamed. " 'At's the word, apprenticeship. Lots o' water over the dam before you graduate from bannock an' beans to whisky, beefsteak an' ten-cent cigars."

While Johnny continued to ruminate about the "early days" and relive the hardships of various mining camps, I pictured him when we first met in Rouyn the summer of 1923. Noranda Mines, or the Horne as it was then called in honor of the discoverer, was a mere prospect, consisting of only a cabin or two for a modest working force. The few hardy inhabitants of the area dwelt in Rouyn, across the lake, amid a virgin stand of pine, poplar and birch. Jimmy Green, half Indian, had constructed the first hostelry from the abundant timber, and there we often congregated after calling for mail and supplies at Dumulon's General Store and Post Office, one of the few other log structures in the settlement.

As I entered the hotel, Johnny was seated at a table paying off a crew of men who had just completed assessment work at Clericy Lake. Before him was a large scattered pile of currency and he laboriously consulted his time book and called out names.

"Paagen."

One of the men shuffled forward sullenly.

"Here, you no-good bastard, sign this," and Johnny opened a soiled receipt book. The man hesitated.

Jimmy Green stood on his toes and whispered in my ear. There had been trouble, apparently; the crew insisted upon being paid for Sundays. Only a moment before, Johnny, who had contracted to perform the work for a mining company and was thus limited in the amount he could dispense if he expected to retain some balance for his own efforts, had laid down the law with characteristic bluntness. There would be no pay for Sundays. Damned ungrateful lads! Hadn't he hired them at good rates when work in the district was scarce? Yeah! Why, he had even packed grub to the camp himself—fresh cabbage too, and lemons. The real stuff, not extracts, by Gawd! And lots of pancakes and corn syrup and bread like mamma used to bake. Everything but fingerbowls and cigars after meals. And for all that they now were whining about being paid for Sundays they didn't work! Well, there ain't no such thing, so come on, line up, quit this frigging around. Sign the receipts, take your money and beat it!

Paagen looked toward his companions uncertainly. They stood in a compact mass, expressionless, like graven river-gods, showing little sign of interest. As for Johnny, he rolled his cigar pugnaciously and spat. Paagen edged forward. We all watched, tingling with suspense. Would Johnny prevail or would the boys rush him and start a free-for-all, the usual denouement of Rouyn's social and economic problems?

With rapierlike swiftness, Johnny's arm shot under the table. Instantly, the atmosphere became electric. This was it! Already the more timid spectators edged toward the door, ready to escape when the fracas commenced. And then Johnny's arm emerged, his hand clutching nothing more harmful than a bottle of whisky.

"Here, have a drink," said he, handing the crock to Paagen.

The man's face wrinkled into an astonished grin. In a twinkling, the bottle pointed roofward and Paagen gurgled musically.

" 'At's enough," grunted Johnny; "leave some for the other lads," and after a short but friendly tussle he recaptured the whisky.

Paagen signed his receipt and was given a wad of bills. Immediately his friends swarmed forward, eyes shining. The bottle was passed about swiftly and dumped to the log floor—a thoroughly dead soldier. Voices rose in song—"Oh, Mrs. Jones, I love your daughter . . ." Then the door was flung open and out streamed Johnny's former workers, laden with cash. The girls and blind piggers would have a busy evening!

Oblivious to their noisy departure, Johnny deftly gathered the remainder of his treasury, thrust the receipt book in his pocket, and yawned. Just at that instant I caught his eye.

"Say!" he rose and faced me. "Ain't you Bob's brother?"

I nodded.

"Put 'er there." He wrung my hand. "Look somethin' like 'im, on'y taller. Well, laddie, Bob's up in Duprat with Freddy Thompson, wildcattin' as usual. Told me you was due here soon. You're stayin' with me till the lads is back. I'm to take care of you, see?" He slapped my back and winked. Apparently, friendships were quick and demonstrative in Rouyn. "C'mon, now, we'll have a spot o' celebration an' the right kinder liquid up to Klondike Jessie's."

We walked into the fullness of a Quebec afternoon. The deep heady odor of bush, flavored with the smoke of wood fires, greeted us while mosquitoes and black flies rose in swarms.

"Gawd-damned hummin'birds!" sputtered Johnny, his hands busy.

The clearing before us had been churned into a fine mud over which crude plank catwalks had been built. These were only about two feet wide, and it was commonplace to see pedestrians—inebriety being an almost normal condition in Rouyn—lose their balance and pitch headlong into the loon dung. Accordingly, we stepped along gingerly, avoiding damaged boards and halting whenever the catwalk swayed suggestively. Johnny, an expert in such travel, led the way. He steered for higher ground where Klondike Jessie cheerfully operated her blind pig. I had heard much about this three hundred pound Amazon who dispensed brew and cracked the skulls of unruly clients with equal facility. I eagerly anticipated our meeting. Her shack, distinguished by a porch and windows decorated with curtains—a curious feminine touch in so male a community—stood boldly on an outcrop of what government geologists described as andesite. It was rare to find rock in northern Quebec, or, for that matter, relief of any kind. The land was a near-perfect peneplain, monotonously eroded; low, rolling, studded with impenetrable bush, cut by lakes, rivers and regional muskegs. I had well understood the incredulity and contempt of a famous American geologist who had been among my fellow travelers on the "Road to Ruin," as the wags had it.

We had taken the battered alligator at Angliers, the end of steel, and pursued a stately course into the arms of Lac Quinze, across the head of Lac Expanse, and thence into the Ottawa. It was a rainy day and the bush stood on the shores like a gloomy sentinel, hemming us in on all sides. Costello, leaning on the rail beside me, snorted.

"This isn't a mining country! Why, you can't even see rock, let alone mineral! And these Christly bugs!" He rubbed his neck and left a bloody smudge where the flies had been busy. "Can't understand why the head office sent me to this miserable place."

We docked at Gendreau's Portage, spent the night in shacks provided with leaky fly nets, and in the morning resumed our voyage at the north end of Sturgeon Rapids, just below the confluence of the Kinojevis River which meandered into Rouyn. This time we transferred into a small cramped motor launch and Costello became more lugubrious than ever. His report on Noranda was already formulated, even before he had seen the property, and it was, of course, a negative one.

"There just can't be a mine in this country," he argued, to reassure himself. "Everything's wrong: no rocks, no carbonates, no gossan, no hills or mountains. Nothing but this hellish bush, as you call it, and flies and mud. Lord!"

He was not a happy man, I recalled, and in view of what happened, not a very bright one. For the area we traveled in those few memorable days is now one of the notable mining camps of the world, with an annual gold production of $40,000,000 and still growing, and several thriving towns boasting more than 50,000 inhabitants. And, as Johnny and I progressed toward Klondike Jessie's, I kept thinking of Costello and I have thought of him many times since. He was a part of *my* apprenticeship.

Johnny Dillon aroused me with a hearty thump in the ribs, pointed a thick finger toward the Pelletier Portage.

"Be Gawd damned if that ain't ole Noah Timmins himself!"

Two men trekked toward Jimmy Green's Hotel. Noah Timmins —it could be none other—strode before his young companion, who was bent under an enormous packsack. The great man was deep in thought even as he lifted his short legs over the mud. Unbelieving, I watched. So this was the fabulous Noah Timmins, already a legend in the North Country, this awkward rotund figure with narrow sloping shoulders who deigned to travel the bush like an ordinary mortal.

It was difficult at that moment to accept the fact that this bush-whacker in a soiled fly-stained shirt had himself financed and developed the great Hollinger Gold Mine and played so vital a part in the growth and success of Porcupine. This story, how he had left his general store in Mattawa and plunged into the maelstrom of Cobalt when the first silver was discovered in 1905, was an epic of the country. Not content with beginner's luck, Timmins, against the advice of wiser men, purchased claims in the newly discovered Porcupine gold area and welded them into the Hollinger, the crown jewel of gold mines. Luck or insight, who could say? Most men safe in harbor and receiving millions in dividends each year would have long ago retired to a life of well-earned comfort, but the "Grand Old Man of Canadian Mining," despite his years, still ventured into that hazardous sea. Now he was mothering the infant Noranda, deaf, as of old, to the protests and crape-hanging of hard-bitten experts.

"I'll introduce you!" bellowed Johnny, wheeling in his tracks. I followed him with some hesitation; surely my new friend did not know Timmins that well! But there was Johnny pumping the great man's hand as he had mine, then relieving Noah's companion of his packsack.

"Meet Noah Timmins!"

The sandy-complexioned man looked down at me. Sensing my awe, his eyes twinkled for an instant.

"All the way from the States," explained Johnny, "still goin' to college."

"Good, good." Despite a slight impediment, the voice was pleasant. "Come back again and stay with the country. It will be good to you."

He smiled, but I could see that his thoughts were far away, probably across the lake where the fate of a mine awaited his judgment.

I was introduced to Alphonse Paré, his nephew, a mining engineer who, I was informed later, was among his advisers.

Johnny skillfully led the conversation to the matter of his own mining claims.

"Alphonse will discuss that later," said Noah absently, and with that, and a brief farewell, the two left us. Johnny shrugged his shoulders and grimaced.

"Too much on his mind these days. Well, sir," Johnny said, brightening, "you kin now tell your grandchildren you met the great Noah Timmins."

Thanking him warmly for this, I mentioned Klondike Jessie. Johnny needed no urging, and once more we negotiated the uncertain catwalk to the comparative safety of higher ground.

Klondike, whose activities were largely confined to evening hours, was surprised to see us so early. We found her standing on the porch, quite filling it with her enormous bulk and completely obscuring the door behind her. Having been told of her weight, I was surprised to find she was hardly more than five feet tall, and this gave her the appearance of some prehistoric monster which had

somehow survived. Johnny had likened her figure to a sack full of moose horns, but a sack full of pumpkins would have been a more appropriate description. Clothed in a gingham dress which gave the impression of having been forced over her like skin on a giant sausage, she was truly enormous. Arms akimbo, feet bare, she regarded us with tiny piglike eyes, shrewd, all-seeing.

"Robbin' the cradle, Johnny?" she asked, nodding toward me. From somewhere within that Gargantuan frame she chuckled. The sound was akin to the rumble of a distant gas engine.

"He's over eighteen, free an' white, you ole sea pig," retorted Johnny. Roguishly he attempted to slip his hand into the ramifications of her bosom. For this he received a resounding slap, but he continued to smile good-naturedly.

"Told you, laddie, she's quicker'n a cat for all 'at blubber."

"None o' that," gritted Klondike ominously, her voice a deep husky rumble. "Know what I done to the Rainbow Kid when he got too fresh, doncha?" Suddenly, to me, "Right in, son, and rest ya weary arse."

With a rolling twist, Klondike squeezed across the threshold, turned and beckoned us to enter. Stepping forward, I could see at once that she had not made any heavy capital outlay in furnishing her establishment. Beside the inevitable tin stove there stood a single table with three or four lopsided stools ringing it. She sat down heavily, first noting that the legs of her seat rested firmly on the floor logs. We pulled up on each side of her.

"What'll it be?" she asked, all business now.

"The usual." Johnny's grin, those days, was more in the line of porcelain. "Lake water, needled."

"Now doncha go givin' this here lad wrong idees," she growled, reaching toward an empty bottle on the table.

"Take 'er easy, Klondike, take 'er easy." Johnny was genuinely worried, for Klondike suffered from no inhibitions and her aim was deadly. "I says beer, diden I?" he appealed to me.

"I thought you did," I said.

"Okay." Klondike's eyes disappeared in a friendly smile. "Two beers comin' up."

Gasping with the effort, she managed to bend down and raise a loosened floor log. From a hidden recess she extracted several dirty bottles of assorted sizes and shapes and these she deposited before us with a flourish, then wiped them carelessly with the hem of her dress.

"There's service for you," said Johnny admiringly, while he offered me a bottle and helped himself to the largest. Pronouncing a toast which Klondike enthusiastically joined while removing the cork stoppers, he lifted the bottle and drank greedily. Not until he sighed and slapped his belly in satisfaction did I venture to drink. . . .

"But you ain't listenin' to what I say!" Johnny's voice, re-
proachful, cut into the haze of the past.

The office suddenly assumed shape and I found myself apologiz-
ing for being inattentive.

"You was smilin' jest now," said Johnny. "What in hell was you
thinkin' about?"

I told him, briefly.

"Oh, Klondike Jessie," and he too smiled. "Good ole Klondike.
Wassen she a moose, though?" Memories flooded his speech. " 'At
day in her shack an' the round of beer we had. Never forget the
expression on your face, laddie, when you swallered the stuff." He
cackled happily. "You looked surprised at first an' then hurt, as
though I'd led you into a poison trap or somethin'. But you come
out of it, I remember; green around the gills, but game. Polished
off the rest o' the crock."

Thereby I had won Klondike's lasting respect and admiration.
And what had become of her through the years? I wondered.

"Dead. Yeah, nine or ten years ago, up at the Pas." Johnny
nodded. "I was there. We give 'er a first-class fun'ral, the best. Poor
ole Klondike, she was the prospector's friend." If possible, he was
becoming sentimental, unmindful of the many crocks Jessie had
broken on his head. "Jeez, but she was big, wassen she? When Jack
Canty come after 'er with an ax that time—he diden have no
gun—'cause she did a spot o' pimpin' for his girl while he was out
in the bush, well, sir, Klondike slams the door in his face, jest in
time. An' while he's out in front hackin' away at the door, she tries
to climb out through the back winder. But she carried too much
lard for that, got stuck haffway, her bow outside an' her stern inside.
Hung up, like. Ha!" he bellowed uproariously. "The door's almost
gone an' she's ready for the carvin'." Jack sees her fanny waitin' an'
works like mad. Guess he overdid it, 'cause Jessie is real scared now
an' gives one helluva push an' down comes the back wall o' the
cabin! Jack hears the noise an' thinks the whole shack's fallin' down
on 'im, so he beats it for Christ's sake. So, Klondike got off with 'er
skin still whole but a bit bruised, you might say. Oh, them was the
happy days, laddie."

Want to go back, Johnny? No, no, but it's pleasant, very pleasant to sit and reminisce. Klondike Jessie, now, you didn't meet her
kind in Toronto or New York.

"We had some great talks in her place after a few o' them
beers, diden we? Discussin' our ambitions, what we'd do if we made
a big stake, remember?"

I do. Your ambition, Johnny, was to remain in Rouyn and

watch it mushroom into a town and the town blossom into a city. And it has happened, too, within our lifetime. When you go there today, amid the restless traffic and the bustle of a young northern city, the townies point you out—one of the old-timers who has returned to roost. And they've named a street in your honor—not much of a thoroughfare; on the fringe of things to be sure—but it is enough; you are immortalized in Rouyn.

"They burned her shack." Johnny persisted in completing the saga of Klondike Jessie. "Right down to the groun'. Even the bottles was melted. Them bootleggers 'at come into the camp later wassen like the early bunch. Scum o' the earth, they was. Diden like the idee of us goin' to Klondike for our beer all the time, so they pour gasoline on 'er cabin, burn it up. She lost whatever she had. Yeah. 'Member the c'llection we made to give 'er a road stake? Well, sir, it diden do much good, she on'y got as far as Duprat Creek an' then the Mounties chased 'er out o' the country. Not much luck after that, poor ole Klondike. She followed the lads to some o' the new camps but the airplane was makin' things too damn civilized for her line o' business. Jest about busted at the Pas, she was, but still hog fat as ever when she kicked off."

Klondike Jessie finally disposed of, we reviewed the intervening years in the north, the moving from one province to another upon reports of new gold discoveries. For Johnny, particularly, the years were not kind. Tiring of Quebec and growing restless, he journeyed to Manitoba and acquired several groups of claims near the Sherritt Gordon Mine, a promising base metal property, only to watch the crash of 1929 destroy his hopes. Before that he had participated in the Red Lake rush, but following the initial Howey discovery, interest in that field waned, and Johnny, with many others, allowed his claims to revert to the crown.

"So I come back to Quebec after battin' round ten years or so," he informed me. "Might as well, I figgered; knew the country best an' had faith in it. Besides I begin to realize the on'y way to beat the game is to hunt in elephant country where they's a big mine or two. When a new find is made the lads think it's another Noranda an' the fun begins—the ole camp is havin' another boom, y'know, a kind o' secon' childhood. Annyways, I diden lose no time, laddie, not I. While the other lads is sittin' an' waitin' I go out an' grab all the open groun' along the belt I kin, Boischatel, Duprat, Rouyn, Joannes, an' Bourlamaque. It was hell payin' taxes an' cursin' in the work but I managed all right. By 'thirty-nine I had me financin' lined up an' the companies is formed. An' then what happened? 'At lavatory rat Hitler come along an' says Boo! an' the British gets scared an' the bottom drops outer the minin' business. Yeah, sure, you kin thank the Englishmen for the war; they coulda stepped on that worm a hun'red times before he growed into a snake but they was too busy fryin' other fishes."

"Weren't we all at fault, Johnny?"

"No, sir, we wassen!" roared he. "We should keep outer them messes in Europe—England's supposed to take care o' that kind o' thing for us. But they diden an' see what happened! Oh, well, annyways," quieting, "I had to find a job, me, Johnny Dillon, the best damn prospector in the North. Too old for the mines, they says, so I come down below to Toronter and get me some work in a factory; defense job, it was called. Gawd, slavin' indoors like a coolie for $250 a month with them income taxes bitin' out a good chunk!"

"But how did the Vega and Rondo happen?" I interrupted.

"Comin' to it." He lit a fresh cigar with a happy motion. "Comin' to it, laddie. Well, sir, you wassen here durin' the war when most of the lads is overseas. The gover'ment protected 'em on minin' claims; servicemen diden have to do no assessment work or pay taxes to hold their groun'. That tied up a lot o' country but jest the same they was still plenty o' stuff comin' open all the time. Y'know how them things is, everyone gets discouraged an' thinks the world is comin' to an end, so what's the use of hangin' on to some muskeg? We see it happen in the last war an' durin' the depression. No, sir, the early bird don't get the worm in the minin', the worms get him!"

"Pioneering don't pay?" I suggested, quoting Andy Carnegie.

"Somethin' like that." Johnny nodded. "It's the lads which come along after we start a camp who gets the big stuff. But I decide I'm goin' to get in there late as well as early. The time to stake is when the lads is discouraged, but what kin I do? I'm eatin' up me salary an' kin hardly pay for miners' licenses, let alone grubstakes an' all. So I speak to some of me chums in the factory about formin' a syndicate to back me, but they laughed, thought it was a great joke. Says they diden know much about minin' but knew enough to keep to hell outer it, an' more such wisecracks. I'm gettin' desperate. I see by the maps they's all kinds o' groun' open along the belt, but what good is it to me if I can't stake it? Them claims'd be worth a fortune in a few years, I knew, but all I kin do is think about it. It fair drove me crazy. After all them years of waitin' for jest such a chance I'm up the creek without a paddle. Sure, I thought of you, but I meet Alec Mosher on the street an' he tells me you're out west in the desert, minin' some hush-hush mineral to provide the U.S. Navy with a fancy new gunsight. I figgered you was too busy winnin' the war to help me, an' annyways the time is gettin' too short to write."

"What happened finally?" I asked.

"A bit o' luck which has been a stranger to me since Cobalt in 1904. Not that it'd've done annyone elset much good," he hastened to add proudly. "One o' me old wildcat companies in Bourlamaque has a directors' meetin', so I takes off the afternoon from the factory an' joins me fellow directors. Nothin' important, routine I believe the lawyer called it, but Joe Adler from Noo Yawk was there—you know 'im, his old man made a stake in Porcupine long ago—an' gets to talkin' with 'im. He likes my idee of stakin' claims in Quebec an' says, 'Okay, Johnny, hop to it, you get someone to do the stakin' an' I'll provide the money.' An' I says, 'Get someone to stake! Are you kiddin'? What's wrong with me?' an' he says, 'Ain't you too old, Johnny?'

"Too old," repeated Johnny. "Kin you beat it?"

The mere recollection of Adler's remark, suggesting that Johnny was a has-been, was a painful one. Hire a man to stake for him, indeed! Johnny's face became grim.

"Yeah, 'at's what he says an' the deal almost bust up right there. I tells him I'm the one to do the stakin'; when the time comes I have to depend on payin' men to do my work for me, why, I'm through with the minin' business. Well, sir, he calms me down an' apologizes an' then we get talkin' turkey about money an' interest. An' what do you think?"

"What, Johnny?"

"He says to write me own ticket!" The golden smile was wider than ever. "Yeah, sure. Now I like that way of doin' things, especially comin' from a Noo Yawker. So, quick as a trout, I says to 'im it's a deal, shake hands on it, we'll go fifty-fifty—my time against his money. An' Joe says, 'Fair enough.' They was no more shootin' the breeze after that. He sits down an' writes me a check for a thousand.

"Well, sir, nex' day I'm on the Northland headin' for Rouyn, it all happened that fast. First thing I done when I arrive is to spend plenty o' time at the recorder's office goin' over the claim maps. So far I'm all right—most o' the groun' I want is still open. I diden wait a minute, no, sir; bought me grub, strapped on me snowshoes an' headed for the Bend o' the Kinojevis. Rough goin' it was, too. Snow fine an' the glass thirty-five below."

"Why didn't you take the stage from Rouyn to the Bend?" I asked.

"An' have a dozen lads follerin' me?" Johnny snorted. "When

I come to town they know somethin' is cookin'! No, sir, I took to the bush fast as I kin. Annyways, I slept in a settler's shack that night—nothin' like the old days when we had to dig a hole in the snow, eh, laddie? Had a good rest an' bright an' early in the mornin' I'm away. First thing I knew I meet a couple o' lads from Amos. They was out for a syndicate, stakin' like me, an' I guess they're interested in the same ground I am. Y'know how cozy I can be when I have to. Tell 'em I'm jest scoutin' aroun', lookin' the country over, an' all that bilge, but I kin see they're plenty suspicious. Be careful, I says to meself, be careful, Johnny; they's two o' them an' they kin stake faster'n you. So I invites 'em to a spot o' tea, very friendly." He chuckled. "They open up after a few shanty tins o' Lipton an' tells me they coulden find no claim lines an' posts —the settlers has blazed new lines all over the country. Well, sir, you know I been all over Joannes since nineteen and twenty-three an' I figger if annyone kin find lines ole Johnny's the boy to do it. So I slipped away very nonchalong. They follered me, all right, but up whips a blizzard an' I lose 'em in the snow.

"They's lines everywhere, but none leads to posts. But I keep lookin' and sure enough I bump into a Concession line. Right in a burn, it was, near the ole Teck-Hughes camp. Diden lose no time after that, I kin tell you. Three days it took me, campin' in the snow an' up before the sun. Snowshoed to the Bend, then, and caught the bus into Rouyn. When I get to the recorder's office I see them Amos lads whisperin' an' connivin' together. An' what do you think? Why, they're goin' to record the claims I jest staked! Raise hell? Say, I went wild. The recorder comes in an' listens to us awhile. Fin'lly he says to me, 'File your application to record, Mr. Dillon, an' also a affydavit that you staked on such an' such a day.' Then he says the same to the other lads but they scared off when they knew they'd have to sign one o' them affydavits. They pulls out after talkin' about retainin' a lawyer but I never heard nothin' from them. Guess they learned who I was an' diden want to tangle with me," said Johnny quietly.

"So that's how you got the Vega," I said.

"No, that ain't the whole story." Johnny shook his head. "There's more to it. At the hotel that same night I was readin' the latest gover'ment reports an' I see where the Bouzan Lake Fault cuts 'cross country jest south of my group. I decide we need protection to the south. I know them maps ain't exact—too much muskeg to foller the break on surface—but I'm not takin' no chances this stage o' the game. Well, sir, it diden take me long to discover who owned them south claims: a French settler, it was, who done some stakin' near his farm. So I'm in his shack the follerin' day with five hundred in a roll o' one-dollar bills. I don't speak the lingo, y'know, but the money did the talkin' for me. On'y a down payment it was, but it did the trick.

"Well, sir," he resumed, breathing happily, "I done more stakin' an' made a couple down payments on whatever stuff I coulden peg. Adler was okay. Whenever I writes for more money he sends it, by wire too. Pretty soon we're nicely located along the belt an' then we set back to wait. By that time you coulden stick a knife blade annywhere in Quebec that wassen staked; we just come in under the wire. Like I knew it would, the war looks better ev'ry day. Then comes the Donalda drillin' nex' to Noranda an' overnight the public learns they's mines to be had. Deals is made like confettii comin' on New Year's. We was in the thick o' things, you kin bet. We wind up with a canoe full o' vendor stock, a nice chunk o' cash an' all our companies financed for drillin'. But the real fun begins when we hit the first ore on the Vega. Think of it, laddie, in the brown o' the muskeg, right under your old trail where we all portaged hun'reds o' times. Not a rock outcrop in miles. Structural bet, the geologists called it, but it took a Johnny Dillon to change a theory into a mine. Yeah, sure. An' since the first good hole we hit ore in so many places she must look like Swiss cheese undergroun'. Ev'ryone wants stock. Fine. They know where they kin get it—on the Stock Exchange."

He rose and stretched noisily.

"And the Rondo, was that some of your staking too?" I inquired, rising with him.

"Nope." I helped him into an expensive Chesterfield. "Threw the Rondo together—old properties sittin' idle for twen'y years." Once more the golden grin. "Don't have to stake no more, laddie; people is jest fallin' all over themselves to deal with me. Johnny Dillon's got the touch of Jesus, they say. All I do now is give the nod an' things happen. Yeah, sure. The Rondo was a cinch. Told the claim owners I was formin' a company an' they could have stock for their groun'. One of 'em wanted some cash but that diden stop me. All right, I says to 'im, we'll buy some pooled vendor stock at a price. He jumped at the idee. You see, I know all the tricks, laddie. So the company's formed, the claim owners get stock for their groun' an' I get stock for"—here he paused and winked facetiously—"for services. I think 'at's the word. Annyways, they make me president an' I lay out a plan of drillin'. First few holes diden click, so I move the rig north, above the fault. An' did we find ore then?" He waved a copy of the *Northern Miner* at me. "Jest read the feature article in this week's issue—Rondo's all over the sheets. Two mines, laddie, two mines, an' more comin' up!" His exuberance flared for a moment, and then he became sober. "Happened all of a sudden, diden it, sure, but they's the other side of the picture too. Nearly forty years of . . . of *apprenticeship.*"

We walked to the elevator.

"All these things is interestin'," confided Johnny, "but the trouble is not many people knows about 'em. Now, if I had any eddjication, I'd write a story about Canadian minin', how it begin an' how it grew an' what it takes to make mines."

We stopped at the sidewalk, shook hands, and prepared to go our different ways.

"Yes, sir, it's about time the real story is told, before us ole-timers is gone an' it's too late." He slapped my back heartily. "An' you're the one to do it. Yeah, sure. Get busy, laddie, an' don't you forget to tell 'em all about Johnny Dillon!"

With a final golden smile, he hurried toward Bay Street.

CHAPTER II

Meet the Boys

My brother Bob and I are a couple of prospectors who received bush training on the streets of East Boston, bordering the railroad tracks. We are not unique in this respect, for some of the best woodsmen in the field were born in large cities. But it is a far cry from a tough urban neighborhood in Massachusetts to the shores of Hudson Bay. To understand how such a transition was possible, some biographical material is necessary.

Our parents were immigrants who settled where they disembarked, in the land of the bean and the cod. Boston is known for its Brahmins, Christian Science, museums, and educational institutions. Less known are the dreary suburbs, somewhat enlivened by the offspring of sturdy and spirited Europeans who fled their native lands to escape persecution and economic depression. In such a typical melting pot of the Promised Land, we were born and reared. There were four of us, all boys, who learned early lessons in life in the teeming streets of our conglomerate neighborhood. The surest way to earn respect—and peace—was with our fists, and at a tender age brother Bob demonstrated that he was capable of taking care of the entire family.

It was a realistic world, where no quarter was given or asked, excellent preparation for the larger tasks which awaited us in adulthood. For one thing, we had few illusions about our fellow beings, and judged them as they did us, on the basis of fundamental qualities. It was a kind of minor jungle existence. Above all, we learned to acclimate ourselves to rapidly changing conditions and came to understand the characteristics of all manner of people, certainly no deterrent in the subsequent rough-and-tumble world of business and mining. I cannot write of those early years without a deep glow of affection for Fred L. O'Brien, local athletic director. By his kindly wisdom and profound understanding of adolescence, he kindled our interest in competitive sports and had no small influence in shaping our lives. The "Coach," I am glad to say, still carries on his good work in a changing world.

That our environment was in no way deleterious or unwholesome is attested by the men of affairs who sprung from it. Louis Cates, the mighty head of the Phelps Dodge Company, was one of our "boys." So was Joe Kennedy, who stormed Wall Street and then dressed in knee pants to be received by England's King. Then there is Norman Corwin, justly celebrated for his distinguished radio work which has, among other honors, earned him the first Wendel Willkie memorial "One World" award. Paul Kirk is one of the youngest judges of the Massachusetts Superior Court. Haskell Masters is Canadian vice-president of Warner Brothers and Hal Horne is chairman of the board of Story Productions, Inc., a new and potent Hollywood producing organization. Henry Bodkin and Irwin Hoffman exhibit their paintings in New York art galleries and have had their pictures permanently hung in museums. There is Bernhard Berenson, now living in Italy, who is considered the world's outstanding expertiser on old masters. When dancer Hal Sherman literally broke up one of the early editions of Irving Berlin's *Music Box Revue,* he was proud to relate to newspaper reporters that he was a native of East Boston and was taught how to fight by his pal, Bob Hoffman.

The matter of education was one of grave concern. Except for my brother Irwin, whose natural talents pointed to a career in art, none of us seemed to gravitate toward the professions. But we were destined for Harvard, of that there was never any question. My oldest brother David decided to concentrate in economics and a possible career in business, but Bob was an enigma. He was a natural athlete and a good student in mathematics and the applied sciences, but his habits were completely unorthodox. He simply could not be weaned from his love of street fighting.

One day he returned home, bruised, bleeding, but triumphant. He had finally challenged the local bully and thrashed him soundly, though not without some damage to himself. There were visitors. One of my uncles, a vaudevillist, was playing at the old Keith's Theatre in Boston, and had brought with him his brother-in-law, Jim Dooley, of the then famous Dooley & Sales team. Dooley, smoking a cigar and sipping a glass of whisky, looked on with amusement when Bob made his dramatic entrance and announcement of victory. My father, a gentle soul who abhorred fisticuffs, surveyed his battered son and wrung his hands.

"My God," he exclaimed rhetorically, "what is to become of Bobbie? He's just a little bum."

"Wait a minute," smiled Dooley. "You were just saying before he came in that he was smart in school. And he's tough too. Well, why don't you make a mining engineer out of him?"

"Mining engineer?" My father was completely incredulous. No one, in his restricted circle, had even remotely thought of such a profession.

"Sure. Why not? He's got the makings." Dooley drank deeply. "I just played two weeks out in Butte, Montana. And the toughest men out there were the mining engineers. Bobbie'll take to it like a duck to water." Then, turning to the incorrigible under discussion, he asked, "Wouldn't you like to be a mining man, young feller?"

"Guess I would," was the prompt answer, and thus was launched into the world one more geologist who was to learn that rocks could be studied as well as thrown at itinerant peddlers and hostile gangs.

The outbreak of war hit us cruelly. David who enlisted early, was killed in action, and Bob was critically disabled. He survived only through a miraculous feat of surgery, but for a period of more than two years was a semi-invalid. This was a hard blow to a once active youth who had excelled in baseball, football and boxing, but at a time when such casualties were all too common he accepted his lot philosophically and improved the time by undertaking graduate studies at Harvard. It was during this period he met J. Mackintosh Bell, a prominent Canadian geologist who had stopped to visit at Cambridge after military service abroad. Bell painted glowing pictures of mining possibilities in Canada. He was seconded by Professor Henry Lloyd Smythe, also Canadian born, who had never forgotten his native land. It was natural, therefore, that when the young mining student, possessor of four college degrees, was given the opportunity to work at the Calumet & Hecla Mines in Michigan, he decided to visit northern Ontario en route.

He stopped at Sudbury, went underground at the various nickel mines, and then swung north to see the budding wonders of Kirkland Lake, Porcupine and Cobalt. From the Goldfields Hotel at Timmins, he wrote a long letter home, describing the strangeness of primitive surroundings, the first wild country he had ever seen. He said, in part:

"When I see prospectors, dirty, ragged, covered with fly oil and grease as they come out of the bush, I thank God for my technical training which has placed me high above them. I shudder to think of the kind of life they lead and take heart in the security I have as a professional engineer."

Young, impressionable, full of the knowledge so recently absorbed in cloistered halls, he little realized that in less than a year he would be a part of that small nondescript army he so patronizingly described. Michigan loomed on the horizon, and he prepared to turn south for what he thought would be the first step in the life of a mining engineer. After Calumet & Hecla, a sinecure at the Cerro de Pasco Mines in Peru had been promised him. Life seemed quite simple. But then he met "Cap" Anchor, the right-hand man of the mysterious "Captain" Joseph R. Delamar. Anchor had just been dismissed by his none too grateful chief, and now he stood at the desk of the hotel cursing mining in general and Delamar in particular.

"You're in the wrong business," the wrathful Dane told Bob. "That is, if you ever work for anyone else. If you do anything in mining, do it for yourself. Wish I had."

"Why don't you now?"

"Too old," muttered Cap, "over sixty, I am. But you!" He looked at the young husky and sighed. "What I'd give to be you, now. The places I'd go to . . ."

They talked for hours. Anchor had his eye on Larder Lake, where engineer George Grey, erstwhile pitcher on the Princeton baseball team, was operating for Associated Goldfields.

"That's the spot," opined the elderly Cap, "Larder Lake. Now, if I only had a partner."

"You've got one." It was pure impulse, a quality which the unique Bostonian was never to lose. "I'll join you."

"You will?" Cap Anchor's eyes became saucer-like. "Ready to go now, say?"

No, that couldn't be done, and Bob went on to explain what awaited him in Michigan. But next spring, 1921, would be the time.

"Oh, I get it." The old man looked drearier than ever. "Next year it is, then," and he shook hands with his phantom partner and took his leave, never expecting to see his young friend again. But he was destined for a surprise.

The Michigan interlude passed swiftly. In the fall the coterie of Harvard professors left for Cambridge and Bob headed west to visit the mining camps about which he had read so much. And then, with the first snows of winter, he returned to Boston, and resumed his studies for the last time. The family was lukewarm to the idea of prospecting.

"That letter you wrote, now," my father reminded, "telling us about those dirty prospectors."

"Yes, I know. I felt that way at the time." Bob nodded, and his eyes were dreamy. "But I want to try it one summer, at least. Learn that end of the business. And the doctor tells me it would improve my health."

Cap Anchor received periodical letters from Cambridge, showed them to his doubting friends in Porcupine.

"Gonna have a damned mining engineer for a partner, by Christ," he boomed, "and a bloody Harvard graduate, at that!"

They met while the snow was still on the ground. Sleeping nights in a rude pup tent, they prospected together during the long hot days. It was rugged bush, partly burnt over, heavy with windfall, and the black flies were vicious. There was rain too, and wet sucking muskeg which made each step forward a tortured adventure. Bending low under backbreaking loads, their tumplines wet with perspiration and glued mercilessly against their foreheads, they made systematic traverses through the bush.

"You'll fill the bill, young man," acknowledged Cap Anchor, almost grudgingly, a month later. "Regular dog in the woods, you are. Never get lost and a nose for rock."

The young hopeful swelled with pride.

There came to Larder Lake one day two prospectors from Gowganda, bent on a little wildcatting spree, Bob Gamble, with jutting chin and rapid tongue, and Freddy Thompson, quiet but smiling with a mischievous fire. They camped with Anchor and Bob a few days. Thompson, a dead shot with a revolver, nipped off partridge heads with deadly but nonchalant accuracy. He was tigerish in the bush, too, in a neat, controlled way. Bob was interested. Cap Anchor had already indicated that this was to be his last season in the field, the effort was becoming too much for a man of his years.

"How about teaming up next year?" Bob asked Thompson. "I haven't much money, but I think we can manage if we're careful."

Thompson, they learned, was parting company with Gamble. He liked the young American, was particularly impressed with the idea of joining forces with a technical man, and so he made his decision quickly.

"All right by me," he said simply, and the two shook hands, beginning an association which has endured to this day.

When Gamble and Thompson left Larder Lake for Gowganda,

Anchor and his protégé continued to scour the bush for gold. The flies were less pestiferous now, but the days were growing shorter. Anchor grumbled interminably, but the former Harvard student made the rounds with a light step. His thoughts strayed ahead to 1922 when, with his new partner, he would really move and not crawl like a worm over the same hellish terrain. So musing one gray morning, he unthinkingly walked into a tag-alder bush. One of the sinuous branches snapped viciously and whipped across his face. He stopped and pressed his streaming eyes.

"Come over here!" bellowed Anchor. "Want to show you something!"

"Can't. My eyes are closed!" Bob shouted.

"Well, take a look and you'll see gold through your God-damned eyelids!"

There was unmistakable elation in the old man's voice. His hand trembling, he lifted his gold pan for inspection. With tortured eyes, Bob looked. A long thin line of yellow clung to the inside edge of blue-black metal. His stomach contracted; this was the real thing.

"Where'd you get it?" he asked tremulously.

"Right here." Anchor tapped a brownish boulder with his toe. "Hunk of float, it is."

"H'm." The geologist searched the ground carefully. "Must have come a long way. Pretty well rounded. And no outcrops in sight."

"It came from somewhere," responded Anchor heavily. "We'll take a look."

And look they did for hours, days, and weeks. They found more float, all of it rich, but no sign of an outcrop which might indicate the original source of ore.

"It's in that draw," suggested the weary Anchor, pointing to a well-defined depression. "We'll have to dig a trench."

They discarded geological hammers for pick and shovel, dug into the bouldery ground. Gravel streamed into their hole, and then water. Disgusted, Anchor threw down his pick.

"Hopeless it is, without timber and a pump. This'll have to be drilled. But we'd better stake 'er first."

Out came axes and four claims were staked.

In Cobalt, Bob conferred with officials of the Coniagas Company and interested them in a plan to drill. Samples of the high-grade float were convincing. An option agreement was drawn and a drill crew sent to Larder Lake. There difficulties arose at once, caused by the heavy overburden. Dreams of quick fortune faded as the swearing men ruined whole lengths of casing in futile attempts to reach bedrock. I would like to record a sudden change, and rich ore discovered in Anchor's draw, but the melancholy truth must be told. Coniagas, dismayed at the expense of drilling, soon found enough reason to abandon the project after two barren holes were completed. Bob and Anchor parted with the knowledge that mines are not to be plucked as easily as grapes from a vine.

While this little drama was in progress, I was a freshman at college, receiving occasional letters from Ontario. The abortive drilling campaign was a real tragedy to me, but fired with the excitement of a prospector's existence I quickly agreed to Bob's suggestion that I join Thompson and him the following summer. Ontario was large and there were many mines to be found. Of the bush and woodcraft I was completely ignorant, but with a younger brother's confidence I had few misgivings. If Bob could make the grade, I could.

Early in June, 1922, I left my anxious parents in Boston, climbed into an upper berth at South Station, and, for the first time in my nineteen years of existence, left the friendly hills of New England. Once above Toronto, I was aware of what "bush" meant. For miles the train sped through a monotony of green flatness, broken only occasionally by rude log settlements. As we progressed north, a few sawmills poked into view, sawdust mounds burning purposelessly. There was about the country a loneliness which dismayed me, nor did the dirty bustle of Cobalt, where we stopped briefly, afford much relief. When I stepped onto the dusty platform at Earlton Junction, where I awaited the branch-line train to Elk Lake, a bleak vista spread before me. I was in the heart of the Clay Belt, farming country, so called, but still crowded in by the inevitable bush. In spots, hardy settlers had managed to clear small areas of land, though blackened tree stumps and roots still littered the landscape. Frame houses and a few barns, none of them painted, added to the gloomy scene. Even the spiritless horses, silhouetted against a gray sky, seemed to reflect my lugubrious mood. In afteryears, this country bloomed unbelievably into a garden spot, but I did not know this then, and so faced Elk Lake with dire forebodings.

Gowganda was twenty-seven miles from the end of steel at Elk Lake, and this distance was negotiated in a vehicle dignified by the name of "stage" for no understandable reason. It was an ancient Ford, even in that year of Our Lord, but it was a fitting accompaniment to the dirt road. So rough and perforated was it that the corduroy sections, where logs floated on top of the muskeg, actually seemed a comfort. At various times, the passengers hopped to the ground and pushed the Ford uphill, Jim Ferrier, the driver, barking detailed instructions. The trip required almost five hours, and I could well understand thereafter why the handful of Gowganda's citizens preferred to remain where they were.

Gowganda itself sat on the edge of a long low lake which lay north and south and threw out narrow inlets, or arms, in all directions. A few of the straggling buildings were of the shack variety, but most of them were the now familiar log cabins with tin stovepipes sticking sharply through the roofs. Dogs trotted around aimlessly or skulked away when anyone approached. Faint voices echoed across the water from a small island where a fire ranger's station pushed above the trees. It was a solemn, forgotten kind of place and I found it hard to believe that only a dozen years ago almost ten thousand people had lived in this one-time boom camp. But the hustle of new money had come and gone, and only a few score human beings—trappers, remittance men, and prospectors—had remained.

Following the minute directions Bob had written me, I entered the poolroom and spoke to the proprietor, Jack Dick. He smiled through his gold teeth.

"Knew you was comin'," he said. "Bob and Fred is in the bush but they're due soon. Here's the keys to Fred's shack."

He conducted me downshore to a row of cabins and indicated the one that was to be my home. There was a largish porch, with a huge moose horn nailed above it. Mineral specimens were scattered along the floor on each side of the entrance. Inside, everything was neatness and order. There were books and reports on several shelves along one wall. A double bunk, one cot (which I found later was specially purchased for my use), a table, a large tin stove, and chairs filled one room. At the back was the kitchen, equipped with a two-burner kerosene range. Two water pails were placed on a rack near at hand. Outside plumbing, apparently, and no electricity. Coleman lamps hung from the ceiling.

A clatter outside interrupted my inspection. I turned to face brother Bob. He looked at me through swollen eyes and shouted a greeting.

"What happened to you?" I asked, alarmed.

"Nothing much. Just black flies. Been out two weeks. Come on outside and meet Freddy Thompson."

Lowering a canoe on the rough quay was a smallish man who performed his task with surprising gentleness. He straightened up as I approached and I looked into twinkling brown eyes. His lips spread into an infectious grin, showing large white teeth. In contrast to Bob, his general appearance was almost immaculate. The black flies, apparently, respected him.

"So you're Arnie," he said.

"The kid brother himself," interjected Bob.

"Welcome to Gowganda."

I helped carry the packsacks inside, marveling at the quantity of food and implements they held. Bob explained why the load was so big: Indians at Hangingstone Lake had sold them a quarter of moose.

"You'll like it up here, kid," he promised through puffed lips. "It's a great life."

But I wondered. Those flies, now, and those enormous packsacks. How did one fight against them? All night long I tossed on my cot, revolving in my mind how I would face this terrible bush. I had never seen this kind of wilderness before and first impressions were anything but reassuring. Home had never seemed so far away.

The next few days were given over to plans and preparations for the forthcoming trip into Matachewan. I learned much in this interval and began to experience a rising interest. For one thing, I recognized that prospecting was a profession like all others. Nothing was done haphazardly. Fred had on file a number of government reports and maps. These were laboriously studied and an itinerary carefully plotted. Food supply was then calculated on the basis of poundage per man per day and then tucked into small canvas bags which were labeled with indelible pencil. Nothing was forgotten: tent, candles, matches, sewing kit, a file for sharpening axes, fly oil, notebooks, pencils, compasses, geological picks, axes provided with leather heads to prevent cutting through the packsacks, whetstones, pots which cunningly telescoped into one another. The chuck was mostly of the dried variety—prunes, beans, peas, rice and the like—and one large slab of bacon completed the meat ration. No coffee, but tea, for in those days dried milk was unknown and canned milk was too bulky and heavy to pack. All our baggage miraculously fitted into two packsacks, and the blankets, two for each man, were rolled up for head loads.

On an unforgettable June morning we loaded the canoe and departed from our base. It was a slow process at first, for the duffel had to be carefully distributed to keep the canoe evenly balanced while allowing sitting room for me in the center.

"You're not Hudson Baying," promised Fred. "There's a paddle for you too."

I was told to first place my paddle across the gunwales and then step squarely into the center of the canoe. This I did, but not without some uneasy rocking. Fred then took his place in the stern. I was instructed to sit on a packsack, a none too comfortable seat, and then Bob occupied his position in the bow. A deft thrust of Fred's paddle and we shot out into Gowganda Lake. Jack Dick, on hand for the occasion, waved a farewell and plodded toward the poolroom. The great adventure lay before me.

Accustomed to the dawdling pace of "canoedling" at resorts along Charles River, I was immediately dismayed at our forward pace. Fred, with a swift, stiff-armed motion, paddled as though possessed. At first I thought this was done to impress me, but as the minutes passed I realized it was not so. I was in for it. These boys meant business. For a time I maintained some semblance of paddling, then my arms began to ache, my stomach muscles groaned in protest, and my back throbbed uneasily. Surely there must be a pause that refreshes! But the gurgle of Fred's paddle became a song as inexorable and interminable as one of Wagner's operas.

"Stiff arm," cautioned Fred, as I jabbed at the water ineffectually.

Oh, Fred, thought I, if you only knew how I am suffering!

Arrival at a portage saved me for a while. The ground was soft and the canoe was allowed to push into the loon dung. Bob stepped out and held the bow between his knees while Fred and I tossed lighter impedimenta ashore and passed the weighty packsacks to Bob, who lowered them carefully. Curtly, I was instructed to help pull the canoe and carry it several yards to flat terrain. Paddles were then tied to the center thwarts. Fred, a bullfit bag on his back, grasped these and then with a sudden effort lifted and twisted the canoe so that the bow pointed skyward while the stern remained on the ground. Then Bob held on while Fred adjusted his coat around his neck and ordered the canoe to be lowered until the paddles rested firmly on his shoulders. It swung level and then walked forward on human legs.

"Get going," said Bob, all business, as I gaped at the disappearing canoe, and he held up a packsack.

I slipped into the shoulder straps and adjusted the broad tumpline across my forehead. The weight was oppressive, which was certainly not helped by the swarms of flies and mosquitoes that greeted me with true northern hospitality. A sack containing tin dishes and utensils was thrust into one hand and a roll of blankets thrown over the packsack. I was then advised to follow Fred along the trail. He was out of sight by this time and I had some qualms about losing him entirely. My early pace, therefore, was somewhat too rapid, and in less than a hundred feet I was gasping for breath and swallowing black flies. This, I decided, was not the life for me. But Bob's heavy footstep was close behind and I clawed at the soft ground with

weakening legs. The whole world was on my back and the tumpline
gave forth low worried sounds. My throat dried, my chest burned,
and into my mouth came that bitter coppery taste which was to become all too familiar. Fortunately, the portage was not long, hardly
more than a quarter of a mile, (a pull-over, Fred called it) and so I
was able to reach the far side under my own power. Fred, who already had the canoe afloat, anchored by a single paddle thrust far
into the mud, helped remove my load. Relieved, I had the strange
sensation of floating through the air. Fred regarded me quizzically.

"She's a son of a bitch, Canada," he twitted.

I could only smile weakly.

No rest. Swift, and it seemed to me frantic, reloading of the
canoe, and once more the killing quick time of paddling. Somehow
I held out until lunch, but then I disgraced myself by nicking Fred's
best ax in an attempt to chop wood. He only looked at me, then set
to work grinding down a new edge with file and whetstone. Discon-
solate, I sat on a log and watched my companions deftly prepare a
meal of bacon, fried desiccated onions, tea and bread with jam. I ate
sparingly, and was almost relieved when the signal was given to resume travel.

By midafternoon I was so exhausted and flybitten that I acknowledged defeat and was allowed to stretch out full length on the
packsacks. It was a bitter pill to swallow, but one more stroke of
the paddle at Fred's pace would have undone me.

We camped along the Montreal River. Out came the silk tent
from one of the rolls, with canvas flooring. No balsam brush was
cut for a mattress—we were only stopping the night. A small space
was cleared and the tent pitched. The front flap was provided with
a small hole covered with netting and barely large enough to admit
us singly. I was the first in, and unmindful of the mosquitoes was
soon rolled in my blankets. Black flies swarmed under the ridgepole
and stayed there, the only decent habit I ever discovered in these
pests. Outside, calls came for dinner but I was too far gone to eat.
I remembered Fred lighting a candle and gently singeing mosquitoes
against the tent, and then oblivion. My first day in the bush was
over. . . .

Fred's reveille was unforgettable, a mixture of English Navy
and Canadian Army lore. His voice, clear as the sunlight, came into
the tent:

> "Come along, all you sleepers,
> Heave out, heave out, lash up and stow,
> Rise and shine, rise and shine, rise and shine,
> Shake a leg, shake a leg, shake a leg,

> Hit the deck, hit the deck, hit the deck,
> There's daylight in the swamp,
> Bean on the tab',
> Little birds're singing the praise of the Lord,
> God damn your souls,
> Get up!"

Oh, that cry, which I hear even yet, and the urgent thought that never would I be trapped in this predicament again. Mosquitoes whined angrily and waited on the other side of the netting. Bob and Fred had run the gantlet; it was now my turn. I tried to act fast, but in my haste entangled myself in the cheesecloth and was bitten fiercely. My language was anything but Harvard.

And so the second day began.

But let us skip two or three months. This finds us swinging up Duncan Lake against a rugged head wind. All three of us are stripped to the waist and paddling rhythmically. At the word "Change!" we take a single additional stroke and then reverse sides, the canoe never slowing an instant. At the first portage, the canoe is hauled up briskly and I, yes, I am under it with confident stride. I have learned to take this great awkward weight and clamber over logs and rocks like a young moose, and when my shoulders sag I know how to lift my head and take the load on my neck. Insects still hover about, but I pay little attention; they are a part of the country. In one hand I hold an ax by the head, edge pointed outward so that a fall will not wound me. I recognize the slightest sound and can follow the trail, however obscure. Rain means nothing to me, for I have traveled for weeks in wet weather without removing my clothes and the only cold I recognize is removed by proximity to a campfire. I can fell a tree in any direction with fair accuracy, and I know where north is without a compass by observing the sun or noting the inclination of trees and the relative sparseness of vegetation. I am often the first one awake in the morning to light the fire, shag water, and cook breakfast. I am an accomplished ax-man, and know how to twist my wrists in chopping so that the thin edge will never strike unfriendly ground. I can paddle two hours or more without a rest and sleep comfortably on the ground. I know that townships are six-mile rectangles named after Englishmen such as Cabot and Connaught, and not settlements where people live. I recognize rocks by their appearance and not as they are described in textbooks. Gold is a dull metal in nature, I have learned, and does not glitter. I am a confirmed tea drinker and salt pork is a delicacy to me. Few in the north can match my profanity, except Bob and

Fred, for I can address the Deity in several dozen ways. Staking a claim is no longer a mystery, for it is a simple rectangle of 20 chain (¼ mile) sides, with posts cut and marked in pencil at all four corners. I will eat fish, venison, muskrat, beaver, dried apples, berries, bacon, beans, bannock and corn mush with equal appetite and I have never been treed by a moose. (Nor has anyone else, despite the popular magazines!) I travel in any kind of weather, for I have been taught to light a fire in pouring rain and keep my necessities dry. Calls of nature I obey swiftly, before the flies can organize, and I can cut almost as neat a ridgepole or claim post as Fred himself. I wear long woolen underwear on the hottest days. My hands are calloused and horny, and I have stopped counting flybites. I am proud of my washboard stomach and the clarity of my vision, and the smell of the bush is as familiar to me as hay and manure are to a horse.

Arnold   Robert

That summer we covered almost two thousand miles, examining prospects, studying new country, staking claims, moving, moving. First Matachewan, then West Shiningtree, and on to the fringes of Porcupine and Kirkland Lake, then down toward Sudbury. No discoveries for us, but a treasure of knowledge and experience. And in the fall I said farewell to my bushmates, with tears in my eyes.

"I'll be back," I promised, as the stage prepared to leave.

"Sure you will," said Fred. "You weren't so bad toward the end."

"You'll do," pronounced Bob, and I turned toward Boston like Shakespeare's soldier, full of strange oaths.

And return I did in the late spring, for Fred and Bob had been grubstaked by Bob's classmate, Quincy A. Shaw, Jr., scion of the Calumet & Hecla founder. They had become fixtures in the newly discovered Noranda field, after having mushed in by dog team from Larder Lake in the waning days of winter. Shaw's assistance was timely; money had become a problem. Fred was ill, suffering from the aftereffects of cumulative gas attacks during the war, and Bob, until welcome word arrived from Boston, was working as a sampler underground at the Dome Mine. It was a curious partnership, possible only in America where patrician and plebeian can unite in common effort. There were differences of opinion, for new and old Boston could not be expected to merge so completely as to lose their distinct entities, but the association, lasting almost eight years, was mutually beneficial and pleasant.

I now was a bushwhacker in my own right. No longer was there the comforting knowledge that I would be home again in the security and ease of Cambridge after a few months' lark. I was in the bush to stay, where travel was hard and long and the outside world of men seemed unreal and nonexistent. Bob and I became "wildcatters," scattering our claim posts from Osisko (Tremoy) Lake [1] to distant Chibougamau. To us, the days were annoyingly short, as with the impatience and ambition of youth, we sought to engulf the entire Pre-Cambrian. Old-timers were amused at our impetuousness.

"You'll slow up," joshed Bert McDonald, our neighbor on Osisko Lake. "Burn yourselves out, you will."

Slow up we did, but not before we had covered prodigious amounts of country. Bob was a stickler for mapmaking and note taking and our Lefax file grew to staggering proportions. It seemed a hopeless kind of life at times, this batting around the bush, for outside interest in Canadian mining was at a low ebb. To me, more

[1] Most Quebec lakes have two names, Indian and French.

easily discouraged than my indomitable brother, we were pitting our training against mere luck. We were simply prospectors, no different from other bushmen who had little schooling and yet seemingly were as well equipped and deserving of fortune as we.

"We'll find a mine . . ." Bob would say, but I would only shake my head. Fred, married now, and still in poor health, was with us only at intervals, and I missed his quiet and humorous cheerfulness.

As I write, the memory of those days fills me with nostalgia. Little did we realize the richness of our life, the deep satisfaction of complete self-reliance and the glowing health which only the north can give. We quailed at nothing, for there were no creaking joints to favor, or family ties which gave us reason to pause. Weather meant nothing to us; rain and snow were a part of the bush, just as were flies, windfall, and the long portages. Yes, we can still travel in the north, but never again with the dash and abandon of Rouyn years.

There was the time, for instance, when we received word that our immediate presence in Kirkland Lake was necessary. All aircraft had left Osisko Lake and a canoe trip would require more time than remained before the hour of rendezvous.

"We'll walk out," announced Bob. "We've got about thirty hours to make it, and it's only sixty-five miles."

We each made a bug from empty tin cans, a candle thrust through the side punctured near the closed bottom. Axes, a pocketful of raisins and prunes, and we were ready. We paddled to the western side of the lake, cached our canoe at Bill Gamble's poolroom, and made for the old Lake Fortune winter road. It had been a wet summer and the roadway looked like a spring freshet. There was no walking along the right-of-way; we had to keep along the shoulders. And what a mess it was! Tree stumps with deep intervening holes sucking at our boots when we were unfortunate enough to miss our footing. Not a word did we speak, for the effort of walking consumed us entirely. Confident, Bob led the way, seeking easy spots.

"Tired? Want to rest?" he called at last.

"A fiver would do, Bobbie."

We sat on a fallen pine. Bob looked at his watch anxiously, then rose.

"Come on, kid, we're behind schedule."

And off we went, our boots squirting brownish water. The pace was fast, even when we were forced to abandon the road altogether and take to the bush. A fine rain began to fall and the road became even more sodden. Each step was accompanied by a dull pulling noise, and our boots were soon heavy with Quebec gumbo. On and on we plodded, slipping, falling, cursing with almost comical vehemence. When night came our bugs were produced (who knew of flashlights there?) and in the wavering candlelight we continued to fight the mud and sorrow of a Canadian winter road in the good old summertime.

Late the following morning we were in Larder Lake. Bob permitted the luxury of pancakes and coffee at Sheldon's stopping place, and then, changing our woolen socks, we took to the bush in what we decided was the most direct route to Kirkland Lake. But we learned that the longest way round is the shortest way home. There were great burnt areas which forced us to detour constantly and old timbered sections were piled high with brush and slash. The day was bright and warm, though, and we forgot the bitterness of extra mileage. And when we at last discerned the white headframes of Kirkland Lake mines rising above the thin jackpine, Bob called a halt. He consulted his watch and smiled triumphantly.

"We'll make it with a half hour to spare," he said with satisfaction. "Rest now."

Later, when we trod the board sidewalks of Kirkland town, we met our old friend Bill Cooper, ex-Mountie and first mine captain at the Hollinger. He surveyed us with astonishment.

"You lads look as though you've just been pulled out of a muskeg! Where in hell've you been?"

Briefly, we explained. He whistled and shook his head.

"Nuts, you are. Kill yourself." But then he smiled. "Oh, well, I was like you once, young, full of piss and vinegar and my tits sticking through my shirt."

Walking toward the railroad station, Bob chuckled happily. Coming from Bill, this compliment was compensation enough for the grueling trip.

"Tits through your shirt," he kept repeating.

The meeting was of no great consequence; we could have arrived late without loss to anyone. But we were true to our promise and that, it seemed at the time, was of vital importance.

Another memorable trip, also negotiated in rain and mud, was coming out of Duprat Township late one autumn. I need not go into the detail of that trek, but one anecdote is perhaps worth recording. We were very low on food, and carried only some cooked bacon which became sandwiches smothered in two soft bannocks, the sourdough bread which is the prospector's trademark. Hunger overcame us as we were crossing a long spruce swamp, and it was decided to stop where we were and eat. It was not a happy place, for the muskeg was perforated with yawning holes where large trees had fallen, leaving their roots to decay. We managed to light a fire, brewed tea and then prepared to enjoy our mighty sandwiches. But I had inadvertently chosen a bad resting place, a giant root elevated with deceiving assertiveness above the mushy ground. When I sat, the rotten wood collapsed. Down I went. The bannock escaped and landed at the bottom of a two-foot hole. Ignoring Bob's unashamed laughter, I threw myself full length on the muskeg and gingerly fished for my food. I snared it finally, but brought to view a soggy-looking mess, covered with soot and decayed wood. But I brushed off the offending debris and bit deeply into the fodder. His laughter gone, Bob eyed me with sudden respect.

"When you can eat that," he declared with finality, "you're tough!"

And then I laughed. . . .

The Red Lake rush drew us above Lac Seul in 1926, but we no longer paddled, for the outboard motor had by then become the accepted mode of travel. It was something of a relief to forgo the elbow grease of paddling, but there was still the task of portaging a heavy-keeled 19-foot canoe, cans of gas, and the motor itself, in addition to the usual duffel. Coming out of what we decided was a hopeless mining camp, we were swamped on Lake Pakwash and escaped with our lives only by the miraculous presence of a tiny rock islet which suddenly revealed itself above the confusion of wind-swept water.

Manitoba, north of the Pas, was our next stamping ground. A quick look at British Columbia that same year convinced us that this outlier was not for us, and so we returned to the country we knew and understood best, around the borders of Hudson Bay. The great rivers, Harricanaw, Ottawa, Kinojevis, English, Churchill, became familiar to us. Later, when the Northwest Territories beckoned, we were among the first to answer the call, locating in Yellowknife and learning much of the arctic and of new and mightier waterways, the Peace, Slave, Athabaska and Mackenzie, and the sweeping stretches of Great Bear and Great Slave lakes. It was strange bushland for those of us who had been hardened in the tangled woods of the lower provinces. The trees were pitifully small and in the summer the muskeg was so dry that we often raised dust when we plowed through it. Only a few degrees below the Arctic Circle, we wondered at the almost perpetual sunlight and found it difficult to fall asleep in the glare of seemingly late afternoon. It was surprisingly warm country for the north, freshened by prevailing winds which kept the flies down. Dry too, with as little moisture from the sky as in many desert areas. More significant, there was gold, and we spread our stakes wide and far.

In a span of twenty-five years we have been fortunate not only to see but also to participate in the winning of the north. Those who have not pioneered can never experience the thrill of visiting camps which in our time have sprouted from nothingness into large communities. And there is satisfaction and pride in knowing that we have helped to make this possible, the kind of payment which can never be valued in dollars. When we walk into the Noranda Hotel now, and Kelley Lightner, the manager, greets us with a cheerful, "Hi, boys, it's good to see old-timers coming back," he little realizes how comforting his words are. We are at home, where we are understood. For in crowded New York we are merely consumers of food and payers of rent like so many millions who think and act alike, and there is a sad lack of camaraderie which only the bush can give. This is the same feeling, no doubt, which soldiers have, the welding of associations made under fire.

In the beginning the transition from the bush to city pavements was a hard one to accept. After months of eager anticipation, intoxicated at the prospect of joys and luxuries, we would hasten to Boston or New York, only to find ourselves completely disillusioned. Our legs ached from unaccustomed pounding of unyielding sidewalks, the fetid air caused headache and listlessness. Above all, there was little community of thought with our friends and associates. They could never talk our language. Articulate as we tried to be, they could not understand us, and more than once we were subjected to good-natured, but none the less annoying, jocularity. We were asked, usually by women and with accompanying giggles, "Do you actually dig the gold yourselves?" or "Is the plural of moose, mice?" or "How many squaws do you have cached up there?" and the like.

One incident stands out in my mind. We had spent difficult months preparing camps and carrying out assessment work on a group of claims in one of the remoter Quebec townships. The nearest waterway was nine miles from our cabin and we were forced to cruise the bush and blaze a portage, later known on government maps as "Hoffman Trail." It was grueling work, for the terrain was swampy and we were under necessity of wiggling around muskegs several miles in width. We were naturally anxious to shorten the distance if possible, for all our food and supplies, including anvil and blacksmith outfit, complete even to coal sacks, had to be carried in on our backs. But long by-passes and detours were unavoidable.

Trail cutting required several weeks, after which Bob and I mapped more than two thousand acres with a Brunton compass, not omitting contour lines. The whole job was accomplished for grubstakers in New York, and after the freezeup we journeyed south for a conference, armed with specimen and maps.

Three men eagerly awaited our coming, for gold had been found and hopes were high. We were properly dined and then conducted to a large office overlooking the busy waters of New York harbor. We told our story amid laudatory remarks, and then spread the large contour map on the desk. Three heads, close together, bent down with interest.

"What's this?" asked benevolent Mr. Humphry Van Hiss, carpet manufacturer de luxe, pointing to a thin winding line through the map.

"The trail," Bob explained. "The trail from the river to Home Lake."

"H'm." The big man looked perplexed. "I don't know much about these things, but it sems to me that if *I* were cutting that trail, I would do so—" and he ran a well-manicured thumbnail across the sheet. Then smugly, "A straight line is the shortest distance between two points, you know, boys."

Invariably, there are friends who have some member of the family who is lazy, unscholarly, refractory, just plain dumb, or vicious, and the suggestion is made that perhaps we could take the young person up north and make a man of him. It was strange, and still is, for that matter, how many people regard the north as a receptacle for remittance men and ne'er-do-wells. In any event, with advancing age has come more tolerance; we philosophically accept the fact that north is north and south is south and never the twain shall meet—except when Boston boys confound the poet.

Of interest, I think, has been the growth of aircraft travel, which we have seen blossom from discarded crates of flying boats to svelte Norsemen winging over every corner of the bush at speeds which never fail to astonish us. This is a far cry from the canoe which, except for local trips, seems to be gone forever. Even more miraculous has been the emergence of Canada from a little-known mining country to a place of approaching world leadership. It has been amusing to watch outside indifference, and even ridicule—so hard to take years ago—gradually change into respect and then desire, desire to own a mine like Lake Shore, which once went begging. But time turns back for no one, not even the indispensable mining companies with offices in downtown New York, and while there are still mines to be found there are far more hunters in the woods now, all of whom possess large appetites.

Today we have a small office in New York to house our growing files which detail the work of a lifetime. The seemingly wasteful trips we made, the false alarms to answer the call of gold which never existed, the futile rushes, all serve their purpose now, thanks to Bob's insistence that we "make pictures" of every property we visited. We believe we know the areas of promise, and while fortune is elusive, we are still not old men and have hopes of a mine or two of our own. We can travel the bush, even at this date, but I am frank to say I would not care ever to repeat that memorable summer in Gowganda.

While our associations have been many, it is with the prospector that our true affections rest. We have known him from Lake St. John to Great Bear Lake, in all seasons of the year, in prosperity and adversity, and it is our proudest boast that we can meet him on common ground, without condescension. For that, no doubt, we can thank East Boston and a Canadian training which began where mines are located—in the bush.

CHAPTER III

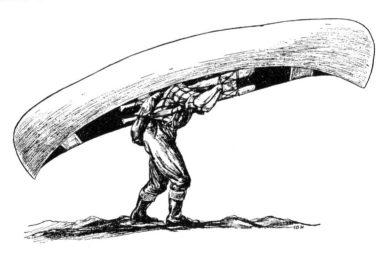

.Patch of Snow

Voltaire, unable to resist the urge to impress his vast audience, contemptuously referred to Canada as a "patch of snow." It was a catchy bon mot, a convenient phrase for statesmen and politicians of France who welcomed an excuse for the loss of the colony to England.

Today Canada stands as the crown jewel of the British Commonwealth. In population less than that of New York State, this vast, sprawling half continent is a world leader in raw material production. Known in the beginning as a source of peltries and timber, and later as the "granary of the Empire," Canada has forged to the front of nations in the last few generations as a reservoir of mineral wealth, so essential to civilization's material progress.

The world has become dependent upon the patch of snow for such necessities as nickel and asbestos. Without Canada humanity would be sadly deficient in gold, silver, platinum, lead, zinc, copper, and other metals. Canadian uranium played a vital role in the development of atomic energy, with its earth-shattering connotations. Doughty Cortez, who blandly informed Montezuma that the conquistadors suffered from a lingering illness which could only be remedied by gold and more gold, would be a happy playfellow in the patch of snow. Off to a slow start, Canada has produced gold at the rate of $200,000,000 yearly, with every prospect that this figure will be appreciably increased. No other geographical entity on the planet offers so enormous a mineral potential, stretching for three thousand miles from coast to coast, thence north to the far-flung reaches of the Northwest Territories, Hudson Bay, and Labrador. To American·eyes, unfamiliar with the rolling tracts of Canada, this might be better understood if we envisaged a series of mining belts reaching from Atlanta to Seattle, with famous bonanzas dotting the route.

Facts and Figures

In 1900 the total mineral production of the Dominion barely exceeded $64,000,000. In 1942 this yearly figure had increased to $567,000,000. At the turn of the century the world was enlivened by spectacular gold discoveries in the Yukon and the subsequent rush of more than twenty-five thousand adventurers into the area. In a few short years, more than $100,000,000 was wrested from frozen gravels and river beds. But this was only a small beginning, the best was yet to come.

British Columbia, which received some attention after the first flush of the 1849 California "boom" had passed, had become a steady producer of metals by 1900. In gold alone this mountain-studded province has produced well over $420,000,000. It is the leading base metal province of the Dominion. To the end of 1944 it yielded in gold (excluding placer), silver, lead, zinc, and copper a total value of $1,433,000,000. In the Sullivan property, located at Kimberley, British Columbia possesses the greatest single lead-zinc-silver mine in the world. Total dividends paid by British Columbia metal mines to the end of 1945 were in excess of $277,000,000.

Ontario enjoys the highest production of all the provinces, providing more than 40 per cent of the mineral wealth of the entire Dominion. To the end of 1945, Ontario metal mines produced $3,-746,000,000 of which $1,617,000,000 has been derived from gold alone. The Sudbury nickel-copper-platinum deposits, the greatest on earth, have accounted for $1,541,000,000 in this same period. Dividends paid by all Ontario metal mines in this time aggregated $1,012,000,000. The gold mines have contributed $490,000,000 and the nickel-copper mines $475,000,000 of this total.˙

In Ontario are located two of the world's most remarkable gold camps, Porcupine and Kirkland Lake. The former, coming into production only in 1911, had, to the end of 1945, produced $846,000,-

ooo, enriching stockholders of the various mines with over $246,-
ooo,ooo in dividends. One mine alone, the Hollinger, has distributed
$121,000,000 in dividends. The camp is still vigorous, with new
properties being developed in an easterly direction.

Kirkland Lake, which started producing in 1918, has yielded
$488,000,000, of which total $203,000,000, an unusually high percentage, has been disbursed as dividends. Here the leading mine is
the Lake Shore, which has paid more than $94,000,000 to stock-
holders.

To those who are attracted by comparisons, the pleasant variety,
it will be of interest to know that Porcupine has already produced
more gold than the much publicized Cripple Creek and Comstock
Lode districts combined. Since 1911, Ontario's gold production has
been twice that of Alaska, where operations started in 1880, more
than twice the entire output of Nevada, which came into production
as early as 1859, and more than twice that of South Dakota since
1876. Of all the states California alone can boast of higher gold output than Ontario, but it must be remembered that more than one-
fourth of that state's $2,000,000,000 production was obtained in ten
lush years, 1848 to 1858, when the famed alluvial deposits were discovered and operated. At present rates of production, however, Ontario will in due course equal and surpass California.

Turning to Quebec, we find that this latecomer, which in 1926
produced only $76,000 in gold, had in 1942 increased this amount to
$42,000,000. To the end of 1945, this hardy infant had produced a
total of $528,000,000 in metals, of which $315,000,000 has come from
the base metal group, copper-zinc, and $213,000,000 from gold. The
Noranda Mines Ltd., which blew in its smelter as late as 1927, has
contributed a substantial part of this total and has already paid its
stockholders more than $110,000,000.

In Manitoba the chief contributor in metals has been the Flin
Flon Mine, one of the Canadian giants. To the end of 1945, this
enterprise, known as the Hudson Bay Mining & Smelting Company,
produced approximately $220,000,000 in gold, silver, copper, and
zinc. Since the beginning of operations in 1931, the company has
paid $52,000,000 in dividends. The province itself first yielded gold
in 1917, a comparatively late date, but by the end of 1945 had produced close to $70,000,000 from the Flin Flon, San Antonio, and
other mines.

Saskatchewan enters statistics largely as the result of containing a portion of the Flin Flon Mine. At the end of 1945 its record of
gold stood at approximately $40,000,000.

The Yukon, from 1886 to 1945, has produced approximately

$211,000,000 in gold, of which close to one-half was obtained in the eight years from 1897 to 1904.

Of great interest at this writing is the newest gold area in Canada—Yellowknife. First coming into production in 1938 with a yield of only $260,000, this camp, located only a few degrees below the Arctic Circle, spurted close to the $4,000,000 mark in 1942. War conditions forced a shutdown of the producing mines of the district, but by 1944 Yellowknife, in seven years of production, had turned out more than $14,000,000 in gold. The pitchblende and uranium of Great Bear Lake have been nationalized, their value being incalculable in the dawning age of atomic energy.

The total value of gold produced by the entire Dominion of Canada, as recorded from 1858 to 1945, is approximately $2,800,-000,000.

Voltaire, if he were alive, would be interested in knowing something of Canada's metal contribution to the sorely pressed United Nations which, incidentally, had much to do with the liberation of La Belle France. In the year 1943, when the situation was at its warmest, Canada produced:

                595,190,000 lbs. of copper
                444,061,000 lbs. of lead
                288,019,000 lbs. of nickel
                610,754,000 lbs. of zinc
                 17,345,000 oz. of silver
                  3,651,000 oz. of gold
                    220,000 oz. of platinum

and quantities of uranium and cobalt and palladium, selenium, mercury, etc.

In the six war years, base metals to the value of one billion dollars were produced; 1,620,000,000 lbs. nickel; 3,600,000,000 lbs. copper; 1,600,000,000 lbs. zinc; 1,300,000,000 lbs. lead.

A fair record for a patch of snow!

The Early Years

Five years after the epochal voyage of Columbus, Henry VII of England, with more foresight than generosity, commissioned John Cabot, the Genoa-born master mariner, to undertake a voyage of discovery. Cabot was to bear all the expenses, the good king retaining a twenty percent interest in the venture. This probably constituted Canada's first mining syndicate, for both king and sea captain were confident that much gold and treasure would be found on the "eastern shores of Asia."

On June 24, 1497, Cabot landed on Cape Breton Island. He found no gold but noted that the natives wore copper earrings. And so, on his return to England, he reported evidence of an abundance of copper. King Henry listened to the story, forgot or suppressed his disappointment at the lack of gold, and in the excitement of discovery appointed Cabot an admiral, at the same time bestowing upon him the princely gift of £10 and a yearly pension of £20. Cabot became a national hero. He had discovered a new northern land, Canada, which was not a part of Asia, and he had given Britain the right to claim it.

Among other things, Cabot reported great quantities of cod in the vicinity of his new-found land. This attracted the Breton fishermen of France, who boldly crossed the ocean in their tiny sailboats, towing black-painted dories and scattering from the Gulf of St. Lawrence to the Grand Banks. It was these hardy Frenchmen who gave Cape Breton its name.

Meanwhile, other European monarchs were roused to action. In 1500, Gasper Corterreal sailed from Portugal in Cabot's wake. Along the upper reaches of the St. Lawrence, he landed for reconnaissance, captured fifty aborigines, and carried them back to Portugal where they became galley slaves. This was a poor substitute for gold, but the "land of laborers" gave the country its name, Labrador. Corterreal sailed west again the following year, but with poetic justice, he disappeared at sea.

The Spaniards poked south, Balboa across the Panama isthmus to discover the Pacific and prove the New World was in truth no part of Asia. The Pope thereupon divided the New World between Spain and Portugal. The king of France, enraged at such presumption, dispatched Verrazano, a Florentine sea captain, to explore the new seas, but the Italian never returned from his voyage. The king then called upon Jacques Cartier, a master pilot in the bustling fishing fleet off Newfoundland. Cartier explored the regions of St. Lawrence thoroughly, brought back natives and reported the existence of mines of precious metals and "stones." On an inland trip from the St. Lawrence, which he named, Cartier related a curious incident. One of the native chiefs seized Cartier's gold-handled dagger (probably brass), pointed up the Ottawa River, and "made signs that such things [gold] came from up the river." Cartier did not follow this lead which might have brought him to the gold of Porcupine and Kirkland Lake and the silver of Cobalt, since the Indian route to Hudson Bay crossed this mineral-laden country. Instead, he bartered trinkets for a small quantity of gold and silver and "precious stones," the latter actually valueless pebbles (probably water-eroded fragments of mica-rich rock which dispersed the light and shone like diamonds). Intrigued with this discovery, Cartier occupied his crew almost a year loading ships with "Canadian diamonds" and returned, at long last, to France.

The king's jewelers soon appraised the worthlessness of the cargo. Cartier's services to the king were not forgotten, however, and the weary voyageur, honored with a title, retired to a seigneurial chateau.

Frobisher's Gold

"All is not gold that glitters," sang Shakespeare, mindful of the sad tale of Martin Frobisher. The good Martin, a buccaneer at a time when that profession was considered respectable, was unique in several respects. He was a good organizer and an excellent salesman, as well as an intrepid seafarer. His public relations man was Michael Lok, a London merchant who had friends in the English court. Divers gentlemen in high places were "sold" on the idea of gold in "the Orient," the route to which Frobisher declared was the "onely thing of the worlde that was left yet undone." And so, after much prodding, a syndicate was formed in the princely amount of £1,600. Money apparently went a long way in those days, for Frobisher was able to purchase two barques and retain a crew of thirty-two men.

Frobisher sailed in June, 1576, and on August 11 reached the northern bay which now bears his name. His encounter with the Eskimos bartering furs had unfortunate repercussions. Five of his men were captured, carried off and never seen again. He, in turn, snatched an Eskimo from his fellows and sailed for England. While he aroused considerable interest with his strange captive, who was pronounced a Mongol, thus verifying that the new continent was indeed Asia, real excitement was caused by a curious "black stone" which he had casually picked up together with various curios. This magic substance was reported to contain gold, though considerable doubt arose concerning the validity of the assays.

London became gold conscious; the boom was on. Stock salesman Lok had an easy time raising £4,400, of which amount Queen Elizabeth subscribed £500. Lok was made governor of the company and Frobisher, with a cut of 1 per cent, was made high admiral. In May, 1577, the new expedition sallied forth with high hopes. Landing in the straits, the eager men scurried about the islands. Cornish miners, imported for the occasion, extracted "two hundredth tunne of golde ore in the space of twentie dayes." The "high grade" was transported to England and various results were reported by miscellaneous assayers. The "ewer" was reported to contain gold, silver, copper, and lead. Other experts declared there was "noe manner of mettell at all." Queen Bess, however, seemed to be convinced that Frobisher had something and ordered a third voyage. Additional funds were obtained and fifteen small ships set sail for the northern El Dorado.

More than a thousand tons of "ure" were shipped to England on this occasion but new tests indicated the stuff was worthless. Lok, without means to discharge the debts of the expedition, became a bankrupt and was sent to prison. Frobisher survived the immediate crisis. Eventually he became a vice-admiral and under Drake and Hawkins served bravely in the glorious repulse of the Spanish Armada. It appears that Lok, the promoter, took the consequences for his associates.

On one of the islands in Frobisher Bay remains of pits have been located. From the dumps have come masses of amphibolite, a dark, highly altered rock containing hornblende and flashing specks of mica. This, it appears now, was Frobisher's "gold."

Samuel de Champlain

While Frobisher's expeditions gave impetus to later exploration by the English in the north, resulting in the discovery of Hudson Bay by Henry Hudson and the eventual organization of the Hudson's Bay Company in 1670, the French were busy establishing themselves to the south. The groundwork for the inevitable conflict was laid, culminating on the Plains of Abraham in 1759 when England seized final control of Canada.

Samuel de Champlain became the first French governor in 1603. That remarkable man, whose destiny is irrevocably stamped with that of Canada, was determined at once to build foundations for a permanent colony. Discovery of new lands was not enough, the mineral wealth of New France must be organized. Coincident with his amazing voyages of discovery and the establishment of Quebec and other settlements along the St. Lawrence, he commissioned picked men to search for mineral. From the reports submitted, it would seem that mines were at hand for the asking. A "mining engineer," Master Simon, reported "mines" of iron and silver at St. Mary's Bay, Nova Scotia. Monsieur Prévert vividly described a large copper mine in the Bay of Chaleur. Champlain's journals are replete with references to mineral deposits. On one occasion he was presented with a foot-long slab of native copper by an Algonquin warrior who described the source as westward, "near a large lake." Could this have been the famed Lake Michigan copper deposits which, at a later time, enriched and helped industrialize the United States? There is no way of knowing. While the indefatigable Champlain did in fact discover the Great Lakes, there is no record of his mineral findings in that remote region. Had he not been so obsessed with founding an empire for France, he might have devoted more time and energy to finding the source of native copper. Such a discovery, if made at that time, might have changed the whole course of history.

A Near Miss

The French made further efforts to found a mining dynasty in Canada, none of them very successful. In 1654 Louis XIV granted a concession to Nicholas Denys to mine gold, silver, and copper on Cape Breton Island. Denys announced the presence of coal on the island, but nothing was done about it at the time. Eventually, under the English, Nova Scotia became an important producer of coal, the first to be mined in North America.

Canadian mining made its bow to the world as the result of Sieur de La Portardière, who in 1667 was sent from France to investigate the iron deposits of Bay St. Paul and St. Maurice Valley. Years later, in 1736, the first charcoal furnaces were built near Three Rivers to treat these ores and convert them into iron, and these remained in operation until 1883, long after the English formally acquired Canada. Thus the earliest mining industry in Canada exploited iron and not gold; the primitive furnaces of Three Rivers constituted the pioneer metallurgical effort in North America.

Of greater interest to the historian is the fateful trip made by the Chevalier de Troyes, early in 1686. At that time a treaty of neutrality provided that Hudson Bay should be held in common by the fur traders of England, the Hudson's Bay Company, and France. To the men roaming the bush, however, this protocol had no meaning. Nor were the governments, unofficially, minded to observe the treaty. The area became a kind of no man's land where ambuscades, massacres, ship burnings, and pitched battles were routine. And so, led by de Troyes and the d'Ibervilles, one hundred *coureur de bois* and Indians made the long arduous trip from the St. Lawrence to Moose Factory on the lower bay, there to surprise the unsuspecting English.

The route led up to Ottawa to Lake Temiskaming and there the voyageurs camped on the historic trail. They were joined by friendly Indians who wished to show them a metal mine on the Northeast Arm of the lake. De Troyes consented to be led to the spot by an Indian guide who told him en route that bullets had been made from the ore. The French captain examined the deposit and noted in his diary that the "mine" was west of a "rock in the form of half circle." The showing failed to impress him and he and his companions hastened on to the shores of Hudson Bay, unaware that a great silver deposit was only a few miles from the mine. A little interest, followed by careful prospecting by so large a party, might easily have resulted in antedating the discovery of Cobalt by two hundred seventeen years. Certainly, if the French then possessed mines which eventually produced 400,000,000 ounces of silver, an unheard-of fortune in those days of hard money, the course of world history would have taken decidedly different directions. It is inconceivable that the French, ineffectual as they were at the time of their fall in Canada, would have surrendered to the British so easily. The country would have been fortified extensively and intendants of merit chosen instead of men like Bigot, an effete favorite of a dissolute king. Above all, a rush of prospecting would have followed, in the course of which other precious metal deposits might have been disclosed.

The mine which de Troyes examined was the property called "Anse à la Mine" in 1741. In later years, as the Wright Mine, it was developed but never did reach the stage of important production. As for de Troyes, his expedition against the English was crowned with success, but his glory was submerged in the swiftly moving tides of history.

Beginnings of Modern Mining

The remainder of the seventeenth and most of the eighteenth century were uneventful in mining. However, events laid the foundation of future greatness. In 1771 Samuel Hearne, a clerk in the employ of the Hudson's Bay Company, penetrated the unknown lands beyond the waters of Lake Athabaska and reported native copper in the Coppermine River area. Alexander Mackenzie, in 1789, followed the river which bears his name and stood on the shores of the Arctic Ocean, the first white man to view the western end of the long-sought Northwest Passage. Both Hearne and Mackenzie did not live to see the results of their discoveries nor did they even faintly realize the size and richness of the domain whose portals they were the first to open.

Not until the wounds of continual warfare, Indian insurrection, rebellion and political strife began to heal did Canada give undivided attention to its mineral possibilities. In 1842 William E. Logan was appointed to organize a geological survey, an event which marked the commencement of the mining industry in Canada. Logan, who was later knighted by a grateful Queen Victoria for his services, set about to organize a "plan of investigation as may promise to lead to the most speedy and economical development of the mineral resources of the country." For this task he was given the magnificent sum of $7,500. Nothing daunted, this Montreal-born Scot, who had studied geology at Edinburgh, proceeded to correlate all the known deposits from Nova Scotia to the Great Lakes. Under his guiding hand the coal deposits of Nova Scotia were firmly established; gold was found in paying quantities for the first time in Canada, copper prospects were investigated and the first commercial deposit of this metal came into production. His early maps, surprisingly accurate as they are voluminous, gave impulse to prospecting and played no small part in the ultimate development and growth of Canadian mining.

British Columbia

One hundred years after Columbus, the Spaniards had penetrated from western Mexico to the northern straits of British Columbia. Because of their vast holdings and preoccupations elsewhere, however, they did not investigate stories of silver, gold, and other metals reported by the natives. In 1778 Captain James Cook, flying the English flag, cruised the waters of the inland passage and sailed northward to the region bordering Alaska. On the vessel was a young midshipman who returned to the Sandwich Islands with his captain. The youngster's name was Vancouver.

Stories of sea otter on the northwest coast eventually brought results. In 1792 Americans, under Robert Gray, pushed their tiny vessel into the Columbia River and claimed the region for the United States. At the same time, the British sent George Vancouver, now a commander, into the same area. Cruising farther north, he failed to find a Northeast Passage, but he established English rights to the territory from the Columbia north to Sitka, the Russian stronghold.

While the fur trade provided incentive to colonization of the new region, the history of British Columbia is largely that of mining. The Hudson's Bay Company, traditionally hostile to the development of an industry which would cause an influx of population and so threaten a monopoly depending on remoteness for its continuance, found itself, willy-nilly, in the midst of a country alive with mineral discoveries. Governor James Douglas of the crown colony was also chief factor of the Hudson's Bay Company, and his dual capacity caused severe embarrassment. Gold in small quantities was being traded at the various posts by Indians who reported the existence of deposits as early as 1852. By 1857 news had reached California that British Columbia was a likely field for miners and a delegation journeyed north to interview Douglas about the possibilities. Despite the governor's edict that the gold areas could not be exploited until authorization had been obtained from the British government, word of finds on the Fraser River caused a stampede of men from the south. In 1863 the take of gold reached the respectable amount of $4,000,000. Douglas issued a series of unpopular proclamations and regulations, and a tense situation arose. Violence threatened, but Queen Victoria saved the situation by persuading Douglas to resign from the Hudson's Bay Company, while remaining crown governor. The new country was designated as British Columbia by the queen, the Hudson's Bay Company obligingly relinquishing all seignorial rights to the vast territory.

As the river gravels were worked, the onrush of gold seekers resulted in a congestion which could only be relieved by the discovery of new areas. Happily, the Cariboo district was discovered in 1860 and in the next year $2,000,000 was recovered by hand methods. This area eventually yielded more than $40,000,000 in gold. When river gravels were exhausted, attention was given to lode mines, which have maintained production to this day.

The first copper at Howe Sound was discovered in 1865, but it was not until 1898 that the Britannia Mine was acquired by the Britannia Mining & Smelting Company. The property passed through various hands, but eventual control fell to G. B. Schley, a New York banker, in 1918. Britannia became one of the important copper producers of Canada and for years supplied the principal revenue of the Schley's Howe Sound Mining Company.

Another successful copper enterprise in the Portland Canal area was the Hidden Creek Mine which finally came into the possession of Granby Consolidated Mining & Smelting Company in 1901, and is still operating.

The search for gold in the Similkameen area culminated in the discovery of copper deposits on Copper Mountain, later acquired by Granby. Operations here were conducted with such efficiency that what appeared to be an impossibly low-grade ore was treated at profit. Granby methods have since become classic, and Granby men, trained in achieving low costs, have filtered throughout the mining industry.

When the Canadian Pacific Railway reached the west coast in 1885, prospectors fairly swarmed into British Columbia. The Nelson area was discovered, shortly to be followed by Rossland, the latter becoming the first great mining camp in the province. By that time placer operations had dwindled to a mere trickle and all hope was centered on lode mines. The LeRoy began to ship high-grade gold-copper ore and this gave rise to a wild boom. A branch line was constructed to serve the area. Among the early visitors was Augustus Heinze. That doughty American, who had left his mark in Montana where he successfully fought powerful operators of Butte and emerged with a fortune of $14,000,000, now formed the British Columbia Smelting & Refining Company which obtained ore from the prolific LeRoy Mine. A smelter was built at Trail, on the banks of the Columbia River, and this was blown in during February, 1892. Meanwhile, the boom had careened to dizzy heights. Hundreds of properties changed hands at spectacular prices; there seemed no limit to rising stock values. In 1898, however, the inevitable collapse occurred. Prices tumbled overnight, with the result that thousands of speculators and operators were ruined. This incident had its reverberations throughout Canada; for more than a decade mining development was seriously impeded. However, the Heinze Smelter survived the chaos. In 1906 the plants were sold to the risingly powerful Consolidated Mining & Smelting Company, now dominated by the Canadian Pacific Railway, which had constructed various branch lines to feed the Trail Smelter and had become a majority stockholder in "Smelters."

By far the most important enterprise in British Columbia is the Sullivan Mine, in the Kootenay district. This deposit today produces more lead and zinc than any other single mine in the world. While large-scale production did not commence until 1922, the property was discovered in 1892 by Pat Sullivan and his partners, John Cleaver and Mike Holland, who had emigrated from the famous Coeur d'Alene district south of the border. Following the discovery, the mine passed through successive ownerships. Just before the turn of the century, the Canadian Pacific Railway constructed a connecting line from Cranbrook to Kimberley and thus made large-scale development of the Sullivan possible. A smelter and a power plant were constructed, and it seemed as though the enterprise was finally to come into its own. The ore proved to be very complex, however, and a complicated metallurgy was too much for the management.

Harassed by debts, the company was placed on the auction block and sold to creditors who at once effected a reorganization. At this point, the Guggenheims of New York took hold, but after limited work concluded that the deposit was hopelessly inadequate. Smelters, which was then operating in Rossland, decided differently, purchased the property and devoted the next few years to finding methods of treating a complex massive sulphide ore. By 1914 the mine was operating profitably, due to selective mining which by-passed the lower grade ores and extracted only the high-grade "plums." In 1922 the metallurgical problems were solved, and a large concentration plant built. The capacity of this mill was steadily increased until it is now able to handle 6,000 tons daily. Owing to the Sullivan, the Consolidated Mining & Smelting is now one of the truly great mining enterprises of the industry. Up to the end of 1945 the company had paid $130,000,000 in dividends from an $830,000,000 production.

The Bridge River area, like others, was first discovered by zealous placer miners. The Bralorne Mine, one of the few lode gold mines in the province to enjoy long continuous operation, has paid over $14,000,000 in dividends. Adjoining it, the Pioneer Mine, starting as late as 1931, has a dividend record of close to $10,000,000.

Up to the present, the largest single gold mine in the province has been the Premier Mine, with dividends of $20,000,000. Situated in the Portland Canal district, the mine was located in 1910 by Bill Dilworth and sold to Oscar Bush, a professional ice skater, for $5,000, finally gravitating into the long arms of the Guggenheims, but not before a local syndicate received $1,000,000 cash for a 52 per cent interest. The property swung into full production after World War I and the first dividend was paid in 1921.

The construction of the Alcan Highway, crossing the northern edges of the province, has heightened interest in these hitherto inaccessible regions. Hopes are high that new mining camps will be found by the many prospecting parties now scattered throughout this area.

Quebec

Canada's first bona fide gold discovery belongs to Quebec. Militant feminists will be pleased to learn that the prospector in this case was a woman who, by pure chance, found a small nugget in the Chaudière River basin in 1823. The find was a small one, however, as placer deposits go, and after desultory investigation received little attention. Twenty-five years later systematic mining was undertaken but, while $2,000,000 was accumulated over a period of time, the area has since passed into obscurity.

Also to Quebec goes credit for Canada's oldest mine, the Eustis. Found near Sherbrooke, this interesting property began to operate in 1865, and to the time of its final shutdown in 1934 produced nearly $20,000,000 in copper and pyrite.

It is in northwestern Quebec, however, that the future of mining rests. The story of discovery, the rise of Noranda, and the flowering of a great mining district will be detailed in a later chapter.

Asbestos

Of decided interest to Tommy Manville and others is the Thetford-Asbestos district, 115 miles northeast of Montreal. This area supplies the world with most of the fiber required for insulation, brake linings, and roofing. The first discovery was made in 1877 during railway construction, but no serious mining was undertaken until 1881 when W. H. Jeffrey, a wealthy farmer, began to mine one of the richer deposits. In New York City, W. H. Johns was manufacturing roofing material composed of paper, pitch, and burlap, and an inferior asbestos obtained from Staten Island. Another interested individual was Thomas F. Manville, who was then fabricating pipe coverings made of sheep wool and clay. Realizing that the product distributed by Johns was superior, Manville conferred with him, and, as a result, the Johns-Manville Company was formed in 1901. In 1916 this organization purchased the Jeffrey property. Two years later the Canadian Johns-Manville Co., Ltd., assumed ownership and has since operated continuously. Despite the 10,000,000 tons already extracted, the district, with its various mines, still has a long life assured. Production to date is approximately $375,000,000.

Ontario

The Lake of the Woods discoveries of gold in western Ontario during the 'eighties provided operators with more headaches than profits. The copper deposits along the northern shores of Lake Superior were largely disappointing, also, though the silver of Silver Islet managed to pay its owners respectable dividends. Iron mining started as early as 1820 but until the recent discovery of Steep Rock Mines, with more than 30,000,000 tons of high-grade ore, Ontario iron had contributed little to Canada. It was nickel, then an obscure and comparatively unknown metal, that gave the province its first real toehold in the mining world.

As early as 1848, Sir William Logan made note of a nickel occurrence at the west end of Lake Huron. Eight years later Alexander Murray, Logan's assistant, reported mineralization containing nickel in the now-famous Sudbury Nickel Range. In 1883, when the Canadian Pacific Railway was pushing westward, one of the cuts exposed copper-nickel sulphides. Following that time, properties were acquired by staking and purchase at the statutory price of one dollar an acre. Among others, Thomas Frood staked what was later to become the most valuable single deposit in the history of mining. Unaware of this, Frood, a timber cruiser, died in penury, long before the value of his ground was established.

On January 5, 1886, Samuel J. Ritchie, a railroad operator of Akron, Ohio, formed the Canadian Copper Company. His first visit to the area had been made in order to obtain lumber for the manufacture of wheel spokes in his carriage factory. In the course of his visit, he met Thomas Tate, secretary to the president of the C.P.R. It was Tate who had picked up the first ore in the railroad cut and from him Ritchie obtained knowledge of the new discoveries. At this juncture, R. M. Thompson, an ex-navy man from New Jersey who operated a copper smelter in Bayonne, New Jersey, appeared in Sudbury. He contracted to purchase 100,000 tons of "copper" ore from Ritchie, but on attempting to treat it he discovered that it contained a high percentage of nickel. This made the ore unacceptable to Thompson. Ritchie, undaunted, set about to discover how he could recover the nickel and make a virtue, and a fortune, of necessity. Accordingly, he engaged John Gamgee, an English inventor and metallurgist who had long been experimenting with nickel, principally with respect to its use in alloys. Within three years, the United States Navy had approved Gamgee's nickel steel plate and Congress voted a $1,000,000 appropriation for the purchase of the new metal. Other countries followed suit, and for the first time nickel appeared to be established as one of the important industrial metals. Meanwhile, Thompson had worked out the so-called Orford process of separating nickel from copper, one of the two standard methods in use today.

A consolidation of the various properties of the Canadian Copper Company was effected in 1901, the principals being Ritchie, Thompson, an American mine operator named Captain Joseph R. Delamar (of whom we shall hear more), E. C. Converse, and Charles M. Schwab. The new company was named the International Nickel Company of New Jersey. This organization, however, was not the sole proprietor of nickel properties in Sudbury. The other principal competitor was Mond Nickel, founded by the chemist, Dr. Ludwig Mond, later Lord Melchett. Mond, a German Jew, had emigrated to

England after he had earned a small fortune manufacturing and selling a soft drink in his native Germany, no mean feat in that land of beer drinkers. In England he developed a process of recovering nickel from a copper-nickel matte by an injection of carbon monoxide gas. Having made this discovery, he sent his engineers to Canada to acquire various properties on the Nickel Range. Among these was Frood Extension, purchased for a matter of $15,000.

Lord Melchett

The Mond Nickel Company became the chief rival of the International Nickel Company until the two organizations were merged in 1928. The necessity for amalgamation arose largely from the development of fabulously rich ore in the lower levels of the Frood Mine in 1927, the dip of which extended into Mond's Frood Extension. Subsequent work on the Mond revealed the existence of a 50,000,000-ton ore body with an approximate grade of $50 per ton in copper, nickel and platinum, unequaled anywhere for size and richness. While Nickel has other mines containing more than 200,000,000 tons of ore reserves, the high grade of the Frood constitutes the "cream," accounting in large part for the company's $500,000,000 dividend record to date.

At the present time, the Nickel Company has 14,584,025 shares of common stock outstanding, valued on the market at approximately $600,000,000. It supports half the city of Sudbury by virtue of an enormous payroll, and owns the bulk of mining properties on the so-called Nickel Range. The estate of Thomas A. Edison, however, retains title to several claims north of the Frood Mine, and Frood Deep Mines owns 480 acres immediately northwest of the Frood deposit on the projected extension of the dip of the ore bodies.

The giant octopus that has spread over most of the Nickel

Range has allowed one other property to escape its tentacles. Falconbridge Nickel Mines, Ltd., is the sole important independent producer of nickel at the present time and serves to lighten the shadow of monopoly. It was located in 1906 by Thomas Edison, who was seeking a nickel supply for the storage battery he had just invented. Accompanied by Mrs. Edison, he tested the heavily overburdened terrain with a magnetometer. Working eastward on the south rim of the "basin" in Falconbridge Township, his instrument recorded decided "kicks." Claims were staked and shaft work started. Unfortunately, the ground was difficult; quicksand was encountered at a depth of eighty feet, and Edison gave up further operations. Eighteen years later, when Ventures, Ltd., acquired the property and sank a shaft, it was demonstrated that had Edison continued his work downward another twenty feet he would have reached an important ore body!

Edison's abandoned claims reverted to the crown. W. E. Smith of Sudbury, waiting for the stroke of midnight when the ground would officially become "open," staked it. Smith had a connection with the E. J. Longyear Company of Minneapolis, a diamond drilling concern. Accordingly, drilling on the property was started in 1916, continuing into 1917. Enough work was done to demonstrate the presence of commercial ore along a strike of 8,000 feet and across good mining widths. The Longyear-Smith group thereupon sold 80 per cent interest to F. W. Bennett, a Minneapolis iron and flour magnate. On several occasions, Bennett was approached by agents of International Nickel Company, but each time complained that they considered the claims a poor risk and offered only a nominal purchase price. This situation was remedied when Thayer Lindsley appeared. Lindsley, who had just organized Ventures, Ltd., accepted Bennett's figure of $2,500,000, a sum he declared was the basis on which he had bought out his own associates. The Falconbridge Mines, Ltd., was formed and, managed by engineer J. Gordon Hardy, developed into a profitable enterprise and an important factor in the nickel industry. A smelter was erected, and from it was shipped a nickel-copper matte to the company-owned nickel refinery at Kristiansand, Norway. By astute agreement with London metal-selling agents, nickel and copper have been sold advantageously in Europe. The fear expressed by pessimists that no independent company could successfully compete with the giant International Nickel Company has not been realized. On the contrary, when the Norwegian plant was seized by the Nazis during World War II, International Nickel provided Canadian refining facilities for Falconbridge.

Cobalt, "Where the Silver Comes From"

Whether or not the first silver in Cobalt was uncovered by an irate blacksmith who is said to have hurled a hammer at a fox and struck, instead, an outcrop of the native metal, this camp mothered the entire mining industry of eastern Canada. Cobalt silver led to the gold of Porcupine, Kirkland Lake, Quebec, and even as late as 1944 welcomed a new grandson in the form of iron deposits in Labrador.

Like Sudbury and Asbestos, Cobalt owes its discovery to a railroad. In 1901, after considerable political maneuvering, the Ontario government financed the construction of a line from North Bay to Haileybury, the edge of which was designated as the "Great Clay Belt," potential farming country. In September, 1903, the right-of-way had been cut through the wilderness—"unexplored country," as it was described on the maps—to a point five miles south of Haileybury. Widespread criticism of the Temiskaming & Northern Ontario Railroad suddenly changed to paeans of praise when the news of silver discoveries was flashed round the world. Evidence points to J. H. McKinley and E. Darragh, crosstie contractors, as the first actual locators, and not Fred La Rose, the hammer-throwing blacksmith with bad aim. McKinley and his partner were attracted by the unusual color of the ground on the southeast shore of Long Lake. Prospecting uncovered thin plates of metal, which McKinley tested for ductility with his teeth. Samples were then sent to McGill University in Montreal, and there Milton Hersey, a metallurgist, found that the material assayed thousands of ounces of silver to the ton.

Meanwhile, La Rose had found a different kind of ore, niccolite, and showed it to his superiors, contractors John and Duncan Mc-Martin. A partnership was formed and La Rose proceeded to stake two claims, McKinley and Darragh having recorded their claims a month previously. Noah Timmins and his brother Henry, storekeepers, purchased La Rose's half interest in the two claims, thus founding the Timmins-McMartin combine which was to affect the entire history of Canadian mining. David Dunlap, a young lawyer of Mattawa, entered the syndicate, his legal talents and business acumen aiding the situation. At the time operations of the La Rose were suspended in 1930, the mine had produced over 25,000,000 ounces of silver and paid close to $8,000,000 in dividends.

Neal King, a fire ranger, sold four claims to M. J. O'Brien for $5,000. This canny lumberman retained the claims, himself financed the development, successfully defended himself in a costly litigation to substantiate his title, and was rewarded with the longest-lived mine in Cobalt, the only one in which the public did not participate. We shall hear much more of Timmins and O'Brien.

Altogether, Cobalt has produced in excess of 400,000,000 ounces of silver and its various companies have distributed above $100,000,-000 in dividends. The camp has long since passed its peak, but the prospectors, promoters and engineers it cradled have gone on to establish mining camps throughout the Dominion.

Porcupine

In view of Porcupine's record of gold production, today's observer is at a loss to understand the almost universal reluctance to accept the first discoveries in 1909. But it must be remembered that Ontario had earned a poor reputation because of the various fiascos in the Lake of the Woods area when rich surface deposits of gold failed to persist in depth.

Long before the Dome and Hollinger discoveries, gold had been known to exist in Porcupine. The area was traversed by a Hudson Bay trail which had been in existence for more than two hundred years. Indeed, prospectors reported in 1909 that when moss was removed from quartz veins, hobnail boot marks were found on rich gold exposures.

We shall learn in a later chapter just how the discoveries occurred and how the new district, suffering from neglect, financial anemia, and a devastating forest fire, at length rose from its trials to become the first gold camp in North America.

Kirkland Lake

When Harry Oakes stepped off the train at Swastika, in June, 1911, the Kirkland Lake gold area, as such, was unknown. The Swastika Mining Company, located athwart the newly constructed extension of the Temiskaming & Northern Ontario Railroad, was just beginning to produce from the first gold mill in the north. The rush into Larder Lake, twenty miles east of Kirkland Lake, had come and gone. Few people were aware that the Burrows brothers, as early as 1906, had found gold and recorded claims in Kirkland Lake, only six miles east of Swastika.

Bill Wright and his brother-in-law, Ed Hargreaves, located their first ground in July, 1911. At the recording office in Matheson, to the north, they learned that considerable ground had been staked from Swastika eastward. Accordingly, they pegged claims just beyond the staked area. When Wright discovered gold, the story was rumored outside. While it attracted only minor interest, the four Tough brothers, who, with Clem Foster, were engaged in building a road from Swastika to Kirkland Lake, decided to stake near Wright and Hargreaves. In the course of their preparations they met Harry Oakes at Jimmy Doige's grocery store in Swastika in January, 1912.

Oakes, who spent much of his time at the recorder's office in Matheson, now offered to supply up-to-date information regarding the status of the old Burrows claims, provided he would participate in any claim staking. Since the trip to Matheson was a lengthy one and the "dope" would require much time to obtain, a bargain was made. Oakes thereupon informed the Tough frères that the claims in question would be open within a few hours!

The party left Swastika early the next morning, and, despite heavy snow and a killing frost of more than fifty degrees below zero, reached Kirkland Lake before daybreak and restaked the five old Burrows claims. The men moved quickly and this proved fortunate, for only an hour after their work was finished Bill Wright appeared, prepared to stake the same ground. Wright, however, did not make the trip in vain, for he staked the adjoining western claims, which eventually became the Sylvanite Mine, a far more profitable enterprise than the Tough-Oakes.

Spectacular gold was soon found on the Tough-Oakes property and a new camp appeared to be on its way. The mine, however, did not live up to early expectations. Notwithstanding, the Tough-Oakes was important, for it attracted the first real interest in the Kirkland Lake area and provided Harry Oakes with a matter of $200,000. This he received ultimately when, after protracted litigation, he was able to sell his stock and devote all his time and money to the Lake Shore.

Momentous events were impending. A diligent prospector, Oakes found a small gold vein on the southern shore of Kirkland Lake and staked two claims. Bill Wright promptly tied on to Oakes, his claims being largely water. Staking under these conditions was difficult, and it was no surprise that Wright's claims were oversize. Arthur Cockeram, a rising young mining man, shrewdly appraised the situation, and since the law provided that anything above the prescribed forty acres per claim was free ground, ingeniously planted his posts to embrace the "surplus" of exactly $7\frac{1}{2}$ acres. This was not an extensive holding, but, as it happened, Cockeram's claim jutted between the Teck-Hughes and Lake Shore properties. Several years later Oakes paid Cockeram and his syndicate $30,000 and 50,000 shares of Lake Shore for this bit of water, for beneath the lake rested the richest section of ore in Canada. Cockeram and his friends, as well as Oakes, were not to know this for some time. In 1937, the 50,000 shares of Lake Shore were worth over $3,500,000, but by that date Arthur Cockeram and the Connell brothers had sold their holdings. Only Shirley Cragg, the fourth syndicate member, retained a sizable portion of his stock.

Oakes, who had formed the 2,000,000-share Lake Shore Gold Mines, Ltd., obtained Wright's claims for a consideration of 200,000 shares, and then began his epic battle to build Lake Shore into a mine. Finally, in 1918, he was able to commence production on a 50-ton daily basis. Since then mill capacity has been increased in stages to 2,600 tons. Ore was of a richness and extent never before seen in Canada. In a comparatively short time the mine became one of the few $100,000,000 dividend payers in history, and Oakes, whose dramatic career will be reviewed in later pages, went on to become a modern King Midas.

Wright fared well. In addition to his Lake Shore stock, he retained a quarter interest in the Wright-Hargreaves mine while Hargreaves sold his interest for a few thousand dollars. The property came under control of a Buffalo group headed by E. S. Miller, Albert Wende and Oliver Cabana, who supplied the first money for production. Known at first as the "mine with a mill without ore," the Wright-Hargreaves confounded croakers and critics by developing into a bonanza second only to Lake Shore. From 1921 to 1945 it produced close to $110,000,000 and boasts a dividend record of $43,000,000.

The Sylvanite Mine, staked by Wright, became a successful, if modest, producer. Since 1927 it has produced in excess of $31,000,-000. Dividends to the end of 1945 totaled close to $9,000,000.

At one time, stock in the Teck-Hughes Mine, staked by the Hughes brothers, sold at less than five cents per share because of the disappointing results obtained by Nipissing Mining Compay of Cobalt, which elected to drop its option. Taken in hand by Charles Denison of Buffalo, the claims were given another chance. Denison and his associates loaned Teck-Hughes more than $600,000. Instead of foreclosing, they caused the company to reorganize, accepted stock for their bonds, and then purchased the Orr claims adjoining, into which the Teck ore zone was dipping. Under the persistent and able management of Dr. D. L. H. Forbes, the mine finally came into its own. Though small in acreage, it produced approximately $81,-000,000 from 1917 to 1945, with a dividend record of more than $41,000,000. The company has enjoyed outstanding success in outside exploration, its prize being the Lamaque Mine in Quebec, a child now mothering its aging parent.

Kirkland Lake Gold Mines, Ltd., was the first property given the right to employ the name "Kirkland" in its incorporation. Acquired by purchase through the efforts of Bob Jowsey, the mine was harassed with innumerable difficulties before reaching important production. Today, however, it is one of the Kirkland Lake mines which appears to have more hope for the future than memory of the past. A dividend record of more than $4,000,000 appears to be only a start toward better days.

Macassa Mines, the westward limit of the producing mines in the area, was a latecomer. Incorporated in 1926 and promoted by Bob Bryce, a mining engineer, this enterprise began as a pure geological speculation, there being no surface expression of ore. Bryce struggled desperately to obtain capital for what was considered a wildcat. After years of effort, ore was encountered at a depth of 1,500 feet. In 1934 the first dividend was paid, and yearly distributions have continued to the present time without interruption. To the end of 1945 these exceeded $7,000,000 from a production of approximately $20,000,000.

Larder Lake

After remaining dormant for more than thirty years, this Rip Van Winkle camp was revived by the development of the Kerr-Addison Gold Mines which in many respects is the most remarkable gold mine in Canada. A detailed history will be given elsewhere. Suffice it to say here that this property, abandoned years ago, has now developed more than 20,000,000 tons of $8 ore and in a few years of operation has paid close to $9,000,000 in dividends. Possibilities are still vast; from present indications, an eventual total of 50,000,000 tons is probable. This will place Kerr-Addison in the Lake Shore-Hollinger-Noranda class.

The success of Kerr-Addison has resulted in renewed development throughout the district.

The Gold of Patricia

This area, which contains the Red Lake and Pickle Crow districts, has already distributed more than $20,000,000 in dividends, the most important producer being Pickle Crow, followed by Central Patricia and the various mines of Red Lake. The first gold in Red Lake was discovered in 1925 by the Howey brothers and the camp received its initial development under the sponsorship of the ubiquitous Jack Hammell. This same man was also responsible for the amazing Pickle Crow Mine. Balked in his efforts to obtain financial assistance from various mining companies, he at length undertook to finance the property himself. Success came in 1935 when production began. Since that year the mine has produced $22,000,000 and has paid more than $8,000,000 in dividends. Adjoining the Pickle Crow is the Central Patricia Mine which was sponsored by Fred Connell, who obtained the property from Louis Cohen's Chalcocite Syndicate. From 1934 to 1945 the Central "Pat" produced in excess of $16,000,000, with a dividend record of $4,000,000.

Thunder Bay

Long the stepchild of Ontario gold mining, this section has become a steady producer of gold. Thanks to the discoveries in the Little Long Lac area and the efforts of the late "Joe" Errington, the district now has several important producers. In the short period of ten years, Thunder Bay mines have distributed $11,000,000 in dividends and the immediate future of the camp appears bright.

Manitoba

The southern portion of Manitoba is a flat, drift-covered area of prairie and forest, and has become justly famous as one of the vital granaries of the world. Its northern stretches, densely wooded, contain a strip of so-called Pre-Cambrian rocks which have proved fertile in the production of mines. Despite the fact that northern Manitoba has for several hundred years been the scene of Hudson's Bay Company's fur-trading activities and had been extensively explored, no important mining occurred until the development of the great Hudson Bay Mining & Smelting Company in the 'twenties.

The earliest gold discovery reported was in 1881, the locality being Black Island on Lake Winnipeg. The first discovery of gold in the Rice Lake area, which now contains the successful San Antonio Mines, was made in 1911. A small mill was constructed in 1912, but this proved a failure. Other discoveries were made, including that of the Central Manitoba Mines, which in 1927 operated a small mill, but all these were disappointing. The Bingo Mine fiasco, where high-grade gold was reported, later found to be "salted," did much to impair the mining reputation of the province.

In 1917 a deposit of sulphides containing copper and gold was reported at the Mandy Mine northwest of the Pas. So rich was this ore that the material was bagged and taken by dog team and sleigh to the Pas and from that point shipped by rail to the distant Trail

Smelter in British Columbia. While the deposit was mined out in its entirety, interest in the area was heightened, with resultant prospecting after the war leading to the discovery of the Sherritt-Gordon Mine.

In 1932 the active Bob Jowsey located God's Lake Gold Mine. In 1940 the Snow Lake area broke into the headlines when Howe Sound drilled what appeared to be a major gold deposit. Meanwhile, the San Antonio Mines, after years of struggle but helped by the liberal purse of Noah Timmins, blossomed forth into one of the important gold producers of the Dominion, with a production of close to $18,000,000 since 1932.

Long considered a white elephant and requiring almost twenty years of travail from the period of discovery to the date of production, the Hudson Bay Mining & Smelting Company has already paid more than $55,000,000 in dividends and has established new precedents in metallurgy and mining.

Sherritt-Gordon Mines owes its existence to Bob Jowsey and Thayer Lindsley, who together revived development of the property after other operators had passed unfavorable judgment upon this copper-gold deposit which at first seemed limited in extent and poor in grade. Recently this company has drilled a promising occurrence of copper-nickel in the Granville Lake area.

Northwest Territories

The greatest interest in this vast region centers in Yellowknife, the hub of the "Territories." Once regarded as a barren arctic outpost, this district, enlivened by Gilbert Labine's discovery of uranium at Great Bear Lake in 1930, has furnished more fireworks in its short existence than any other of the camps. Owing to its romantic situation, the atomic energy furor, and the richness and frequency of gold discoveries, the "last frontier" has captured the imagination of Americans as well as Canadians. A constant stream of publicity, much of it puerile, has accompanied field developments, but this does not detract from the undoubted possibilities of Canada's newest mining area.

Summary

As countries go, Canada is still young. For two centuries it was occupied with discovery and colonization while enduring monotonous warfare between settlers and Indians, English and French, in addition to various internal ruptures. With confederation at last realized in 1867, Canada was unified for the first time, and was able to give its undivided attention to the pursuits of peaceful nation-hood.

Not until the turn of the nineteenth century did mining become important, and since that time its forward progress has paced Canada's coming of age.

Canada has been described as a geographical, historical and political monstrosity, with its 11,500,000 population centered along the southern border and composed of divided French and English elements, each jealously maintaining a distinct way of life under the common shadow of the United States. And yet, this enigmatic Dominion, sprawling from one coast to the other and reaching toward the thin regions of the North Pole, has emerged from World War II with a new consciousness of power which places it among the select countries of the globe. More poised and mature, Canadians have come to realize their own peculiar heritage, neither British nor American, and in this realization they stand at the threshold of a greater destiny.

Canada surprised itself with the vastness of its own war contribution. At a time when a large part of society has gravitated toward uniformity and standardization, this Dominion offers welcome contrast as the champion of individual expression. Its armed forces consisted almost entirely of volunteers. By comparison, we in the United States would have required almost 10,000,000 enlistments. Of the RAF personnel, one-quarter were Canadian. Practically all the airmen of the empire were trained in Canada under the British Commonwealth Air Training Plan. From a country whose navy was nonexistent in 1939, Canada became second only to the United States in shipbuilding, and at V-E day operated an armada of almost a thousand fighting vessels. Prodigious amounts of arms were produced and shipped to England, along with precision equipment which had never before been manufactured in Canada. Within its borders was located the largest small-arms factory in the empire. And in food products Canada proved to be England's breadbasket.

In metals, above all, Canada outdid itself, not only in the quantity, but in the quality and diversity supplied. The medical services of the entire United Nations depended largely upon Canadian radium, and atomic bombs, which cut short what probably would have been a long Pacific war of attrition, were made possible by the uranium of Great Bear Lake. Over two billion pounds of nonferrous metals annually came from Canada's mines at a moment when mechanized warfare was consuming metal in astronomical quantities.

As an agricultural entity, implemented by wood products and furs, Canada would have remained a mere appendage of the British

Empire. But mining transformed the economy and social life of the Dominion, giving it the stature of a great power with an arresting position in the complex world of today. Canada leads all others in the production of asbestos, nickel, platinum, iridium, and palladium; it is second in zinc and cadmium; third in gold, copper, magnesium, and cobalt; fourth in silver and lead. Because of plentiful water power, Canada has the largest aluminum treatment plants in the world, and in a single war year produced more of this indispensable metal than did all countries combined in 1939. In British Columbia the largest new mercury mine in the Western Hemisphere came to the rescue when a shortage threatened early in the war, cut off as we were from the usual Spanish and Italian sources of this strategic mineral.

Canada must export or die. It produces far more than it requires in almost every essential, and while its industries along the St. Lawrence have increased, raw products obtained from the hinterland comprise the lifeblood of the nation. In the 18-year period from 1927 to 1944 the value of mine exports exceeded those of farm or forest, constituting almost 34 per cent of derivative products sold abroad. In addition to being the premier extractive industry of the country, mining's impressive gold production, normally $200,000,000 a year, has given Canada a compelling position at international monetary conferences, besides furnishing domestic currency and credit requirements.

Mining is the broad foundation of Canada's internal structure. The railroads, half nationalized, would be a grievous burden to the small population were it not for the substantial tonnages of mineral output. With imports, this amounts to more than a third of the nation's freight traffic. The industry absorbs 17 per cent of developed power resources, helping Canada achieve the distinction of having the largest per capita power consumption in the world. The Canadian miner receives a larger weekly wage than workers in all other industries. With his family and those dependent upon mining products for their livelihood, he constitutes 7 per cent of Canada's population, with $200,000,000 yearly spending power. The industry, in addition, purchases from $100,000,000 to $150,000,000 annually in supplies and equipment, thus maintaining a goodly proportion of Canada's industrial plant. And the taxes obtained from mining have been, and still are, enormous, enabling Canada to maintain a pay-as-you-go fiscal policy, the big reason for its unique refusal of Lend-Lease during the war, the only country in the family of the United Nations which did not take advantage of Uncle Sam's generous paternalism.

In short, Canada would not be the modern, virile country it is today without the mining industry. Despite already impressive achievement, Canadian mining, if handled intelligently, is still capable of great expansion, and in this happy situation can be compared to the American West as it stood two generations ago, before the final immensity of so many camps was established.

Agriculture, it might be contended, makes for a happier people. But in the "Granary of Empire" days, dislocations in the loosely strung Dominion were severe whenever the wheat market fell into a decline. It has been proved, too, that 90 per cent of Canada's terrain is unfit for farming. And when we turn to Canada's gigantic storehouse of timber, we find that lumbering, though admittedly important, is basically locust-like in character. While providing large revenues, these operations are itinerant, sweeping as they do through large areas and leaving them uninhabitable for years. The fur trade, too, is neither constructive nor of any fundamental value in an industrial society, and actually has retarded colonization and settlement, since by its very nature it requires an undisturbed forest remoteness.

Canada has long been misinterpreted as a land of ice and snow, habitable only on the more congenial fringes along the south. This ancient canard persisted for more reasons than Voltaire's famous, or infamous, wisecrack. Most of the early Canadian exploration was devoted to search for a Northwest Passage, and explorers approached the land from the north. Journals of the time were replete with references to icebergs, snowy wastes, Eskimos, and the like. And the fur trade, as we know, encouraged this belief. For two centuries Canada's chief export was peltries, later augmented by wheat and wood products. The world wrote Canada off as a country good for only a few raw materials, otherwise inhospitable.

To mining Canada owes the breakdown of this dangerous myth. A new and providential life began as prospectors and engineers penetrated the bush, pitched their tents, and built rough log cabins in the virgin woodland. Industrious towns rose where only moose and bear had lived before; railroads pushed forward, hungry for traffic, and a small army of settlers and tradesfolk trekked north. Farmers began to prosper in latitudes which had been too quickly written off as hopeless. As the land responded bountifully to plow and harrow, untouched powersites, once mournfully regarded as wasted, were put to effective use. Mines meant new money and this, in turn, meant new business, and for the first time Canada experienced the comforting knowledge that its bush was an imperishable asset. Mining, let it never be forgotten, supplied first practical proof of the friendliness of the north, which today is growing in population at twice the rate of the sheltered south.

The service of mining in pushing back the frontier cannot be overemphasized. It has given to Canada a pioneer quality, a spirit of independence, self-reliance, and confidence, a species of rugged manhood which has become a curiosity in many countries. It has colored every aspect of Canadian life in strong, certain tones, and despite the cleavages among its people, has furnished a close-knit singleness of purpose which will in time overcome sectional differences. Canadians look north instinctively, as do, indeed, all thinking men everywhere, for there lies the future, the true crossroads of the world.

The provinces, by their liberal mining laws, have given every encouragement to individual effort. Except for Labrador, large concessions are unknown. There is no land grant as in Africa, where the "chartered company," so dear to the hearts of English speculators, has proprietorship over the large part of South African mineral wealth. In Canada, anyone over the age of eighteen, regardless of nationality, can purchase a miner's license for $5 or $10 (the amount varies in the different provinces) which entitles him to stake a designated number of claims each year. This freedom from restriction is unique in present-day society, when most countries adhere to a rigid nationality and geographical groups clamor for nationhood. The prospector is circumscribed only by assessment work requirements; he must perform a specific number of days' work on any claim he stakes. (Failing this, his ground reverts to the crown and may be staked by others.) Usually he is granted a patent or its equivalent after he has completed five years' work and from that time on need pay only a nominal tax as permanent owner of the land. The old era of the sourdough is giving way to a modernized version of the mine seeker who is well equipped and employed at a salary by syndicates and mining companies. Nevertheless, the Canadian prospector is still a mover at will, a free-lance operator who has escaped regulation in an age of government centralization.

Ottawa has contributed to the north by its geological survey programs, but critics have been vociferous in condemning a halfhearted attitude which they say is fashioned by the as yet relative insignificance of the northern electorate. It is shown that frontier roads have been few, and those finally built are pitifully inadequate to serve the boundless territory still unexplored. In their defense, politicians say they are loath to authorize expenditures of public funds where they cannot see an immediate or urgent objective. The north is, however, objective enough. The discovery of the Cobalt area was completely fortuitous, the unexpected result of railroad construction undertaken by an Ontario government motivated only by hopes of colonization. The results of this courageous step have been far-reaching, not only in the princely wealth of mineral and high revenue won, but in benefits measured in terms of human values, incalculable by any evaluation device.

The constant pressure exerted by the mining industry upon the Dominion for assistance in various forms may be said to spring from entirely selfish motives. And yet the fact is incontrovertible that Ottawa has been generally dilatory, even indifferent, in forwarding the advance of an industry on which the broad foundations of the entire nation rest. Unless leaders rise to the occasion and accept a greatness fairly thrust upon them, they will watch the stature of their country steadily diminish and make mockery of their venerated statesman, Sir Wilfrid Laurier, who, in a moment of supreme eloquence, declared, "The twentieth century belongs to Canada!"

Voltaire's "Patch of Snow" Has
Yielded:

Classification	Period	Production	Value
All Minerals	1886 to 1945		$11,147,443,287
Gold	1858 to 1945	94,723,542 oz.	2,786,858,311
Silver	1887 to 1945	893,786,525 oz.	501,172,826
Copper	1886 to 1945	10,198,665,789 lbs.	1,196,680,616
Lead	1887 to 1945	8,912,378,667 lbs.	385,553,028
Zinc	1898 to 1945	7,433,600,000 lbs.*	311,884,088
Nickel	1889 to 1945	4,425,979,394 lbs.	1,198,630,143

Dividends Paid by Canada's Metal Mines to December 31, 1945—$1,534,129,851.

* Estimated.

CHAPTER IV

The Prospector

September 27, 1928

J. A. Riddell, a former Coeur d'Alener, now residing at Broken Hills, Nevada, recently returned from Rouyn, Quebec, home of the big Noranda Mine, where he spent about three months. In a letter to a friend in this city he says, "I did not like it up there and three months was enough for me. That country is no place for a desert rat, up there among the muskrats. I found out one thing, that if a prospector can't find a mine in America, he will not better himself by going to Canada, for that is the hardest in the world to get into and look for a mine. It is the toughest country I was ever in."

Wallace (Idaho) *Miner*.

Pop Kenyon, his head propped against the grub box, his legs sprawled before the campfire, sniffed contentedly. We had examined his claims—"the hasty glance," he called it—the dinner of partridge and bacon was good, and more important, his pipe was drawing well.

"So you're from Bosting, Massachu," he chirped. "I know the town; they got an orchestra or somethin' down there, ain't they?"

I laughed in assent.

"There two days," he announced. "Didn't like it much. Them people ain't a bit happy."

And what was this crickety oldster of the bush doing in the city of the bean and the cod?

"Peddlin' claims, what do you think?" he explained. Reflectively, he chewed on a bit of wood. "Only I didn't sell any."

Lying before us, his deep-blue eyes smiling and his white hair moving in the gentle breeze from the lake, he might have been a banker enjoying a vacation trip in the north. Only the bronzed weather-beaten face, the soiled ragged clothing, betrayed his calling. As with so many prospectors, he breathed contempt for technical men, but missed being offensive by reason of an ever-present sense of humor.

"What would you do, Pop," I asked when he had finally dispatched Massachusetts and engineers to oblivion, "what would you do if you made a really big stake?"

"What would I do?" He chuckled at the prospect. "Why, I'd buy me the largest pair of snowshoes in Manitoba, first thing. An' then, by God, I'd cache 'em in the biggest pine tree I could find an' go to Califo'nia for the rest of my life!"

Of the old school also, but of different disposition, was the late Jake Davidson. More creeks were named after him than any other prospector in Canada. In his lifetime, old Jake was a favorite subject over many a campfire. A lone traveler always, his actions never failed to elicit wonder and comment. For one thing, he scorned the use of a tent, and for a time merely slung a hammock, which he himself had sewed from discarded clothing, between two trees, defying flies and weather alike. Later, he sought out caves, no mean feat in a generally flat country devoid of limestone. One such shelter has since become famous, Jake's habitation when he staked and prospected the now producing Young-Davidson Mine in Matachewan. Jake was tough. He made his own canoes, much as the Indians did in the time of Champlain, covering the birch-bark sections with strips of metal salvaged from old tin cans. By some it was rumored that he had set bush fires the better to prospect the country, but from silent Jake came never an admission or denial. Matachewan, where he made his headquarters for many years, abounds with versions of his exploits.

"Did you ever hear about Jake diving for pearls?" asked Paddy

Plaunt, when I met him picking specimens on the Young Davidson, years ago. "No? Well, he decided there was money to be made on the bottom of the Montreal River, so he sheds his clothes—"

"Just a moment," I interposed. "How about the flies?"

"Flies, hell. Jake didn't mind 'em no more'n he did cream puffs. Used to cover himself with grease. Stunk like hell, he did. He just didn't have no feelin's about anythin'. Well, sir, he dives into the water and comes up puffin', his hands full of clams—you know, them fresh-water things. And he keeps divin' and comin' up with them clams until he has a pile five feet high. Then he throws on his greasy pants and shirt and sits down to examine his ketch. With a knife he opens every single one of them things. Lookin' for pearls, he says. Yes, sir, he done that one whole summer. It was somethin' to see, I tell you, when he comes up for air, soundin' out like a big fish, only he's covered with hair like a gorilla. You could folly his trail along the river by them piles of shells."

Jake was in Rouyn early. Scorning the immediate vicinity of Noranda, which was too crowded for him, he followed a creek leading from the Bend of the Kinojevis. More than twenty years have passed since his battered canoe pushed through the horsetails of that twisting, log-strewn waterway, and now Jake has been immortalized by the creek and a regional fault named in his honor, astride which sits the Rouyn Merger Mine, about to produce gold for the first time. His old claims, long ago abandoned, are today worth a fortune. Thwarted in Rouyn, he lived to see Hollinger take over and operate his Young-Davidson Mine where today visitors can see his cave, boarded and carefully preserved.

And there was Sam Otisse, moose hunter par excellence, half Indian, another lone wolf who divided the Matachewan area with Jake. After a brief interlude of prosperity during Elk Lake boom, he staked what is now the Matachewan Consolidated Mines. Sam decided to enjoy his new-found wealth. He purchased an automobile, covered the back seat with canned goods, and started on a tour west. But before he had gone very far, difficulties arose. Having been instructed by his bank to communicate at once if he found himself in trouble, he had the following wire sent from Sault Ste. Marie:

HAVE RUN OUT OF CANNED GOODS. SHIP 500 LBS. IMMEDIATELY.

The bank's reply is not on record.

Little known outside of Gowganda, but a character in his own right, is Billy Bourke. For years he alternated between his duties as fire ranger and prospector, a circumstance which caused him no end of embarrassment and confusion, since government employees are forbidden by law to stake claims. A rapid talker, and not too discreet, he often found himself speaking in the wrong role, but with comical nimbleness he always managed to extract himself from an awkward situation. When I first met him, he was a ranger, but his heart was in mining. Whenever he returned to town for supplies, he invariably showed up at our cabin with a specimen.

"Annythin' to it?" he would ask hopefully.

"We'll assay it and let you know," was Bob's reply.

"If it kicks, there's another Hollinger waitin' for youse lads. On'y, don't be forgettin' Billy, d'ya hear?"

We promised to be faithful, but the assays continued to be low —until one day a sample returned $7 a ton in gold. This was it, the break we had been waiting for, and though we had just returned from a hard trip through Cabot and Connaught, it was decided to hunt up Billy and his partner, Joe Ophelia, immediately. A few cautious inquiries gave us the needed information, and we were off for Duncan Lake at the crack of dawn, spirits high and hopes soaring. We met our men sooner than expected, in the middle of Obushkong Lake, not more than fifteen miles from town. Fred gently directed our canoe broadside to that of the rangers.

"Hi, fellers, what's up?" cried Billy, while his partner, impassive as ever, regarded us with solemnity.

Knowing Billy's excitability, we had prepared to lead into the matter of the assay gradually, but Billy, with unpredicted shrewdness, had divined that something unusual had happened. Our hesitation heightened his suspicions.

"You got the assay?" he shouted.

"Yes, we did." Fred Thompson tried to appear casual. "Not too bad, either. Seven dollars."

"Seven dollars!" Billy smacked his paddle on the lake surface and sprayed us all, then stared at us wildly through the wetness. "It's another Hollinger! I told youse I'd get it! Men, it ain't a vein, it's a whole formation!" He continued to thrash about, uncontrollable, while silent Joe plied a busy paddle to prevent the red canoe from upsetting.

After diligent effort, we managed to calm Billy down long enough to discuss a plan of staking. But our man insisted upon being protected by an agreement. Out came Bob's Lefax, and in a few minutes Billy, head cocked like a parrot, was listening to the cryptic phrases of a contract. An oath broke from him.

"Never mind them whereases and all that loon dung, I don't understan' a word. Give me your meat hooks, partners, an' we'll let 'er go at that. Youse boys is honest, so what t'hell."

Even as we reached over the gunwales to shake hands and seal the compact, we quickly made plans. The find was two days' travel north, and all five of us would make for the spot at once.

"No more fire rangin'!" cried Billy.

The canoes turned round, Billy leading the way, and my first gold rush was on.

The trip was unforgettable. Billy insisted upon taking several short cuts, and this meant negotiating creeks. They were so full of deadheads and beaver dams, so winding and tortuous, that in the end we required almost a week to reach our destination. Day after day we toiled; for a time it appeared we would never again see the friendly surface of a lake. Billy cursed the fire rangers, who were supposed to keep the waterways clear, forgetting that this was his assigned task. Whenever a log obstructed our way, he hopped out of his canoe, straddled the offending stick which glimmered under several inches of water, and let go with his ax. At each stroke, a geyser of water showered him.

"Son of a bitch," he choked, his face and clothes dripping, and down would go the ax, viciously.

"If I on'y had me five-poun' ax!" he gasped, before the next deluge hit him. "Them bastard fire rangers!" More water. "Pig-ruttin', squaw-hoppin' . . ." Water, water everywhere, and how the gallant Billy did drink! Joe looked on quietly. Both he and Billy were oblivious to our convulsed laughter. Our suggestions, when we could talk, that Billy keep his mouth closed, were ignored.

Before the trip was over, Billy was not overly fond of beavers, for their innumerable dams added to our difficulties, requiring dozens of pull-overs. But at night, when the day's trials were over, he sat before the campfire and regaled us with stories, most of them humorous but unprintable. One of his sage observations, however, deserves mention. Apropos of nothing, he declared that balsam gum, taken internally, was a sure cure for gonorrhea. We guffawed in open derision.

"Wassamatta?" Billy glared at us defiantly. "I been drinkin' the God-damn stuff all me life, an' jest lookut me! Sound as a bear cub!"

We reached El Dorado at last, somewhat less hopeful, for Billy's enthusiasm had waned noticeably as we neared our goal.

"Where's the showing?" asked Bob.

"You're standin' on it," replied Billy without hesitation.

"Let's eat," suggested Joe, the first words he had spoke since the meeting on Obushkong.

One look at Billy's "formation" and we agreed that Joe's idea was not bad. After lunch we made a more careful examination and decided that Billy had stumbled upon a narrow and flat-lying rhyolite, sparsely mineralized with pyrite. Certainly, the showing was nothing uncommon. We broke off samples for later assay, roasted and crushed some, and tried panning, but never a "color" of gold could we see.

Weeks later, all the assays returned blanks, and then Bob, re-examining his files, discovered that he had inadvertently mixed Billy's original sample with one taken near Kirkland Lake.

"An expensive mistake," he said ruefully.

"Oh, I don't know," said Fred. "We saw a bit of new country, had a bellyful of laughs, and Arnie can now go back to the States and tell the folks he participated in a gold rush."

As for Billy, he was wonderfully calm about the whole thing, once the facts were known. But all through the summer he offered to perform little tasks for us, thus betraying concern about our attitude toward him. An opportunity to serve us came when Jim Thompson, one of our good friends, asked him to carry a message to us. We were out in Hangingstone Lake area at the time, and Billy and Joe were headed in the same direction.

"If you see them," instructed Jim, "say that they should come out at once. Pete Graham wants Bob to get in touch with him at New Liskeard about a show Ed Horne staked in Quebec."

Days later Billy spotted us as we were leaving the north end of a portage. There was a small but dangerous rapid intervening, but Billy elected to make the run, aware that if he and Joe stopped to cross the portage we three would soon outdistance his canoe and the message would be undelivered. Though he and Joe were expert canoemen, they exposed themselves to possible destruction. But this was no deterrent. Yelling instructions to the unmoving Joe, the intrepid Billy sent the canoe into white water. A few quick twists of the paddle, a bad moment or two when rocks scraped their bottom, and the fire rangers were catapulted safely into the quiet waters of the lake.

We turned to meet them.

"I've got somethin' to tell youse," shouted Billy, standing up and waving his paddle. "Jim Thompson says for youse . . ."

Once more, as earlier in the summer, the red and gray canoes were saddled together.

"Le's see," Billy looked worried. "Jim says for youse . . . he says . . . le's see . . ." and poor Billy rubbed his unshaved jowl in misery. "Now, what in Christ did he say? You remember, Joe?"

Joe smiled and shook his head with imbecilic gravity. To us, it was inconceivable that these men had just risked their lives to deliver a message they had already forgotten.

"By the Jesus, I don't know," wailed Billy. "It's somethin' about seein' someone somewheres or other." He pummeled his head savagely. "Ain't no use, fellers, I can't remember."

Our comments made even Billy blush.

Jim Thompson learned of this misadventure (the message to Garcia, we called it) after the freezeup. It was too late to see Pete Graham, who, in the interim, had closed a deal with the Noranda group. In consequence, the Hoffman-Thompson partnership did not reach Quebec until the winter of 1923.

Big Jim himself made history in Quebec, later. A veteran of the Klondike, he spent many years in Gowganda fighting a losing battle to develop a silver mine west of Spawning Lake. Tall, powerfully built, erect, he is the proverbial man of the north, a type which would gladden the jaded heart of a cinema director. When Austin Dumond discovered what later became the rich O'Brien Mine in Cadillac, Jim found gold directly west of Dumond's stakings and this ground became the Thompson-Cadillac Mine and for a time appeared to be a worthy rival of its fortunate neighbor. The stock went above $1 a share and Jim seemed well on the road to a competence. But a combination of difficult underground conditions and uncertain management resulted in the suspension of milling, and the stock dropped to a few cents.

Reviewing the experience, Jim had this to say: "Some people sell too soon and some too late, but me—" and his wide eyes twinkled—"I didn't sell at all."

As I write, the property, having gone through bankruptcy, is being energetically developed once more, under the name of Alger Mines. Jim, older but still active, continues to prospect.

Sarkis Markarian, may his tribe increase, found no mines, but his indomitable spirit enriched those of us who enjoyed his tenacious friendship. This lovable Levantine was proof enough that Armenians can do more than sell carpets, for he was made of the rugged stuff of life. I first met him in 1922, when he was caretaking at the Silver Bullion Mine. Above medium height, he appeared short, due to a barrel-chested torso and long powerful arms which were never still. He was cooking lunch at the time and wielded an enormous knife, fully as large as a sword, the weight of which was in itself sufficient to slice bread.

"Make him myself," he explained, "f'um ole saw blade, an' moose horn for handle. Is very sharp, so look out."

His huge brown eyes, somewhat myopic, smiled at me in friendly fashion. A thick, coarse walrus mustache did not quite conceal two rows of large strong teeth, which even Teddy Roosevelt could not have matched.

Sarkis, it appeared, was having trouble with his water supply, for a family of beavers insisted upon building a dam in the wrong spot. Each day Sarkis would place a small charge of dynamite under the mass of branches and blow out an opening, but the industrious beavers would repair the damage during the night.

"Is no use," he sighed. "Dem li'l debbil too smart for Sarkis. I have to carry warrer quarrer mile."

Several weeks later he stayed at our shack as my guest when Fred and Bob had gone "out" for a few days. Sarkis could neither read nor write. But he could talk. And while he stirred the oatmeal, a process which required more than an hour, he reviewed his life's history for my benefit, as I lolled on the cot. He fled from Armenia at a tender age, after his family had been destroyed by the Turks in one of those hideous massacres which was the shame of the Middle East.

"Turk bassards," said Sarkis, waving his spoon. "So ignoran' keep date by moon, like savage."

He fought in the interminable Balkan wars, against his inveterate enemies, of course, was wounded several times and finally went off to sea. For a time he served in the Argentine Navy, but, disgusted with South American "barbarians," he transferred to the British Merchant Marine. While the oatmeal cooked, he told a story of his ship stricken with fever off the coast of Africa. Sarkis was the only able-bodied man left, and he alone stoked the furnaces and headed the vessel out to sea, far from pestilential shores.

"Sunumunbitch job," he nodded. "T'row in coal, run up ladder, turn wheel, run down stairs, t'row in coal, run up ladder. . . . Pfui!"

Years later when one of his shipmates quit the sea to try prospecting in northern Canada, Sarkis joined him. After a short stay in Cobalt he drifted into Gowganda, where he and Fred Thompson became friends and partners for a time.

"Is good fella, Fred," said Sarkis. "Hard-work' an' hones'."

His obsessions were the Turks, the Catholic Church, Argentina, and a voting machine in which he and President Wilson were the unfortunate stockholders.

"Is good for Pres' Veelson is good enough for Sarkis," he explained, with a toothy smile. "But"—and he shook his head like a Punch and Judy mannikin—"is lose money for us bot'."

Thereafter I was employed at odd times writing letters for Sarkis. His dictation was generalized, of course.

"Tell sunumunbitch," he would say, "tell 'im is claims wor' more dan one hundra dolla, an' he go stick money hup his hass."

He somehow managed to scrape up the wherewithal to send for his numerous relatives in Armenia, but none of them took to life in the north and soon deserted him.

"Bassard no good," he said mournfully. "They go Detroit an' leave Sarkis alone."

A bushwhacker without a peer, Bob and Fred hired him to accompany them on a longish trip to Hudson Bay. Sarkis was to cook and perform the various camp chores, leaving the others to devote themselves to prospecting. The old boy was a joyful companion. At sundown he would gravely perform a facetious Moslem ritual, kneeling and salaaming and reciting a gibberish of prayer. On the highest hill he could find in the Harricanaw basin, he constructed a large wooden cross.

"So Frenchmen won' be firs'," he explained.

One night Bob and Fred thought they would have a bit of sport with their helper. They had been out late and darkness was upon them as they approached camp. Sarkis was puttering around the fire, putting last touches to a dish of trout which he had freshly caught. Creeping forward silently, Bob and Fred suddenly rushed toward the fire, brandishing their arms and whooping like Indians.

Without turning, Sarkis reached for his ax . . .

On one of his rare trips to Toronto, Sarkis fell into the hands of a tough cab driver who drove madly from Union Station through the streets of the city. Sarkis, in terror at first, held on for dear life, then reached forward, and with a gorillalike arm encircled the driver's throat.

"Sunumunbitch," he gritted, "you doan' kill me firs', den I kill you!"

Needless to say, the cab halted immediately.

Toward the end, lean times forced him into the more prosaic life of a restaurateur, and he fed prospectors in Elk Lake with the most delectable dishes of the East, grumbling all the while and wielding the famous knife which he carried with him as a virtuoso carries his violin. And when he died in 1936, aged eighty-three, the news reached us tardily, too late to bid him farewell and send him away with our blessings. It was some comfort to learn that in his last moments he spoke of nothing but Fred and the Hoffmans, their kindnesses, and their patience.

"Ole man, no spik good Englis', no money, but good fren's," were his last intelligible words. . . .

Sandy McIntyre paddled easily while I sat facing him, the troll line resting in my hand. As the bearded Scot talked, he spat skillfully through a gap in his front teeth, sending faint ripples over the smooth surface of Red Lake.

"Yea, mon," he said, "Oi staked two projucers an' todae Oi'm flatter'n piss on a plate."

He sighed, but not very convincingly, for his eye was merry as ever. It was a different Sandy, though, from the one I had known around Larder Lake, an articulate and intelligent Sandy who was wonderfully sober. With almost psychic intuition, he guessed my thoughts.

"Surprised, hain't ye, as Oi'm sober."

He shook his head, and went on to explain that he was all right in the bush, but that the moment he hit the steel the old urge was upon him again.

"Oi'll drink annythin' then, lad," he admitted. "Lydia Pinkum's compoun', hoss mejicine, annythin' Oi can get me han's on."

He was proud that the newspapers had played up his arrival in Red Lake, stressing the eagerness of tenderfeet to stake near the famous locator of the first McIntyre claims in Porcupine.

Sandy and I were old friends. I had seen him about Kirkland and Larder many times, when, with glazed eye and well-lubricated tongue, he stopped me and spoke with the extravagance of a man whose mind was entirely free of inhibitions. There was the time, I recall now, when he spoke of killing a black bear as it entered his cabin window. The animal, in its death throes, had become firmly wedged in the sash, and Sandy was unable either to pull it inside or thrust it outside.

"So Oi had to cut 'er up with me ax where she lay," he explained. "Whittlin' her down like, ontil she slid out."

Sandy is dead now, gone to the Valhalla of prospectors where quartz veins are a mile long, half a mile wide, and fairly bursting with gold. Incorrigible to the last, he was one of the few of the early mine hunters responsible for the first important gold discoveries in Canada. I doubt whether another Sandy will ever appear.

His real name was Alexander Oliphant, but this became Sandy McIntyre when he threw off the yoke of marriage after a particularly disagreeable domestic tiff and emigrated from Scotland to Canada. There he found bush life more to his liking, and his blue eyes and reddish beard soon became familiar throughout the north. His vital part in the great McIntyre Mine brought him more fame than wealth, but he bore no resentment. No one seemed to know just what Sandy did receive for his Porcupine claims; estimates range from $8,000 to $18,000. In any event, he did not enjoy his affluence very long. Deciding to visit the old country, he left the bulk of his "stake" with a local banker in Timmins and then departed for Scotland. There he did his best to consume more Scotch than his native land produced.

"But Oi couldna make 'er," he said, reporting the incident, "though Oi tried hard."

He bade farewell to Scotland for the last time and returned to Canada. In Porcupine he was informed that all his money had been dissipated in an ill fated Night Hawk Lake speculation. Relating the incident, Sandy told me:

"Thet miserable banker forged me signature on a pow'r of attorney, he did."

Retribution? None, save a hearty round of curses which Sandy showered upon the financier. Then he set himself to repair his fortune. The Hughes brothers had purchased one-eighth interest in his Porcupine ground for $25. Now, in a generous but practical gesture, they offered Sandy a job to prospect their own claims in Kirkland Lake, promising an attractive bonus if he found gold. Sandy readily accepted. While his ability as a prospector has been somewhat exaggerated, he was good, and to the jubilant Hughes boys he soon presented a discovery which became the nucleus of the Teck-Hughes Mine. Sandy was promptly given 150,000 shares as a reward. The stock, in later years, climbed to more than $10 per share, but luckless Sandy sold out long before that. Montreal was the scene of his downfall; the temptations of a large city were too much for his simple nature. The entire block of stock went for $4,500 in a single transaction. I asked what he did with the money. Sandy, in honest surprise, answered:

"Why, Oi spent it on the drink an' sech. What's monaie for? Easy come, easy go, thet's Sandy McIntyre."

So, instead of basking at ease with the proceeds of his two "projucers," Sandy continued to lead a precarious existence in and out of the bush.

Sandy McIntyre

Like most prospectors, Sandy was quick to join the Canadian Army in 1914. He was anything but a model soldier. At the Montreal training depot, he answered a routine questionnaire on previous military record by detailing imaginary service in India, South Africa, and the Sudan. When presented with multitudinous campaign ribbons, Sandy's exuberance waned, especially when he learned that such misrepresentation might result in a court-martial. He confessed to the error of his ways and was dismissed with only a reprimand. At Folkstone, in England, where the Borden Battery received combat training, Sandy, notwithstanding vociferous protest, was made to remove his beard before the troops embarked for France.

"He was only in the line a few months," I was informed by one of his officers, "and half of that time he was in the clink for various offenses. When he called one young leftenant a pig rutter and threatened to blow his head off, we transferred him to a school of gas techniques, and for a while he did well. But on the same day he was made corporal, he was broken and transferred to a headquarters company. For a time he directed traffic behind the lines and finally was sent to Scotland cutting timber with the 'Cold Footed Thumb Suckers.' "

Home again, Sandy built a cabin near Kirkland Lake and staked a number of claims on which he performed desultory assessment work. The Red Lake rush stirred him into activity and he was among the early arrivals there. For a time he appeared on the way to another stake, but with the Howey initially a disappointment, Sandy lost heart, dropped his claims, and returned to Kirkland Lake. There, as the years passed, he became a familiar figure, his beard somewhat grayer but his tongue as spicy as ever. Just before the end it was popularly supposed that he received a small monthly pension from the McIntyre Mine. Judging from Sandy's activities, however, he lived more on the bounty of his numerous friends who stood by him to the last, especially those who had served overseas with him during World War I.

Our cabin, on the southeast end of Osisko Lake, was among the earliest built in the Rouyn area. Near it, connected to the mainland by an ingenious floating bridge, was Bert McDonald's island, an oasis of land in a desert of water. Bert's place never lacked for residents, the regulars being Bert Airth, Gus O'Donnell, Bobbie Kent and last, but not least, "Major" Blake. No one seemed to know Blake's first name but it was easier to call him Major, a title of uncertain origin, but pleasing to the old man, nevertheless. Blake was an Englishman of distinguished appearance and clipped speech, speech, I might add, that was in constant operation. He was the exception proving the rule that the British are reticent. The Major was anything but that. He loved to refer to his English "interests" and "principals" but, loquacious as he was, he never disclosed their identity. After a while we all began to suspect that his grubstakers, like many of his oft-repeated experiences, were mythical.

"Did I ever tell you lads about hunting flamingos on the Nile?" he would ask, and before we could reply emphatically in the affirmative, he was off again on that celebrated trip, shooting the big birds with his trusty rifle and carelessly flinging them over his shoulder.

"Hold on," said Fred Thompson one day, "you say you killed eleven of those flamingos and carried them on your back?"

"Eleven, one short of a dozen, that's right, sir."

"Well," said Fred quietly, "I've been in that country and as I remember those birds go fifty pounds or more."

"A bit high, a bit high," returned Blake, not in the least embarrassed, "these were small ones, about half that weight, and all the load I could wish for, sir."

Almost twenty years before Horne's discovery, Blake had been in the Chibougamau rush, and spoke with poignant nostalgia of his "Chibougamau Indians" who could pack a man in a canoe, run rapids, and perform other wonderful and miraculous deeds. We began to hate those Indians for their perfections, that is, until we got to Chibougamau ourselves. Then our dislike changed to sympathy, for, as we suspected, they were just Indians. Confronting Blake with these realities accomplished little. He snorted and spoke with bitterness of the enervating effects of civilization which had contaminated his beloved aborigines at last.

His pet hatred was the French, and he never passed up an opportunity to malign them. This all derived from a sad experience, which the good Major repeated so many times that we soon knew the story by heart. After almost twenty-five years, it is still fresh in my memory.

Blake, it seems, was a participant in the Bousquet rush which occurred in 1911, the same rush which first drew Ed Horne into Quebec. But Blake fastened to Cadillac Township, where, he boasted, he had found the gold where now the O'Brien Mine is located. He was too early, however, and could obtain no backing to pursue his work. Regretfully, he abandoned his show. But in Quebec City he was not forgotten, for the gentlemen of the Department of Mines decided to name a small waterway "Blake River."

"I deserved it," related the Major, "I bloody well did. And then what do you think, gentlemen? The cartographer—mapmaker, you know—being French and cursed with the stupid ignorance of that unhappy people, read my name as 'Black' when he drew the river on the latest maps. He was a literal bastard too, bad luck to him, and so he committed the crime of translating the rutting name, so his miserable countrymen could understand. And that, gentlemen, is how it became 'La Rivière Noire.' Well, sirs, I made a special trip to Quebec and protested; they promised to rectify the mistake, but on and on it goes, like the Liberal party."

On one of the frequent occasions he told this tale of woe, a party of noisy habitants passed the island. Blake looked up quickly and eyed the revelers darkly.

"I'd shoot at the cattle," he muttered, "but I might hit my favorite bitch. Shouldn't've let her out in the bush this morning."

Ironically, "Blake River" finally appeared on all government maps, together with the "Blake Series" of rocks, but too late for the Major to enjoy his triumph. By that time he had gone to his final rest, where, I hope, the flamingo hunting is good and Chibougamau Indians are many.

I can never think of the early days in Rouyn without recalling the Benbow incident. Benny Benbow was badly bushed, poor fellow, his particular obsession being his might as a hunter. He visited us in Joannes years ago, and tired us out recounting his prowess in the woods. He killed moose in herds apparently. Wherever we went, he struck dramatic attitudes, holding up his hand for silence as he detected signs of prowling animals. Though we had been without fresh meat for weeks, the woods were full of game for Benbow.

"You've got to keep the eyes open," he told us. "You can't go to sleep on the trail. Before I pull out you lads'll be eatin' fresh liver an' blood puddin'."

Benny's opportunity came sooner than expected. One of our gang, Joe Hill, left for the workings with a box of dynamite before the rest of us, and as we followed him, after washing the dishes, Benny led the way, gun in hand. In a few minutes he sniffed the air suspiciously, then called a halt.

"Been a bear here," he muttered, and his eyes darted along the trail. "Ah, there she is!" He stuck a forefinger in a fresh mound of dung. "Knew it, knew it." He faced us glowingly, dilating with pride. "Takes Benny to find 'em. You'll have bear for supper, lads!" and with that he darted into the bush, leaving us weak with laughter.

For, had he been less precipitous in his departure, he would have observed that the bear, in this case Joe Hill, had fastidiously left a handful of Scott Tissue only a few feet from the trail.

We were among the first to utilize the services of Hans Lundberg, the eminent geophysicist, when he first came to Rouyn, fresh from his Boliden triumphs in Sweden. Our arrangement with him was simple. We had several thousand acres of claims and he had the device that could locate mineral deposits beneath lake, swamp, and overburden; the combination would be attractive, that is, if ore was present. In any event, we proceeded with our plans, hired a gang of bushwhackers in Rouyn and began to cut lines preparatory to electrical survey. Our men were tough, but not tough enough to endure the heaviness of constant work, the frequent changing of camps, packing such mean loads as storage batteries, and forgoing the delights of town for months on end. Our labor turnover, therefore, was so high that when work ended in the fall (short of mines but long on equipment and experience) we had with us only one man of the original personnel, Joe La Fitte. He was our Man Friday, our faithful follower, who never let us down, except on one or two minor occasions. There was the time, for example, when I asked him to carry my lunch into the bush, where I would meet him at noon. I gave him a whole pie, freshly baked, in addition to the sandwiches, and considered this ample for Joe, his two axmen and myself.

I arrived at the appointed spot somewhat late; Joe and his friends had already eaten. Munching my sandwich, I noticed that the pie was gone. Now, I am not overly fond of sweets, but I considered that this gluttony was unlike Joe, and so remarked:

"Where's my pie, Joe?"

"Dere was t'ree piece pie, dat's all, an' we heat hall hup."

Sternly, I reminded him that there was a *whole* pie, which I had given him myself.

"Sure, boss, I know dåt. But," he added, with friendly conviction, "dat pie, when we cut 'im hup, she on'y make a t'ree-piece pie!"

Men came, and men went, but Joe went on forever. When the gang was finally paid off and most of the boys scattered in the Rouyn direction, we informed Joe that in consideration for his loyalty we were taking him with us to Kirkland Lake for a special holiday at our expense. He capered with joy, and made a happy companion on the trip out.

Arriving at Kirkland, we put up at Charlie Chow's Hotel, giving the exulting Joe a room to himself. But he disappeared before lunch and was gone for hours. When he finally returned, he burst into our littered room which we had converted into a temporary office.

"By da Jeez," he cried, before we could say a word, "I just have a woman!" and he blew a kiss into his fingers so hard that his false teeth rattled in protest.

"Any good?" I asked, continuing my writing.

"Good?" His jaw dropped at the impertinence of the question.

"Why, boss, she merveilleuse; you go too. By Chris'—" he excitedly shook my arm to gain full attention—"when she take off da dress, she have SILK UNDERWEAR!"

Bob Gamble, the leader of four brothers, is one of the select prospectors who can boast of major financial success. A stormy petrel in more than one mining situation, he started at the bottom of the ladder, a mere bushwhacker. Money came only after years of effort, when he had fully mastered all the arts of his profession. He traded as hard as he traveled; not many mining companies and promoters could best him in negotiations. After fruitlessly participating in the various rushes, starting with Cobalt, he came into his own when Noranda was discovered, there to achieve undisputed possession of the world's record in staking claims. His brother Bill, rotund and amiable, was content with operating a poolroom, but brother Wesley was a valuable bush assistant. After claims had been staked, companies were quickly formed, and activities passed to brother Kellard, the public relations and promotional genius of the family. Gamble companies came out of Rouyn in rapid succession, and from them have emerged two mines, the Senator and Stadacona, one near miss, the Granada, and two promising prospects, the Astoria and Pelletier Lake.

"Grab all the ground you can and stick with it," Bob always said, and suited action to the word. Few could sustain his pace in and out of the bush.

In 1914 he and Fred Thompson, his partner at that time, entered the famous 200-mile canoe race at Ottawa. Against trained sportsmen equipped with specially built craft and dressed in fancy trunks and jerseys, they cut sorry figures in their patched Peterboro and bush clothing. But laughter turned to respect when they far outdistanced their swanky competitors, running the Long Sault Rapids, trotting over portages, and breaking the record by many hours. In addition to receiving gold medals and diamond cuff links, the winners had their names engraved on a large silver cup permanently kept in the club lobby. Gamble, who considered the effort worthy of greater reward, shocked the judges with suggestions concerning disposal of the silver trophy.

An engaging talker, contagiously optimistic, thoroughly at home in bush and office, it was inevitable that his ambitions would be realized.

Like all self-made men, Bob can be headstrong, as he demonstrated in the matter of his Haileybury house. He still maintained this residence, though most of his interests were in Quebec, where he spent the greater part of his time. Rising tax rates angered him increasingly.

"An outrage," he called it. But he did not confine his resentment to words. Not Bob. He had the house cut into sections, placed on flat cars, and taken into Noranda, where it was reassembled. And the taxes, perforce, were reduced drastically, for he was the owner of a vacant lot now.

For a time he established himself on Bay Street as a stockbroker, but the interlude was short.

"Those Bay Street boys are too much, even for me," he said ruefully.

Today he resides in a Toronto suburb, still interested in mining. But the old spark is gone since the loss of his only son, Robert Jr., who died gallantly while serving with the RCAF.

Merle "Bud" Mallory, one-time Idaho cowboy and private in the American army which fought so dismally in the Philippines in the backwash of the Spanish-American War, was by his own admission a twentieth century Casanova. "The ladies, God bless 'em," was his cheerful dictum. Of medium height, dark, his lively brown eyes were constantly sparkling with the light of reminiscence.

"Those eyes," he admitted modestly, "are my fortune."

One June day in 1924, Fred Thompson and I were caught in a downpour of rain in the midst of claim staking and took refuge in Bud's tent near the old Rouyn Lake portage. He welcomed us with a whoop. As we fell into a discussion of prospects for a railroad, he sighed wearily.

"Don't talk shop, boys," he admonished. "Let's have a go at the ladies."

And thereupon he began anew to recount his youthful escapades in Idaho. If he could be believed, his memoirs would have been a perfect cinema vehicle for Errol Flynn. Stabbed once, chloroformed twice by enraged amorata, he managed to survive the onslaughts of love, but decided that a change of environment would probably extend his life span. And so he drifted by stages into Canada, and prospecting.

"There was a woman," he said, "what was a woman. In the Philippines. She was my lotus flower."

And he went on to describe their intimate moments together, climaxed when his dusky mistress caressed his cheeks with the soft bottoms of her bare feet.

"It was wonderful," he breathed, wriggling in the eiderdown which he used as a back rest. "She was a regular contortionist. If she was in town here she'd make more money than the Noranda."

But Bud did more than linger in the past. He was an excellent bushman and prospector, and like most men who dilate on old affairs with the fair sex, he was a devoted husband and father. In 1922 he accompanied Ike Waite into Rouyn when the first examination of the Horne Mine was made for the Thompson-Chadbourne Syndicate, and at that time staked a 200-acre claim next to the Powell. This was his only asset when, late in 1924, he was stricken with lung trouble. Advised that only a trip to the Southwest would save his life, Bud enlisted the services of my brother Robert through whom the Mallory claim was sold to a New York financier.

Bud, with a few thousand dollars in his pocket, left for Arizona, there, in time, to die. Meanwhile, the claim was brought to a patent in 1925. Lying idle since, it is now centered in the most active section of the Noranda district, a highly coveted piece of ground which will command a kingly price when the New York heirs decide to sell.

Adjoining the Mallory claim to the west is the actively developing Marlon Rouyn Mine, the destiny of which is held in the palm of erstwhile prospector Jack Coghlan, now one of Canada's top mining men. This genial son of Ireland managed to survive more than twenty-five years of lean trekking, but stuck to his convictions tenaciously. Marlon is only one of his creations. There is the Heva Cadillac, also in the process of sinking a shaft after a highly successful drilling campaign, and a stable of budding prospects all along the Quebec belt.

"You can't get mines by warming your rear in a New York office," Jack told me not long ago. "Trouble is, you and Bob don't get out enough."

Certainly, *he* gets out enough, though today he is ensconced in a Toronto office which he manages with surprising efficiency and éclat. Jack, beneath a bluff exterior, is shrewd and well versed in all aspects of mining. His integrity is high, and those of us who know him well rarely ask for a written agreement. He is referred to as "Hundred Per Cent Jack," and this pleases him more than his recent appointment as director of the Prudential Trust Company and manager of the Continental Diamond Drilling & Exploration Company.

Another Quebec pioneer, but not so fortunate, is Mel Robb, who, with his brothers, covered much of the outlying sections of Rouyn. To his credit go several spectacular gold discoveries in Montbray and Hebecourt townships. For a time he rode the crest and modestly accepted the congratulations of his many friends. But, alas for Mel, his finds proved to be disappointing in every case. He demonstrated that the hackneyed rule of "Gold is where you find it" was made to confound him. Some gold he found, yes, but most of

Rouyn's gold has a way of running into the properties of others.

Though he has been tormented by teasers thus far, Mel's fund of good nature continues to bubble undiminished as he scouts properties for the Wright-Hargreaves Mine. For a year he managed the newly organized Haileybury Hotel, but he couldn't condition himself to a sedentary life.

"Almost drove me nuts," he explained. "Had to listen to the boys always coming in with stories of new finds."

It was Mel who dug up the promising Bartec Mines for the Teck-Hughes organization. The claims were purchased from a Frenchman and his wife whom Mel assiduously entertained, a task much to his liking. Shortly after the incident, Fred Thompson and I drove to Barraute for a bit of staking on our own account. We met Mel in the "hotel." He was stretched out on the iron bed in his room, dreamily smoking and gazing at the ceiling. At our entrance he came to life, greeting us warmly.

"Have a beer?" he asked.

We nodded. He pushed the door open with a foot, and cried, "Monseer O'Brien, encore some beer!"

In a few moments there was a discreet knocking and into the tiny room came the "Irish" proprietor, a smallish man so French that he did not forget to tip his cap deferentially after he placed his tray of beer bottles on the table.

"So that's O'Brien," I said, when the little man had left.

"Yup, that's him. Just about as Irish as patty der foiy grass. Can't speak a word of English, but that don't bother me. I picked up enough French lingo when I was overseas to get along here fine."

Later Mel reviewed the succession of misfortunes that have plagued his efforts.

"Always a bridesmaid but never a bride," he described himself in conclusion. But he is still comparatively young, and hope springs eternal.

Gone, but never to be forgotten, is the "Russian Kid," he of the giant stature and ready tongue. He made the transition from the gambling tables and hills of Rossland to the flatness of Kirkland Lake and the sodden bush of Quebec with ribald cheerfulness. In the bush he demonstrated that he had mined extensively in the West, for his gophering in the clay of Dasserat Township was a marvel of ingenuity and hard work. The Kid found gold, built a cabin on his claims, and there lived with his sister and brother-in-law, Mike Mitto, who has since become one of the most publicized prospectors in Yellowknife.

The Kid's pet aversion was the engineer.

"Dem guys can't tell da diff'rence between dere arse an' a poker chip!" he roared. "If dey come here, I'll t'row 'em inter da lake!"

Bob and I visited him in company with Dr. Hugh McKinstry, then geologist for the Homestake Mine and now professor of mining at Harvard. We had been in particularly rough bush for several days, and the unsuspecting Russian Kid conducted us on a tour of his property. Half his conversation concerned the stupidity of geologists. When he showed us a quartz vein with sections of visible gold, he became bitingly sarcastic.

"See dat yeller stuff? I put it in dere meself, vid a shotgun, d'ya see? Sure, dat ain't real. I oughter be in jail, saltin' da country."

When he was informed later that he had unwittingly entertained geologists, his declared enemies, he expressed unfeigned astonishment.

"Dem fellers ingineers? Vell, kiss me rear an' serwe me vid demitasses! Dey had dirtier clothes den vhat I vear, an' dey stunk twicet as bad."

One of "dem fellers," it transpired, had attempted to negotiate for the claims. The discussion waxed warm, and then furious. After listening to the final arguments and the detailed plan of financing, the Kid shook his massive head in contemptuous refusal.

"Dat a deal? Know who ya talkin' vid, young feller? Da Russian Kid, dat's who, an' not no ignoran' sonuwabitch, d'ya see? All you askin' me to do is sell my rear end an' fart t'rough me ribs, d'ya see?"

There was no deal.

The Kid is dead but his claims are very much alive. Charley Wright, former member of the New York Stock Exchange, has supplied funds for drilling, and the property is now called Bordulac Mines.

Fred W. Thompson has the distinction of staking more mines and earning less thereby than any prospector in his class. A bushman with hardly an equal, he is deficient in one respect—acquisitive instinct. His life has been exciting and colorful, and yet modesty and self-effacement are as natural to him as braggadocio is to lesser men.

Born in London, he attended the Greenwich Naval School at a tender age but became involved in a boyish prank (painting a red nose on Lord Nelson's statue) and this ended his academic career abruptly. Enlisting in the English Navy, he found the kind of existence that suited his restless temperament. All went well until a bullying petty officer singled him out for special attention. Never an aggressor himself, he often evoked pugnacity in others, but always to their ultimate regret. And so it was with the petty officer. After thrashing him soundly, Fred decided to forgo a long term in the brig by sliding down the anchor hawser and swimming ashore in Sydney Harbor. There he was soon lost in the anonymity of the waterfront.

Fred Thompson

The next act occurred on the sailing vessel *Swanhilda* on which Fred signed as ordinary seaman. Becalmed en route to Panama, part of the crew mutinied against a brutal captain. Fred, the chief offender, was thrown into irons, but he managed to escape when the ship docked in Panama. There for a time he worked as a laborer on the Canal project, after which he became first mate on a fruit steamer. Tiring of this, he drifted through Central America and finally was appointed admiral of the San Salvador Navy, in command of a single ship.

When war broke out with Nicaragua, Fred stormed the enemy port of Corinto. Wounded in the hand by a machete stroke, he nevertheless routed the three-ship Nicaraguan navy led by F. F. Worthington, a Scotsman. By a strange coincidence, the two admirals met again years later under different circumstances, this time as Canadian officers in a communications trench during the Somme campaign. Worthington, incidentally, remained in the Canadian Army and rose to the rank of major general in World War II.

In 1907, Fred received word that his family had emigrated to Canada and purchased a farm in northern Ontario. In a moment of sentimentality, he decided to join them. For a time he worked with his father and four brothers at clearing the land, but quickly realized that farm life was not for him. Stories of mining stirred his rover's blood and in a short while he dropped the plow and assumed the prospector's pick, which he has carried ever since, and with distinction. Gowganda was his first camp, and there he teamed with Bob Gamble and Sarkis Markarian, wildcatting betimes and working underground when funds were short. In 1914 he enlisted in the famous Borden Battery. Except for a three months' period when he was wounded on the Somme, he remained an active machine gunner to the last day of action, at which time he had risen from private to captain. He was one of the few Canadians who received both the Military Medal and Military Cross decorations.

In the course of twenty-five years he discovered and staked two producers, Island Lake and Thompson-Lundmark, as well as the O'Neil Thompson (staked with his brother Bert), now a part of the Rouyn Merger. The Donalda was one of his early "babies," now, alas, in other hands, as well as the Arrowhead, Duquesne, and Wright-Rouyn. At one time he turned minemaker and acquired the Golden Manitou in Quebec, a mine now producing almost $2,000,000 annually. But luck was not with him. One of his associates, en route to mail a check for claim taxes, was struck by a tram in Ottawa. The letter was never mailed and consequently the property was lost. The Duquesne, staked by Fred and his brother, Walter, was slow to respond to development, and the brothers, under pressure of necessity, sold their stock "too early." The Donalda, which he staked with Robert, was sold for a mere pittance in the early days, and passed into luckier hands. And the Thompson-Lundmark, which marked the first discovery of a Canadian mine from the air, was so involved with participating syndicates that the luckless discoverer received only 25,000 shares of the 1,250,000 allocated to the vendors.

A devoted father, he left his wife and three daughters to enlist in the Canadian Army in 1942.

Now, as field manager of Frederick Yellowknife Mines, Fred is seeing better days. In the 1945 season at Yellowknife, he brought in two properties, the Andrew and Slemon, both of which show promise. His unusual talents are beginning to provide the kind of substance he has so long deserved.

His favorite story concerns a Frenchman whom he and Bob met while walking from Larder Lake. Upon being asked by the stranger where they were bound, Fred replied, "Rouyn."

"By da Jeez, I go dere too!" exclaimed the native of Quebec. "You look for work, no?"

"We look for work, yes," replied Bob.

"By da Jeez, me too, I hunt da job. But dere's one place, by Chris,' Johnee Rougeau she keep away lak from da black fly."

"And what place is that?" inquired Fred.

"Dat? Why, she's da Thompson-Hoffman camp in Joannes. Doan work dere, my fren', wit' dem feller. Dey regula' bastard, dem two."

"How do you know?" asked Fred innocently.

"How I know? By Chris', dat's good, dat's veree good! How I know? 'Cause I work for dem sonabitch las' year, an' by da Jeez dey work so hard da harse she drag over da groun' an' bump along lak da stoneboat!"

Fred MacLeod, president of the company that bears his name, is proof that a prospector can master all the problems of discovery, finance, and executive management. He prospected faithfully since the early beginnings of Gowganda. At one time he crossed the Dominion to British Columbia where a friend had informed him of a possible new gold area deep in the interior. After trying vainly to obtain a partner to accompany him, MacLeod was obliged to venture forth alone. It was a grueling trip. Lost half the time, he lived largely on game and fish, wandered along unmapped lakes and rivers. And then when he had decided to turn back he met a band of Indians. "They stank," he reported, "worse than a dead moose." But one of the squaws had a gold ornament crudely hammered from what must have been a large nugget. MacLeod tarried, hopeful that he could learn where she had found it. The squaw, though coy, was completely uncommunicative about gold, and after a period of several weeks, MacLeod departed.

"Couldn't stand the squalor any longer," he explained. "I was out four months and more broke than ever."

Fate was kinder in the east, where after a fruitless session in Rouyn, MacLeod met with better fortune at Little Long Lac, Ontario. Today, as president of the MacLeod-Cockshutt Mine, a dividend payer, he manages a large enterprise with the poise and judgment of a seasoned executive. He accepts his position with quiet temperance, genial and simple as ever, unspoiled by success.

I first met him in the late spring of 1924, en route to Rouyn via the ancient Lac Quinze steamer. The trip required an overnight stay at Gendreau's Portage, where we transferred to a light motorboat. The night was warm and the flies were bad, and so we passengers, or most of us, huddled around the comfort of an outdoor fire until morning. Fred was traveling with Jim Bailey, and for the benefit of a young Frenchman and myself, whom the prospectors took to be greenhorns, the conversation emphasized the hardships of the north, especially during the winter.

"So cold here," remarked Bailey, "that your spit is froze before it reaches the ground."

Others chimed in, and painted a terrible picture of limitless ice and snow. Fred MacLeod, his blue eyes reflective and his baldish head softly reflecting the light of the campfire, finally spoke.

"Talk about cold," he said, "you men don't know anything. Why, I was out in Labrador a couple of winters ago, and there it is really cold. Pitiful. I remember seeing mountain goats jumping from one peak to another, and it was so damnably cold that they froze stiff, right in mid-air."

I had had two summers in the bush and so, wise to the ways of these prospectors, maintained a discreet silence. But my French companion, new to the north, was outraged.

"That's impossible, sir!" he cried.

"And why is it?" asked Fred naïvely.

"Because it's against the law of gravity, that's why!"

"Oh." Fred smiled. "That. Well, lad, it was so hellish cold that the law of gravity was frozen too."

"Foghorn" McDonald, so named because his mere whisper was reputed to carry half a mile through the bush, has long been dead but his memory lives on. Even during his lifetime, Foghorn stories were legion. The favorite, I think, concerns one of his exploits in Cobalt where he had landed after prospecting the American West. Foghorn was engaged in sinking a shaft at the outskirts of town in the early days. It was his custom to take weekend holidays to ease the tedium of six-day work periods, and on these occasions he scrupulously measured the depth of shaft before his departure. Trusting no one else, he rode the bucket to the bottom of the shaft and then roared for the tape to be lowered by his helper. Carefully noting the footage in his book, he then returned to the surface and made for the bright lights of Cobalt. This performance would be repeated dutifully when he returned, somewhat the worse for wear, for Foghorn was adamant about keeping pace with shaft progress during his absence.

One day Foghorn's assistant, by arrangement with the other miners, tied a large loop in the tape before lowering it. Foghorn, eager to be in Cobalt, hurriedly marked the footage at 96 feet, and left his men with admonitions to "shake the lead outer their arses" and put on the heat; shaft progress, as ever, was lagging behind schedule. His weekend was extended over several days, but at length he reeled back into camp. Through force of habit he at once demanded to be taken down the shaft in order to make the regular check of footage. This time the tape was stretched its full length. Foghorn, rubbing his eyes in wonder, saw the thin sliver of steel stop at 81 feet. He shook his massive head, rubbed his eyes, and looked again. There was no mistaking it—the shaft had lost 15 feet while he was in town.

Back at surface, he studied the men who sat about with prearranged nonchalance, then cleared his throat with a rumble like distant thunder.

"Men!" he roared. "When I leave you a few days I don't expect no miracles! But in Christ's name I do expect you to hold your own! Now get down there an 'make up for that lost footage!"

One of the earliest residents of northern Ontario, whose arrival in the Haileybury predated the construction of the T. & N.O.R.R., is bespectacled Major Eddie Holland, now the staid postmaster of Cobalt. Eddie can look back at a career which brought him the coveted Victoria Cross in the Boer War, as well as a long experience in the bush. Still vigorous, his memory is infallible; he remains a veritable encyclopedia of information. In his younger days he was famed for his practical jokes, some of which he carried to interesting lengths, and useful, too, as in the Gillies Limit episode.

This large tract, leased for its timber to the Gillies brothers of Braeside, Ontario, was withdrawn from staking immediately after the silver discoveries in Cobalt. In 1912, however, the government rescinded the order, throwing open the Limit to prospectors. The deadline was set, and men flocked into the area from every corner of the Dominion, bent upon staking what was generally considered valuable ground.

On the memorable date, at the hour of midnight, groups of men were stationed throughout the Limit, their posts cut and conveyances waiting to rush them to Haileybury, about twenty miles north, where the nearest recorder's office was located. Eddie Holland, foreseeing the stampede, had made interesting preparations. One of the hardware stores in Cobalt was advertising a new type of dynamite by placing dummy sticks, containing nothing more lethal than sawdust but covered with the familiar brown waxed paper, in its display window. Holland obtained a half dozen of these, prepared real fuses, and with his partners leisurely made his way through the crowds at Gillies Limit, about twelve miles south of Cobalt.

Studying his watch, as did all the others, Holland sprang to his feet on the dot of midnight, lighted his fuses and threw two sticks of "dynamite" into the brown of rival stakers.

"Fire!" he shouted. "Fire!"

At the familiar and dreaded cry, there was a mad scramble to leave. Holland and his partners were able to stake their claims without hindrance.

But Eddie's men had not provided swift horses to speed them to Haileybury and so they were among the last to arrive at the recorder's office. Almost a thousand men were massed in front of the door, impatiently waiting to be admitted. Eddie forthwith produced several more sticks of "dynamite," lighted the fuses, and charged into the crowd wildly. Once more came the desperate cry "Fire!" and the mob scattered. Thereupon Eddie calmly walked into the office and made the first recording of Gillies Limit claims.

The Limit proved to be a complete flop. Some claims were sold at first but development work was universally disappointing. Eddie obtained little more from the experience than another of his inimitable yarns.

Bill Wright, another venerable survivor of the Boer War, counts his northern ventures in terms of coin of the realm. A native of England, where he was once a butcher in a Lincolnshire town, he answered the call to the colors when the Boer War broke out. In the course of his army duties, he became friendly with a Canadian volunteer with whom he returned to London after the war. His friend decided to marry and live in England and offered to sell Wright a Veteran Lot in Porcupine which the Ontario government, in line with a policy of rewarding returned soldiers, had granted him. The consideration was £10. Wright, who had no ties in England, accepted, and then left for Canada to investigate the value of his purchase. His brother-in-law, Ed Hargreaves, was residing in Haileybury, and there Wright went for what he supposed would be a short stay. But Cobalt was then in its flower. Wright and Hargreaves were soon in the swim of things, not, as might be expected, as miners, but as painters, their first job being that of decorating the Mining Corporation mill. Wearying of such prosaic work in a mineral country seething with stories of new discoveries, they decided to try their luck prospecting. Their claim stakings, and Wright's happy ability to wait matters out, are indelible pages of Canada's mining history.

It is difficult to appraise the fortune which Wright accumulated in his time. He is supposed to have retained all his Wright-Hargreaves and Lake Shore stock until recently, when, upon the advice of George McCullough, he "sold some securities" and bought the Toronto *Globe & Mail,* one of the largest newspapers in Canada.

A bachelor, he lives in almost spartan simplicity, unknown to the public and most mining men, to whom he is merely a fabulous name.

Bill Wright

"For he that hath, to him shall be given" finds its truth in the Bill Wright story. The old "Vet" claim in Porcupine, which originally supplied the reason for Wright's emigration to Canada, was to reward its multimillionaire owner in an unexpected way. While Wright was occupied in Kirkland Lake, the rise of Porcupine after World War I reminded him of his acquisition years before. Unfortunately for him, he had either neglected to record his purchase at the Land Office or was unwilling to pay the required fee. In any event, he now bestirred himself. A cable was sent to London requesting the necessary signature for transfer, but the exciting news of Porcupine had preceded this message. The original owner, sensing Wright's difficulty in legalizing ownership, was now openly negotiating with outside groups eager to acquire the ground. Finding cables ineffectual, Wright decided to visit London himself.

His old friend, now a confirmed family man, proved stubborn, and before Wright could obtain the signature he was obliged to hand over $20,000. An expensive mistake or economy it had been to neglect the transfer of title, but Wright, thanks to his Kirkland Lake winnings, was able to rectify the situation with money.

A quarter of a century passed before Wright found the buyer able or willing to meet his price. In 1945 the Buffalo Ankerite Gold Mines paid him $525,000 in cash and stock. This was a matter of satisfaction to Wright, who had waited so long, and also to the Ontario and Dominion governments, which will have so much more to collect in succession duties.

In the town of Larder Lake today a small paunchy man may be seen lounging about the hotel or walking aimlessly along the main street. Few would recognize Jack Costello, once the saucy dean of prospectors in the area, now almost the only surviving old-timer of the camp.

Jack, an Australian and one-time sailor and lightweight boxer, never departed from his beloved Larder Lake after his arrival in 1906, except for a period of overseas duty in World War I. He was an indefatigable worker. It was his discovery of the Costello Vein that supplied the main reason for continued development in a once-expiring area. His financial return was negligible, however, and to-day a sad little man, he ekes out a precarious existence, completely forgotten. But Jack in his prime was a cocky, provocative bantam and his never-failing enthusiasm, articulated in the juiciest kind of Australianese, was a thing of joy.

Of the Jake Davidson type, he scorned a partner. Never traveling far, he was interminably engaged in digging trenches and proving up his claims. Bothered by too-frequent visitors, he decided to build a one-man cabin, and this, when completed, was the size of a largish dog kennel. Jack was able to lie in the five-foot bunk and reach the stove for a teapot. A man of normal height could rest his elbow on the roof or span the front wall with outstretched arms. Trouble came one day, however, when Jack was entertaining one of his cronies. A small gasoline lamp exploded; both Jack and his friend tried to leave through the door at the same time. A jam resulted, and before the men could extricate themselves, the miniature cabin was burning briskly. Jack's curses, even for him, reached a new high.

George Grey, an American engineer, first assumed charge of operations for Associated Goldfields in 1920, and Jack acted as his guide to the Reddick property. On the way from town they passed the shack of one of the sporting girls, a hefty wench who was none too popular with the prospectors. The road was strewn with rotten potatoes which had fallen from a supply truck and had been out in the sun for more than a week. Maggie was occupied with gardening, her ample derrière exposed to the pedestrians. Jack reached to the ground, picked up a choice fruit of Ireland, and with deft aim struck the inviting target squarely. Maggie, springing to her feet, found Grey watching her with unbelieving eyes while Jack Costello walked ahead.

"The language that woman used," says Grey, reporting the incident, "was something unbelievable. Jack, of course, was the picture of innocence, and Maggie naturally assumed I had attacked her."

On another occasion, Jack's canoe was upset on Larder Lake by a motorboat carrying a mixed party of fisherfolk. Unable to swim, Jack clung to the overturned canoe with grim desperation, while the launch made a wide turn and hurried to rescue him. As soon as he was within hearing distance, Jack sputtered forth in his inimitable accent:

"Seein' as 'ow ya have a boatload o' bitch aboard, Hi won't sigh what Hi was goin' to sigh, but arseholes to the bloody lot o' ya!"

Arthur Cockeram, like so many top-notch Canadian prospectors, is a small man, but his capacities for intelligent mining work are large. His keen observation led to the staking of the choicest part of the Lake Shore Mine, but unlike Harry Oakes he readily joined the Army when war came in 1914. Returning from France, he was employed by the Thomson-Chadbourne Syndicate and played no small part in the eventual success of the Noranda. When the International Mining Corporation was organized by the same group, Arthur was chosen as a director and manager of Canadian field activities. He is one of the few prospectors who has ever sat at board meetings in Wall Street.

A native of England, he emigrated to Canada, working for a time at trapping and railroad construction with his equally famous prospector brother. Arthur proceeds cautiously, in interesting contrast to the more volatile Bobby who has always remained a free lance of the bush. His career has been one of constantly alternating success and failure. After making a stake as an outgrowth of his fortunate Prospector's Airways venture with the late Pete Graham, in the course of which Opemiska Copper and McWatters Gold Mine were found, Bobby became a gentleman farmer. He learned, however, that this was a poor vocation for a man of his mettle and, leaner in purse, he returned to mining. When the heat is on, Bobby responds valiantly, and sure enough, he recouped handsomely by joining Bill Hosking in the promising Rouyn Merger and Hosco developments.

Other brother teams have made mining history. The seven Mc-Donoughs, Joe, Eddie, Charlie, Mickey, Pete, Tim, and the late Jack staked the Amulet Mines. Eddie had much to do with the Cobalt Products Company and Joe, the leader, picked up the anemic Madsen Mines in Red Lake and built it into the leading producer of that reborn camp.

The Moshers, Alec and Murdock, staked the Central "Pat" Mine and are still young enough to envisage an interesting future. Born in Nova Scotia and raised in Cobalt, they took to the bush like black flies. No longer partners now, Murdock directs the growing activities of Mosher Long Lac and Lundward Mines, while Alec is absorbed in the developments taking place at Snow Lake, Manitoba.

In one of the few airplane mishaps of northern Canada, Leo Springer came to an untimely end in 1936. He and his brother Karl had, at that time, discovered the Opemiska copper-gold deposits, after having trapped for years in Boischatel Township, long before Ed́ Horne discovered the Noranda. Karl, still young, carried on alone. His syndicate discovered what is now the profitable Leitch Mine, but credit here must be divided with "Russ" Cryderman, an elderly Sudbury prospector who had covered the Pre-Cambrian of Canada as few others have. He it was who found the first gold of the Leitch, in this case on a patented claim owned by others, but an equitable arrangement was made by Springer, and the Leitch, a dividend payer, resulted.

Not content with this, Springer formed the Springer-Sturgeon Gold Mines, which in time has become one of the active exploration units in the industry, with properties from Yellowknife to Nova Scotia. Profiting by knowledge he acquired in attending special prospectors' classes sponsored by the government, Springer recognized the presence of barite in Nova Scotia, where he had gone to examine a gold prospect. With admirable energy and intelligence, he organized the Canadian Industrial Minerals, Ltd., which is now one of the world's principal shippers of barite, sufficient proof, if any is needed, that makers of mines can spring from the humble ranks of prospectors.

The old order changeth. The sourdough is becoming a curiosity, for prospecting is now a streamlined business, calling for younger, more highly trained men to whom the airplane and radio are routine equipment. And with this change, something of the color has gone out of the bush. There are still characters of the Sandy McIntyre type, but their numbers are fast thinning. The present-day prospector is of a different breed, responsible, trained, and full of serious design. He is undoubtedly more efficient than the old-timer, but in his conformity he is far more prosaic. Efficiency, like virtue, is commendable, but hardly interesting.

I have been frequently asked by the uninitiated just what are the qualities that make for successful prospecting. In answer, I always say that much depends upon temperament and a willingness to face hardship. Familiarity with the woods is not enough. There must also be unfailing optimism and acceptance of the underlying element of luck, and a determination to spend a lifetime, if necessary, in search. Lively imagination is essential also, for otherwise it is hard to see possibilities of a mine in tangled underbrush and untracked muskeg.

Fred Thompson's answer is much simpler.

"All you need to be a successful prospector," he maintains, with a grin, "is a strong back and a weak head. Only one prospect in a thousand makes a mine, and even prospects are hard to find."

In speaking of the prospector, I emphasize the men who actually seek and find. The country abounds in countless others, loosely designated as "prospectors," who should be more aptly described as stakers or "tier-on-tos," which in itself is a profession. But only those who stay in the bush and make discoveries deserve the dignity of the name. They are no overnight bushmen who appear like mushrooms when the provocative word "Gold!" is flashed. We find them, a devoted handful, continually appearing and opening up new territory through the broad expanse of the Dominion.

The old-timer is a simple man predominantly, generally unfitted for the complexities of urban society. Bob Fennell, a leading Toronto attorney, who has numbered among his clients dozens of famous bushwhackers, illustrates this in a yarn about an early prospector who had just received a substantial cash payment. Joe (not his real name) insisted that his solicitor celebrate with him, and so the two repaired to the King Edward bar. At midnight the barkeeper announced closing time. Joe was furious.

"Call the manager!" he roared. "What t' hell kind o' joint is this?"

The manager, suave, solicitous, appeared, explaining the dead line rule on serving drinks.

"I'll buy the Gawd-damn place then," fumed Joe. Reaching in his pocket he extracted a messy roll of bills which he stuffed into the manager's reluctant hands. "There y'are. I own the hotel an' bar an' everything!"

Unseen by Joe, the manager slipped the money to Fennell, who then urged Joe to leave. After some trouble, Joe was escorted to the curb.

"Cab!" he shouted. "Cab!"

Several minutes elapsed and Joe's anger rose.

"What in hell's idea keepin' me waitin'? I kin buy all the cabs in Toronter. Know that?"

When a taxi finally arrived Joe stepped in and questioned the driver.

"How much you make a week? $25? Aw right, I'll pay you $35. An' what you want for the auto? $900? Fine. You sold it. An' now take me home, bud. From now on I'm givin' orders when I want to go places."

And for a month Joe cruised about in lavish style, until he began to realize that outgo is much swifter than income.

Amusing, no doubt, but somewhat pathetic too. Traditionally, Joe and his fellow prospectors are easy meat for suave businessmen and promoters. They usually return to the bush stripped of their winnings, but probably happier spirits, for the outside is beyond their ken. To their more sophisticated contemporaries, they are queer fellows, freaks of the human breed. True enough, they are not ordinary mortals; average men could not endure an existence of killing hardship and devastating remoteness. Those who persist in such a life must of necessity come from a special mold; they cannot be fairly and sympathetically judged from the comfort and convention of metropolitan society where few people know what it means to supply all their own fundamental wants.

In the north we find the last survivors of a braver age when frontiers were still unconquered and pioneers carried the world with them. Sprinkled among them are a few who have won substance in worldly goods, but the large majority is found in the Sandy McIntyres and nameless others, weaker or unluckier than those who have prospered, but none the less deserving for the service they have rendered Canada.

Tom Middleton, co-staker of the Hollinger Mine, is still alive, a shell of a man waiting to die. I talked with him recently, after having sought him out in a shabby Swastika cabin where he is terribly alone. One of his legs has been amputated at the hip, and he shuffles from bed to table by means of a stool he himself built. It is sad to see this ghost of a vigorous giant who once blithely conquered the bush and helped to make the Hollinger Mine possible. For him no well-earned security or service ribbon to show ancient honors, but an old-age pension which barely keeps him in food and tobacco. His red-rimmed eyes, still bright in a sunken skull, speak of deep inner suffering, born of shameful neglect and indifference. But a spark of the old valiant Tom still remains, and even from the ashes of his wasted life an undying spark of humor persists.

"One of my flippers is gone," he says gamely, "and I'm sinking stern first. But I've held some good poker hands in my time, so I ain't complaining."

Undoubtedly, I am a sentimentalist. But as I left his cabin and walked slowly toward the station, I was overwhelmed by a sense of pathos, not unmixed with shame. It is not so much money that these men, the Tom Middletons and Jack Costellos, want as the comfort of knowing they are remembered and not cast aside like worn-out boots. Surely a mighty industry cannot afford to abandon them in their extremity, for was it not their gay, lighthearted touch that converted a waste of land into community wealth and created fat dividends and balance sheets for today's proud mining companies? To paraphrase Winston Churchill's deathless words, "Never have so few done so much for so many for so little!"

CHAPTER V

Noah A. Timmins

Mine Makers

"'Hope is the flower of desire; faith is the fruit of certainty."
Honoré de Balzac

Mattawa, a station on the C.P.R., from whence adventurous travelers embarked upon the uncertain branch line that reached to the foot of Lake Temiskaming along the Ontario-Quebec border. Frame houses, wooden boardwalks, a sleepy cheerless main street, alternately dusty and muddy. An undistinguished town cut out of the bush where few men would care to tarry; certainly the last place where great events might be expected to occur. And yet, Mattawa occupies an imperishable niche in Canada's Hall of Fame, for here the seed of a northern empire was planted.

It was a raw cold day in the fall of 1903 when a rotund and moon-faced little man swung with relief from the wheezing branchline train. There was an hour or two to kill before the main liner bound for Ottawa and Hull would arrive, and so Fred La Rose, blacksmith by trade, strolled up the street and walked into the Timmins General Store. It was like any other such establishment which dispensed necessities in a frontier community, but the man behind the counter was different. Alert and with searching wideapart eyes, he studied the visitor curiously.

"You Noah Timmins?" asked La Rose.

The storekeeper nodded.

"Wanter show you somet'ing," and forthwith he produced a small canvas bag heavy with specimens. These he dumped on the counter unceremoniously.

Timmins selected a few of the larger pieces, rubbed his fingers along the rough nodular surface and studied the curious steely quality of the rock.

"Where do they come from?" he asked.

"Long Lake, up on da T. & N. O.," replied La Rose, carefully gathering his samples in the bag. "Lots silver dere."

"Ah, silver." Timmins spoke quietly, but there was a note of suppressed excitement in his voice. This, then, was evidence of the fabulous rumors that were circulating the country. His young lawyer

Fred La Rose

friend, David Dunlap, had gone north with Dr. Willet Miller, the Provincial geologist, weeks before. Miller, mentor of Timmins and his brother Henry, both of whom had been fruitlessly prospecting and grubstaking others for fifteen years, was eager to investigate reputed silver discoveries. Dunlap, after staking a few claims, had returned to Mattawa with the story that a new camp appeared in the making and Dr. Miller, deciding to stay, had named the place Cobalt, after the mineral which he perceived throughout the district. And now here was La Rose himself, claimant of the first discovery.

Timmins questioned his new friend, bade him good-bye regretfully when the warning whistle of the approaching train echoed through the town, and sat down to ponder the significance of what he had seen and heard. His body stirred with that old quiver of ambition which repeated failure had never downed, and now, with the true instinct of a mine finder, he reached for pen and paper and composed a letter to his brother Henry in Montreal. La Rose must be reached in Hull at once and an attempt made to purchase an interest in his claims. Mailing the fateful letter at the station, Timmins returned to his humble store and awaited developments.

Henry Timmins lost no time arriving at Hull, but there, he learned, the city was full of La Roses. For three days he paraded up and down the streets, knocking at doors until he located the blacksmith with the silver nuggets. Negotiations were complicated by the fact that La Rose had already given half interest in his claims to his employers, railroad contractors John and Duncan McMartin. But Henry was a persistent trader, and did not return to Mattawa until he had purchased a quarter interest in La Rose's holdings for $3,500. The brothers then hastened to Cobalt, there to meet Dr. Miller, who congratulated them on their acquisition. But bad news was not long in coming. La Rose's claims were jumped by ambitious and not overly scrupulous newcomers who swore under oath that they had made the first silver discovery on the claims. A complicated and expensive court action loomed ahead.

Timmins conferred with the McMartin brothers, whose half interest was in jeopardy also. It was decided that David Dunlap take the case, and when approached, the lawyer agreed to handle matters for a contingent equity in the ground. The men shook hands all round, and thus was born the Timmins-McMartin-Dunlap combine that was to play so vital a part in the development of Canadian mining.

After protracted hearings, a verdict favorable to La Rose was handed down. In the joy of victory, Noah Timmins did not forget a promise he had made to himself and his brother. The claims were fairly owned now and there was no reason to withhold from La Rose a desire to buy the still outstanding quarter interest. There was a discussion. La Rose, no doubt, was impressed with the manner in which Timmins had carried out his obligations in the lawsuit, without which, perhaps, the entire group would have been euchered out of their holdings. Accordingly, he agreed to option his remaining interest for $25,000. Before the time limit expired, the Timmins brothers produced the necessary cash, thanks to several rich silver shipments.

The La Rose was no grass-root property as commonly supposed. There was a little silver on the surface but far more smaltite, a cobalt arsenide. Noah Timmins, self-taught in mining and mineralogy, took the lead in the development, guided by the benevolent advice of Dr. Miller. Shaft sinking proceeded almost a hundred feet before the first real silver shoot was encountered, and from that time on the mine continued to respond faithfully. But, as with all beginnings, there were rough moments. Miners had to be paid, supplies and equipment purchased, all of which required money. The Timmins brothers had thrown everything they had into La Rose, and by the time silver was found they were scraping bottom. Accordingly, Noah went to Haileybury and applied for a $5,000 loan at the local bank, offering for security two cars of ore which were being loaded for shipment. He had the estimate of Dr. Miller that the silver was worth $30,000 minimum. The bank manager, incredulous, refused to grant the requested advance. Timmins, frustrated, returned to Cobalt, where he ingeniously managed to obtain the wherewithal to meet current obligations while the ore was in transit. In a few weeks the settlement check arrived from New York. Timmins left for Haileybury at once, there to confront the refractory bank manager with a $50,000 check bearing the potent signature of William Guggenheim.

"But I can't cash a check that large!" cried the banker. "There isn't that much money in the bank!"

"Oh, I don't want your money," answered the silver miner. "I just wanted to see if the check was all right." Then: "This is the security I offered you for a $5,000 loan. We won't be troubling you further. We have made arrangements for another bank to come into this country and there'll be no objections to taking mining accounts."

La Rose was not the only lucrative Cobalt venture. Ever alive to new opportunity, Timmins secured a $200,000 option on five claims west of the O'Brien Mine and hired a small crew to do assessment work. In a month Charles Flynn, fresh from Mexico and Colorado, negotiated a sale to Barney Baruch and the McCormick brothers of New York for $600,000. Thus did Baruch, today's elder statesman, unwittingly help to finance the Hollinger, for it was this money in part which went into the development of North America's largest gold mine. More came from the $1,000,000 sale of the La Rose, an equitable transaction for all concerned, for before it ceased to produce, the mine paid $8,000,000. Timmins did not stop to live off the fat of his Cobalt winnings. On the contrary, he was just warming up.

To Noah himself must go full credit for the Hollinger; he alone picked up and carried the burden while more cautious associates remained on the sidelines. His nephew, Alphonse Paré, a mining engineer, first heard the news of Hollinger's epochal discovery from Johnny Suavé who was among the earliest visitors in Porcupine. Paré telephoned his uncle in Montreal. With characteristic energy, Timmins left for Haileybury on the first train and the next day cornered John McMahon, the man who had grubstaked Benny Hollinger. The bartender had a power of attorney signed by Hollinger and was therefore authorized to deal with Timmins or anyone else. But he was too excited about reports of fabulous gold showings to talk rationally. Realizing that this was an inopportune moment to reach satisfactory terms, Timmins elicited a promise that if it was decided to sell the claims, he would have the first refusal. With that he returned to Montreal.

There he tried in vain to persuade the McMartins to join forces with him. They were interested, but expressed doubts about gold in Ontario. If it was silver, now, something they understood . . . Noah stoically packed his bag and prepared to return to Haileybury alone. Just as he was about to leave, his brother Henry telephoned.

"I'm going with you, Noah," he said. "The thing sounds all right to me."

And so, at the eleventh hour, the brothers Timmins were again united in common purpose. It was a good augury for the future. McMahon proved to be more amenable to reason this time, though several days of discussion passed before he agreed to sell the Hollinger claims for $330,000. But it was a close shave at that, for McMahon was about to depart for Porcupine, his canoe loaded, just as the Timmins brothers arrived at Haileybury. It is doubtful whether the claims would have been sold at the agreed figure if McMahon had carried out his purpose to visit the claims, for his partners on the ground talked of nothing less than a $1,000,000 purchase price.

Later, when Timmins purchased the Gillies claims from Jack Miller, the McMartins experienced a change of heart and asked the intrepid mine maker for a participation. The McMartin dynasty, which today supplies New York café society with some of its raciest gossip, hung in balance as Noah Timmins debated an answer. Finally it came. He would be willing, provided lawyer Dunlap be included in the syndicate. In Noah Timmins's own words, this was agreed "after some discussion" and the McMartins, who not long before this time were petty contractors, now graduated from silver magnates to gold kings. This was their last important mining venture, but it was enough.

To Noah Timmins, however, the Hollinger was another steppingstone. The urge that took him from Mattawa to Cobalt was still strong. In Porcupine he found time to look about, bought three claims west of the Dome from Hugh Sutherland, an active Toronto promoter, for $5,000. Within a few months he sold this ground, along with other claims he had unobtrusively acquired, to the English firm of Bewick Moreing, then the outstanding mining organization in the British Empire. A company was formed and development energetically pursued, but the property did not respond. Timmins, keenly aware of his responsibility, came forward with an interesting suggestion. The McIntyre claims could be purchased for $90,000, he informed his English friends. Why not buy them? He would then throw in three of the northerly Hollinger claims and a company could be organized on a fifty-fifty basis. Reviewing the incident twenty-five years later, Timmins remarked, "Mr. Moreing rejected this suggestion, and the magnitude of his mistake may be gauged from the fact that McIntyre has since paid more than $20,000,000 in dividends, while our addition to this would have been double that."

The prices Timmins paid for the Hollinger, Gillies, and Miller Middleton properties aggregated close to $1,000,000, an unheard-of sum in those early days of Canadian mining. His faith must have been the fruit of certainty, for he stuck to the Hollinger Consolidated Gold Mines like a leech, unmindful of the doubts and condemnations sounded on all sides. When success came, he resisted advice to retire on his laurels, for in mining exploration he had found his love, and nothing could draw him from it. His N. A. Timmins Corporation scoured Canada and South America for mines. Noranda, deserted and friendless, found succor in him, and when the Sisco Mine threatened to close for lack of funds, it was a combination of Noah Timmins and Thayer Lindsley that came to the rescue. Not only was the mine saved, but the entire Quebec district picked up from the low point at which Timmins found it and has gone on to produce over a half billion dollars. In Manitoba, the San Antonio Mine hoisted distress signals, and once more Timmins converted a struggling prospect into what is now the leading gold mine of Manitoba. It was Timmins who financed the Outpost Island venture in Great Slave Lake long before Yellowknife became a camp. It was Timmins, again, who founded the first chromium smeltery in Canada. And the Hollinger Mine, stimulated by the vision and enterprise of its vigilant president, developed the Ross Mine and went on to uncover Canada's greatest iron deposits in Labrador.

Timmins was no beater of drums, no lover of publicity and acclaim. Reticent, perhaps unduly so because of a slight speech impediment, he was characterized by an unfailing enthusiasm, tempered by a strong sense of reality and sobriety. His instinct almost never led him wrong. In December, 1927, he made a historic statement which was well remembered later. "Many people," he declared, "are going to have a rude awakening soon when the current mining-share boom in northern Ontario collapses. They will be the very people who can least afford it."

Old in experience, but young in heart, he found it hard to resist the allure of a new mining venture. And when he died in January, 1936, at the age of sixty-nine, a pall of sadness hung over Canada. For the Grand Old Man of Canadian Mining, as he was affectionately called, had passed on, and we all knew there would never be another like him.

One of the first buyers of Cobalt silver ores was E. P. Earle of New York. As the shipments continued and grew in size and richness, he consulted Captain Joseph R. Delamar. Together, they repaired to Cobalt, and assisted by Arthur Ferland, Haileybury hotel-keeper and brother-in-law of Noah Timmins, they quietly bought up 846 acres in the heart of the district that soon became the Nipissing Mines. Delamar listed the stock on the New York Curb and induced William Boyce Thompson, a rising young mining promoter, to accept low-priced options on several hundred thousand shares of stock. Thompson, of whom we shall hear more, at once launched a high-pressure sales campaign. He knew all the tricks and worked off his cheap stock rapidly. There was one disquieting note, however—most of the buying toward the end came from one persistent source. Tapping his many facets of confidential information, Thompson was astonished to learn that the purchaser was none other than Delamar himself! Sensing that he had been euchered, Thompson rushed to Cobalt, there to confirm his suspicions; Nip had recently discovered a series of fabulously high-grade silver veins. Delamar had in some strange way learned this before anyone else, and the old fox did not hesitate to repurchase stock from Thompson at considerably higher levels.

Who was this Delamar? Shrouded in secrecy, he appeared only at decisive moments and then disappeared again like an eel in mud. Overly sensitive of his foreign accent perhaps, he rarely attended conferences. He was known largely by his accomplishments and these were truly prodigious. Canadian Copper Company was an obscure producer until this mysterious little man regarded the situation with his dark glittering eye and conceived the grand plan that matured into the elephantine International Nickel Company, now

Captain J. R. De Lamar

providing 90 per cent of the world's nickel supply and leading all other mining organizations with a staggering dividend total of $466,000,000. Assisting him in this and the Nipissing venture was Robert C. Stanley, who has since become president of Nickel.

When Charles Denison vacillated and suffered from a case of cold feet at the time Dome Mines was offered for sale, Delamar rose to the occasion. Pulling at his goatee, he walked over the ground, looking, looking with a hungry stare.

"We'll dake id," he announced briefly, and the Dome was no longer without a parent.

Delamar's name appeared infrequently; obscurity was one of his methods, apparently. Taciturn, suspicious of the press, he made few statements. When he did speak it was to voice a decision or a command. He employed technical men and assistants freely but formed his own conclusions. I have met many of his old associates in the West and in Canada, and from conversations with them over a period of years I have been able to piece together some semblance of a portrait, but my picture is by no means complete. The late Cap Anchor, my brother Robert's first bush partner, supplied many facts and opinions. As factotum to Delamar for many years, beginning with the Delamar, Nevada, venture in 1881 and continuing for a quarter of a century, Anchor had a unique opportunity to observe his strange employer, but even the observant Dane was unable to close many gaps in the story.

Joseph Raphael Delamar (or De Lamar) was born in Amsterdam, Holland, on September 2, 1843, the youngest in a family of two girls and four boys. His father, a banker, had left Paris to settle in Amsterdam at the behest of paterfamilias Delamar, himself a banker in Paris who wished to establish a branch in Amsterdam. Joseph's father, Maxmilian, an ardent lover of art, bestowed upon his youngest offspring the distinguished middle name of "Raphael" because of an intense admiration of the Florentine painter. Joseph's mother, Johanna Tenne, was of German descent. According to Anchor, Delamar was Jewish and the name was an assumed one, taken from the French *de la mer,* "of the sea," when the youngest Delamar became a sea captain. Of this there is no official proof. In any event, Delamar found himself an orphan when he was six years old. He did not remain in Amsterdam long. Barely in his 'teens, he stowed away on a Dutch sailing vessel bound for the East Indies. Upon being discovered at sea, he was put to work as the cook's helper, and received the munificent pay of 40 cents a month. By the time he was seventeen, however, he was a mate, and three years later, when the captain died, he guided the ship into port and became a full-fledged sea captain.

A man of Delamar's capacities could not remain a prisoner of routine. Attracted to the possibilities of submarine salvage after the Civil War, he became a deep-sea diver and then a submarine salvage contractor with headquarters at Vineyard Haven, Massachusetts. In all, he raised more than forty sunken vessels. A near tragedy put an end to this underwater interlude. Imprisoned below the surface for thirty-six hours when a sudden shifting of the tide entrapped him beneath a rolling hulk, a comatose Delamar was finally rescued and restored to life. This was enough; there would be no more competing with fish. He now turned to a plan which had long been activating in his ever restless mind. In the course of his wide travels he had remarked that South African trade was unorganized and haphazard. Natives toiled to the southwest coast from the interior and bartered their scanty ivory, gold dust, and hides. Why not penetrate the jungle by navigating a small schooner up the rivers Gambia and Jeba and trade in large volume close to the sources of supply? It was a novel idea and Delamar proceeded to make it a reality. Purchasing the requisite ship in Massachusetts, he obtained a skeleton crew and officers and made a bee line for Africa, laden with cheap cotton goods and trinkets and thoughtfully provided with small cannon, a dozen blunderbusses, and numerous rifles and side arms.

For three years he was swallowed by the hinterland of the Dark Continent, pursuing ways which were never recorded. All that is known of this period is that he was forced to quit when all white members of the crew had succumbed to fever and the large force of blacks had been reduced to a pitiful handful. Delamar himself seems to have escaped unscathed. Ever a trader, even in adversity, he succeeded in selling his ship and trading posts to an English firm. Then he sailed for New York, the Conradian episode of his singular life only a memory.

The year was 1878. Stories of fantastic riches in the newly discovered Leadville, Colorado, camp appealed to the adventurous Delamar, and he was soon journeying westward. At Leadville he rubbed shoulders with a polyglot humanity, purchased a few claims on the outskirts of the district, and then began to realize that he was totally unfitted for mining. A fortuitous meeting with "Colonel" Enos A. Wall, an adventurer like himself who had gravitated to mining and later became justly famous as the first owner and sponsor of the great Utah Copper enterprise, resulted in Delamar's going to Chicago, where he placed himself under the tutorship of a professor learned in mining and metallurgy. Thus fortified, after six months of study, Delamar returned to Colorado, but not to Leadville. Knowing that the state was a wide one, he preferred remoter localities where his special talents would have greater play. Alone, friendless, speaking the language badly, still rolling in his gait, he appeared to be a hopeless apology for a mine hawk. Prospectors and engineers had already combed the state, but this weird man, self-taught and confident, nevertheless conquered the gods of chance.

In Custer County, he noted that road builders were using a different kind of fill, soft, white, heavy stuff, specimens of which he casually collected. Then, in the solitude of his hotel room, he made a series of blowpipe tests at which he was adept, thanks to his Chicago study, and, as he suspected, the "rock" proved to be cerrusite, the richest kind of lead ore. With studied carelessness, he made a few inquiries, learned the identity of the owners of the pit from which the material had been excavated, and bought the land for $3,500. In time this became the Terrible Mine, ironically named, for it made Delamar a millionaire and paved the way for even grander triumphs.

To follow his subsequent career through the great American desert which bloomed for him, to untangle deals and negotiations, to record purchases and sales, to study the tenuous methods which brought forth mines and near mines is a task no one has as yet attempted, for Delamar's tracks were covered while he lived, and since his death the traces of his trail are well hidden in the sands of time. His remaining western monument is the ghost town of Delamar, Idaho, where he came, dug gold, sold out, and like an Arab melted away on new conquests. Utah Copper was his "almost" masterpiece, for he was in Utah early and purchased a large interest in what was then considered Colonel Wall's dubious prospect. Delamar regretted the $25,000 he had spent, for, upon reflection, he concluded that the ore was too low grade ever to make a commercial operation. So, weary or piqued, he instructed his retainers to sell, himself departing for European watering places where he hoped to remove an abdominal pain which never left him. New York newspapers hailed his transit, comparing him to an Asiatic potentate laden with gold.

Returning from Europe, he was informed that his equity in Utah Copper had been sold. Asked the purchaser's name, his secretary replied, "Spencer Penrose and Charles MacNeill on the recommendation of Daniel Jackling."

"Den I haf made a misdake!" cried Delamar. And, true enough, Utah eventually grew into the world's largest copper mine.

For a time Delamar served as a member of the Idaho state legislature and was appropriately chosen chairman of the Finance Committee. Later he was offered the governorship but declined the offer in favor of residence in New York. His town house was carefully chosen on Madison Avenue across the street from J. P. Morgan's mansion. At Glen Cove, Long Island, Delamar founded an estate worthy of a prince. His long-dormant instinct for creative art was now given free rein, and in short order he possessed an important collection of paintings and sculpture. A virtuoso on the organ, he had installed in his country house the largest privately owned instrument in the country. His love of flowers and plants took expression, also; his conservatories housed exquisite orchids and tropical plants, many of which had never been seen by Americans. Delamar's two yachts elicited wonder and envy among the horsy Long Island set, and his house parties, conducted in the grand manner, provided a wealth of gossip and caused haughty dowagers to lift aristocratic eyebrows. Delamar married brilliantly. His wife, Nellie Virginia Sands, was a celebrated beauty and a direct descendant of John Quincy Adams.

Amid this unaccustomed splendor, the old sea captain did not forget his ramified business affairs. New York became his base of operations, and in time he was known as the "Mystery Man of Wall Street." His Canadian projects took rapid form, but he did not confine himself to mining. His interests spread to sugar, phosphate, tobacco, and general speculation. Among others, he held directorships in the American Bank Note and American Sumatra Tobacco companies.

Cap Anchor showed me a letter which Delamar had written him

in 1914. Anchor was carefully instructed to gather information about available mining claims in an inactive section of Porcupine. The last paragraph, departing from the impersonal text, ended with this phrase, "and keep your damned mouth shut!"

"The old goat was a regular Napoleon," said Cap with asperity. "Things had to be done his way, or else. But toward the end he was a sick and unhappy man. First he was crazy about his wife, but then he found some letters in her room, all of them from the Khedive of Egypt, a gent the Delamars met on one of their European trips. Guess the monkey was in love with the Mrs. and the captain blew his top. There was a hell of a stew, ending in divorce. Anyway, the old boy was all broken up about it. Told me it was all a bad mistake, he shouldn't have lost his head, his wife was a wonderful woman, and all that. Between the divorce and his bad gut, he didn't enjoy living much, in spite of all his chasing around."

Said one of the early Dome engineers, "We called him 'Hard Cash' because he always kept a wad of money in his office safe and dished out cash whenever he bought anything. Story was that he got caught in one of the early panics and never trusted banks again. Was he smart? Say, you never met anyone quite like him. That man could smell ore. Only asked a few questions, but they went right to the point. Listened to everybody but said damned little himself, just pulled at that little muff under his chin. This fellow Jules Bache was a wise old bird too, but he stumbled on the Dome by pure chance. So I've been told, at least. Seems that he was playing around with one of the captain's lady friends in New York and she told him about the sea captain who owned one of the best gold mines in the world. Bache, who never missed an opportunity, bought in all the Dome and Dome Extension when Delamar's estate was liquidated."

Delamar died on December 1, 1918, following an operation for gallstones. His will, as was to be expected, was remarkable in many ways. Delamar could not be ordinary. As a preface, he made this extraordinary statement: "I declare I have never been married to anyone except my late wife, the mother of my daughter, Alice Antoinette Delamar, and that I have never had a child born to me except my said daughter."

There were various sizable bequests to servants and retainers, among them $50,000 to his secretary, and $25,000 each to two companions of his daughter. One brother, Abraham, still living in Amsterdam, was generously remembered, as were the numerous children of his deceased brothers and sisters. The sum of $10,000,000 was given in equal thirds to the Harvard Medical School, the Columbia School of Physicians and Surgeons, and the School of Hygiene at

Johns Hopkins University for purposes of medical research and the institution of endowed lectures "to give to the people of the United States generally the benefits of increased knowledge concerning the prevention of sickness and disease, and also concerning the conservation of health by proper food and diet."

Nicholas Murray Butler exulted: "This is a magnificent bequest and we are very grateful to his memory."

Delamar's predilection for medical schools probably derived from his own ill-health and a psychological desire to sanctify the memory of his wife. Her uncle was one of the most prominent American surgeons of his time, and the Sands family was justly proud of a long line of scientists. In any event, a $10,000,000 trust fund which the will provided for Alice Delamar contains a significant qualification—the large principal is to go to the three universities should the present beneficiary die without issue.

Sic gloria transit!

Overlooking the broad waters of Lake Ontario near Oakville rises the majestic edifice of "Edgemere." Its twenty-five acres contain a Japanese water garden, complete to painted wooden bridges, bronze fountains, and priceless Oriental carvings and paintings. There is a Buddha garden also, guarded by a three-ton metal god, and an outdoor dancing pavilion with green marble flooring. The barbecue would do Hollywood proud, for it is extensive enough to accommodate a hundred guests. The house itself is laden with objets d'art. A small head of Christ was once a gift of the notorious Rasputin to the Czar of Russia. Old masters adorn the ample walls. Titian, Corot, Rembrandt, Constable, Gainsborough are all represented in this private museum. Intricate carvings, ancient pietà groups are tastefully arranged throughout the mansion. Nothing in Canada can compare with this magnificence.

Who is the proprietor, commuting to Toronto in a high-powered motor launch, to spend only an hour or two in his extensive office? None other than incorrigible Jack Hammell, prospector and mine maker extraordinary, who came up the hard way. Uninhibited in speech and action, colorful, irrepressible, he has cut a wide swath in Canadian mining. He has become a legend and to him, as to Sam Goldwyn, have been attributed countless stories and bon mots.

This one is typical. His confidential secretary submitted an important letter which required an immediate answer.

"What shall I say in reply?" she inquired anxiously.

"Tell him," replied Jack, as his eyes darted over the paper, "tell him to kiss my rear."

On another occasion, when he had received $300,000 for his share of the Flin Flon claims, it was suggested that he retire.

"Retire? Hell, no!" he exploded. "Retiring is like sitting behind a chicken and picking up the eggs!"

Jack Hammell

John E. Hammell was born in the quiet town of Beeton, Ontario, in 1876. As a young man he ventured for a time in the prize ring, known to the sporting world as Kid Walton. Later he tried his hand at newspaper reporting, in the course of which he became something of an authority on the underworld of New York, picking up a vocabulary which defies comparison. Cobalt silver discoveries brought the wanderer home to his native province, and in short order he became a marked man in a camp famous for its colorful characters. Teaming with Mike Hackett, Jack Munroe, a burly, mild-spoken giant who was reputed to have bested Jim Jeffries in a boxing contest, Joe Acton, once champion wrestler of England, and Tommy Saville, who spoke Ojibwa like a native and later won renown as the husband of an Indian princess, Hammell and the "Gang" supplied Cobalt with some of its choicest anecdotes. And they made history when they were grubstaked by W. S. Mitchell and left Cobalt to discover and stake the Casey Mine.

Hammell was quick to move when the new silver camp of Elk Lake was found in 1907 by Leo Ernhous, erstwhile circus performer. Ernhous, tiring of the bush, had returned to the footlights, soon after to be stricken with mastoid. A quick operation in New York saved his life. During convalescence, he was surprised to learn that his surgeon, Dr. Harbeck, had been to the north on frequent hunting expeditions, in the course of which he had found silver-bearing calcite veins along the Montreal River. Ernhous asked for specimens and to his amazement he saw in them an abundance of the precious metal. An agreement was made at once; Ernhous would stake a group of claims on joint account with the good doctor. Returning north, he went in to Elk Lake. His map was accurate and his bushmanship perfect, for he soon located the doctor's old campsite and the calcite veins nearby.

When the news arrived in Cobalt, Jack Hammell and his friends were foremost in the rush to Elk Lake. With a good head start they were able to stake choice claim groups. It was a wild boom, for Cobalt supplied a noteworthy example of what silver could do in Ontario. Ground changed hands at high prices, but when the deposits were found to be shallow and limited, prospectors who had "sold out too quickly" were the only real beneficiaries. Among the more fortunate was Jack Hammell. Trading in town lots brought him a handsome revenue and his position was further enhanced by the election of his sidekick, Jack Munroe, as mayor of Elk Lake. But it was not a part of Jack's nature to become complacent. His theory was that the world belonged to the energetic. Outstripping his friends, he began a series of undertakings which placed him in the front ranks of mining.

Porcupine called and Jack answered. Quickly perceiving that the choicest ground there was already staked or purchased, he cast about to gain a foothold. Meeting his old friend Barney McAnenny, for whom Benny Hollinger and Alec Gillies had, with an abundance of generosity, staked a claim south of the Hollinger, Jack convinced him that the ground, if properly handled, could fetch a goodly price. And, of course, Jack was the man to do the negotiating, and this for a mere 10 per cent of the proceeds. McAnenny agreed, and Jack left for Cobalt.

There he sat with Sam Cohen, manager of the profitable Crown Reserve Mine, spread the map on a desk and expounded upon certainties of a mine. Cohen was impressed. What was the deal?

"You can have it for $300,000," flashed Hammell.

Cohen reflected, then asked if the property could first be examined by company engineers. There was no objection to this, and the men left for Porcupine on the first train.

A week later, Cohen received the detailed report. He read it carefully, then communicated with his directors. Even Hammell, the speed boy, was surprised at the dispatch with which Crown Reserve acted. The first cash payment was promptly made and the balance completed when Porcupine Crown Mine became a steady gold producer.

The way was now open for more deals, and Hammell was not long in presenting Cohen with another opportunity, this time the Teck-Hughes Mine in Kirkland Lake.

"It's a hell of a lot better than the Crown," said the ebullient Jack.

Once more engineers were sent north to make the prescribed examination, and a long report was sent to Cohen. He read the introduction, a description of the entire district, the geology, a discussion of the timber and water-power resources. Impatiently, he thumbed through the pages until he reached a summary of samples and assays. His brow wrinkled in disappointment; the values were spotty.

"Sorry, Jack," he apologized, "but this time I think you picked a lemon. There just isn't enough gold in this one."

In time, when "Handsome" Charley Denison and his friends, chagrined by their failure to retain a majority interest in the Dome Mine, took hold of the Teck and nursed it into one of Kirkland Lake's Big Three, under the astute management of D. L. H. Forbes, Jack Hammell decided to follow his instincts and "hit the ball hard." He would go places on his own steam. And go he did, first at the Flin Flon where he paved the way for the Hudson Bay Mining & Smelting. The Howey, up in the "Indian Country" of Patricia, was his next scene of triumph, and then in succession came Pickle Crow, the full flower of his hope, Hasaga and Starratt-Olsen. There were failures, some of them bitter, such as the Uchi, and teasers of the Harker and Greene-Stabell stripe, but through it all Hammell rose to a commanding position, outspoken and Napoleonic as ever.

Beneath a façade of garrulity and roughness, lie intelligence, acumen and warmth. Called upon to speak before a distinguished gathering of mining men, he gave a remarkable analysis of Canada in relation to the country's mining possibilities. Concluding, he said:

"There is much more to this life than a mad scramble for dollars. Let us mine the rich veins of character in youth as well as the veins of gold. . . . Let's make this country the finest place in the world. . . . With a northern plan we can do it, and our work for young Canada will be our monument."

We shall hear more of this rapid-fire mine maker in subsequent pages, for he is a large part of the story of Canadian mining.

In the summer of 1924, a tall rangy man walked into our camp in eastern Joannes Township. It was no ordinary hike. Almost ten miles to the Kinojevis River, our trail was largely muskeg, and we had trouble finding men who were willing to walk and pack over this tortuous path. Bob greeted the stranger, for whom we had cut fresh spruce and balsam brush so that his bunk would be restful.

"Meet Thayer Lindsley."

As we shook hands, I said that I had preceded him by only an hour, having packed in from the trapper's cabin.

"You must have had a load," he said quietly. "Your heel marks were rather deep, I noticed."

He was with us by arrangement, George Ellis, a prospector, having agreed to paddle into Bousquet Lake from La Sarre on the Transcontinental Railroad to meet him on our ground. Then the two would make a tour of the country east. Bob, it appeared, had suggested Ellis for the trip.

The next day was given over to examining our "showings" and Lindsley walked along the veins completely absorbed by what he saw. There was a quiet seriousness about him, a mild courtliness which seemed strange in the bush where most men proclaim friendships and ideas loudly. And when George Ellis appeared, white haired and dour, to whisk away our visitor, I had a premonition that Canada would soon hear about this gentle stranger. Nor were my instincts wrong. Today Thayer Lindsley is the exploration king of Canadian mining, a crown he wears with a modesty which is closer to self-effacement.

"Keep working," is his favorite maxim, "keep working and the Pre-Cambrian will in time reward you."

This advice he has scrupulously followed himself. Lesser men, confronted with the problems he has faced in a period of successive world crises, would have disappeared long ago. But in fair weather and foul, he has pitted his unusual talents against a country at times unresponsive and even hostile, and in the end succeeded brilliantly. With imagination, fortitude, and energy matched only by his uncanny geological intuitiveness and financial genius, he builded a mining dynasty across the rambling Canadian hinterland from coast to coast, southward to his native United States and on to the mountains and jungles of Latin America. A truly globular pioneer, he is today nibbling at Africa and other continents.

"Show him a property no one else wants," states one of his associates, "and he'll eat it up."

"You can't do anything with a man like that," a field scout of a rival organization once complained. "He travels the bush himself and if he likes a showing he hands a prospector five hundred cash. He'll ruin the exploration business."

Ironically, this same engineer turned to Lindsley when, years later, his company refused to continue a development he had unequivocally recommended. Lindsley arranged to have the incumbent's stock purchased by several of his subsidiary companies, and the prospect later waxed into a sizable mine.

This mine maker is of an unobtrusive disposition, with all the breeding and instincts of a true gentleman. Soft voiced, almost deferential in manner, he has yet literally swept Canadian mining into his lap. His deeds have been so impersonal as to be colorless, but few others before him achieved so much with so little. To him, money has little significance except as it may be employed in the furtherance of mining property. For the duration of the late war, he allocated his income to the Canadian government. He has made fortunes for others while his own earnings have been modest. In accomplishment and endeavor he finds his own special compensation.

Educated at Harvard as a civil engineer, he was first employed in 1904, when the Brooklyn-Manhattan subway was being constructed. Underground excavation fascinated him and he began to think of mining, influenced as well by his older brother Halstead, a practicing mining engineer. He left Manhattan, and for the next six years wandered about the various mining camps, returning to New York for a period of study at Columbia under the tutelage of Dr. James Kemp. In 1911 he was in Porcupine, and as a result of what he saw he wrote one of the few "papers" of his career, a review of the then struggling district. A later day found his prognostications amazingly accurate. For a time he vainly tried to engage the attention of American mining companies in the young Canadian field. Meeting with constant rebuff, he went west again and was happier trying to solve the strange laws of mineral deposits. In the desert he schooled himself in the science of ore hunting.

Interruption came in 1917. After service overseas as an artillery officer, he continued what he had begun. Now he gave undivided effort to the Homestead Iron Dyke Mine in Oregon and brought this abandoned property back to productiveness. The mine was sold in 1923, and Lindsley, with a stake of $30,000, turned northward where there was room for his budding talents. For associates he chose his brother, Joseph Errington, Colonel C. D. H. MacAlpine, and General D. M. Hogarth. Together they provided funds for various new enterprises in the Noranda district, aided by Toronto brokers. The Sherritt-Gordon Mine suddenly becoming available for fresh financing, Lindsley took a quick plunge, and the first of a string of mines came into being.

His fertile mind, never in repose, conceived the idea of an exploration company and forthwith Ventures, Ltd., was organized. The stock was sold to friends entirely, but outside demand became so insistent that a public issue was decided upon. At the time, Lindsley sounded a strong note of warning. He stated that the project, as the name of the company suggested, was entirely speculative, and those who could not afford to lose were urged to look elsewhere. In spite of this declaration, or perhaps because of it, the stock offering was greatly oversubscribed. Lindsley now possessed a sizable fund.

The first direct result was the acquistion of the Falconbridge Nickel Mine. In 1917 the Ontario government, mindful of nickel's importance as a war metal, published a long detailed report of the Sudbury Nickel Range. Mining men and others had been reading this tome for ten years, but until Lindsley appeared no one had acted upon the voluminous information. Now action came swiftly. The Falconbridge, already drilled extensively, needed only guidance by a bold hand. The claims were purchased in record time, and with Ventures and the public furnishing the capital, the property became the largest independent nickel producer in the range.

While the depression deflated mining exploration generally, Lindsley doggedly continued on his way. Coniagas Mines, after struggling ineffectively next to the McIntyre, willingly turned over the reins to Ventures. Mindful of his earlier study of Porcupine, Lindsley was confident that by stealing down with the shaft, as he expressed it, the mine could be made to pay its way toward deeper horizons where more favorable conditions might be expected. In this he was aided by the higher price of gold, but no other group would have dared tackle this kind of long shot. While the Coniaurum has not developed into a bonanza, it has become a profitable gold mine.

Another typical Lindsley effort was the Beattie Mine in Quebec. Here a large porphyry mass, finely mineralized, was drilled and found to contain medium to low gold values. Large-scale mining and the solution of a complicated metallurgy were necessary, but this did not deter a man of Lindsley's character. The time—1930—was not propitious; security values were depressed and money was not easy to find. Most men would have bided their time, but like all empire builders Lindsley was jealous of time. He applied himself and resolved the riddle of funds. The Nipissing Mines, which had reached the end of silver-producing days, was inertly sitting on a $3,500,000 treasury. Lindsley purchased a block of the stock and interviewed officers of the company. Not long thereafter, Nipissing agreed to buy a million shares of Beattie at forty cents per share, for which it was given options to purchase more stock at somewhat higher prices. With Ventures also contributing, Beattie went ahead, not without numerous problems, to become a dividend payer. Criticism, which had cut deeply into so sensitive a nature as Lindsley's, was stilled and replaced by rising respect for anyone who could "put over" a marginal project of the Beattie type and at the same time instill new life into a sleeping dog like Nipissing.

At the Canadian Malartic Mines, an earlier mine-making attempt, too much for even Lindsley, was resumed in 1933. Thanks to the happy selection of "Ernie" Neelands as managing director, this low-grade property achieved one of the lowest cost operations in Canada, and leads all the Malartics in dividends. Another bright page in the Lindsley record is the La Luz Mines, which was wrested from the inhospitable jungles of Nicaragua. It was necessary to ferry equipment by airplane, construct a water-power site, and perform the heartbreaking task of building a tropical prospect into a self-sustaining community. Again choosing the right man, this time George W. Tower, Lindsley had the great satisfaction of seeing one of his newest creations sparkle in the mining sun.

During World War II, his ramified organization, which has been likened to a Chinese puzzle, one box within another, turned from gold to strategic metals. None of these efforts, in a corporate or financial way, was very profitable, but the yield was of incalculable aid and comfort to the United Nations. Quicksilver came from Peru, tungsten from California, rutile from Australia, zinc from Virginia, alumina clay from North Carolina, magnesium, iron and graphite from Ontario, and lead and zinc from Quebec. Least heralded, but of greatest importance, were the accomplishments of Metal Hydrides, which pioneered the commercial production of uranium so that it was made available to atomic bomb scientists. This little-known company also provided enough calcium hydride to meet requirements of the United States Signal Corps, with some surplus for the hard-pressed RAF.

The threads of gold were again picked up when the war ended. As if to reward him for his abnegations, fate presented Lindsley with the Giant Yellowknife Mine, which appears to be the long-sought "plum," the culmination of a generation of toil. Before this, he rejuvenated Eureka, Nevada, where a long-slumbering district woke to the touch of a master hand. Drilling there disclosed major lead-zinc-silver ore bodies which had been faulted away from the original workings. This was a case of phenomenal memory; Lindsley carried an impression of Eureka for a quarter of a century, returning at long last to put his old theories, mellowed by time, to the test.

Meanwhile, his engineers roam the bush, shafts are being sunk throughout Canada and drills probe the rocks for secrets which slowly yield to his clear, three-dimensional mind. His conceptions are wide, his energy boundless, and his resources unlimited. His methods are well known, and others are free to follow them and become the Cecil Rhodes of Canada—if they can.

A friendly lumberman and fried onions had much to do with the career of genial Bob Jowsey. Gray, and somewhat stiff at the joints, he can look back with satisfaction at a productive life in the bush. Starting as a prospector, he is now the dean of mine makers, equally at home in the bush or at a conference table.

Bob Jowsey

The son of a United Empire Loyalist who gave up a military career to pursue the peaceful life of a farmer near Ottawa, Bob was brought up close to the soil. As a stripling he could never forget a story related to him by Bill Purcell, a neighbor. Purcell, a retired lumberman, had cut timber in South Lorrain, twenty miles from Cobalt, in 1874, and always remembered that his foreman there, Pat Manion, had carried away a sample of "lead" which he found in a curious way. In those days timber had to be squared in the bush before it could be sold to the lumber mills. Accordingly, small trees were first dropped to provide a protective mattress for the large timber. In the course of this work, Manion detected a fragment of interesting-looking rock exposed by an uprooted pine. Curious, he pocketed a specimen which he took to be lead, and then blazed a nearby tree on four sides to mark the spot. Years later, Manion was told by an expert that the "lead" was in fact silver, whereupon he returned to South Lorrain. But he could not find the squared tree. Others, hearing the story, tried also, but without success.

"That decided me," says Bob, in discussing the incident. "I made up my mind I was going to find that silver."

In 1907 he left the farm and went to Haileybury, there to join forces with J. M. Wood and Charles Keeley who were willing enough to search for Manion's elusive silver. In South Lorrain, their first reconnaissance revealed that Manion's son had staked a number of claims, but failing to locate the tree and the silver, had allowed his claims to lapse and wandered on. The Jowsey trio had better luck. They found no tree with four old blazes but they did discover silver, and after a series of mishaps the Keeley Mines, Ltd., was incorporated and financed through the Home Bank of Haileybury. Ore reserves were not easy to develop, however, and when the bank failed liquidators took title to the mine. Thereupon, Dr. J. Mackintosh Bell, of Great Bear Lake fame, purchased the property on behalf of English principals, and after the acquistion of more claims from the active Jowsey combine, went on to discover the Woods vein. The Keeley, in a few hectic years, paid $2,250,000 in dividends.

"Didn't make a hell of a lot out of it," Bob Jowsey commented on the experience, "but it was a good start, a nice way to get my feet wet, and I've stayed with mining ever since."

Seasoned now, he represented a syndicate headed by Noah Timmins and went into the Harricanaw district of Quebec in 1913. On his way back to Haileybury, he decided to visit Kirkland Lake and so dropped off the train at Swastika. The day being late, he registered at Joe Boisvert's hotel, there to meet Albert Wende. Wende, an old-time lessor in Cripple Creek, Colorado, had heard about rich ore at the Tough-Oakes mine and thought he would investigate. He and Jowsey agreed to travel into Kirkland Lake together.

"We were awakened," relates Bob, "by a terrible smell of frying onions. It was still dark, but Wende and I decided to pull out before we were asphyxiated. If we hadn't, the history of Kirkland Lake would've been entirely different."

For, at the end of the trail, they espied a twirl of smoke, which, upon investigation, proved to be Bill Wright's campfire. Wright was mixing pancakes, before leaving for parts unknown. The visitors were welcomed, and as they ate they questioned Wright closely. The Tough-Oakes was in Clem Foster's hands, he informed them. Weldon Young, the broker, had purchased all of Ed Hargreaves's vendor stock in the Wright-Harvreaves Mine, only to sell most of it in Buffalo. Wende saw bigger game here than a lease. Wright, strangely communicative that morning, probably because he desired new neighbors, turned to Jowsey and informed him that McCane, a plumber in Haileybury, was anxious to sell his claim next to the Teck-Hughes.

Jowsey and his companion left for Swastika that afternoon, Wende hurrying on to Buffalo where he purchased Wright-Hargreaves stock from a lumberman named Symms and interested a syndicate to reorganize the company and finance an entirely new development. Jowsey, at the same time, buttonholed McCane in Haileybury and acquired his claim for $3,500. Told by McCane that seven adjoining claims were available, Jowsey hunted down the owners and bought this ground for $1,500. The entire group became the Kirkland Lake Gold Mines, today one of the select producers of the district.

After his return from overseas in 1919, Jowsey turned to Manitoba, where the Mandy Mine had shipped 10,000 tons of copper-gold ore during the war for an amazing return of $5,000,000. That looked good enough to our mine maker, and so he made the long jump to the Pas. Hearing that an Indian named Philip Sherlet had reported a new copper discovery, Jowsey joined a party to examine the find. But his companions deserted him en route, and a chagrined Jowsey was forced to return south alone. Some time later Carl Sherritt and Dick Madole, trappers, restaked the Sherlet claims when they were allowed to lapse, and James Young, who acted as their agent, persuaded J. D. Gordon of Winnipeg to take an option. Gordon passed this on to the Nipissing, and when the option was dropped the International Nickel took over. Once more work proved disappointing and Nickel's tenure was also of the "hail and farewell" variety. Thereupon the Victoria Syndicate, an English company, appeared on the scene. In charge of work was Eldon Brown, a Canadian, and to him Bob Jowsey, an interested spectator, now went, asking for a chance to participate in the new try. Informed that it was too late for this, Jowsey replied, "I'll wait, especially with an English crowd holding the option. They'll never stick, and anyway no mine is worth a damn until it's been turned down five or six times."

Laughingly, Brown promised to communicate with him if events proved him correct. Back in Toronto, Jowsey discussed the situation with Thayer Lindsley, who expressed definite interest. Satisfied, Jowsey departed. Then came a frantic wire from Brown announcing that the Victoria Syndicate had decided not to meet the cash payment due on the option that very day. Jowsey rushed to Lindsley's office but was informed that "T.L." was out having his hair cut. Being a prospector, the resourceful Jowsey soon located his man. Together they composed a telegram, and before the day was over Manitoba's much-optioned copper prospect was in new hands, there to stay. Of the 200,000 shares Jowsey received, ten per cent was allocated to Brown, who remained as manager.

Acting upon information supplied by Dr. J. F. Wright, a Dominion government geologist, Jowsey himself staked the God's Lake Gold Mine, also in Manitoba, and provided one of the few examples of the same individual staking, financing, and developing a prospect into a producing mine. His Bobjo Company, started in 1928, became a junior Ventures, Ltd., reaching out to all corners of the Dominion. For novelty, perhaps, Bob, now in his seventies, is scratching around Saskatchewan, seeking oil. For this mine finder, like most, has the lust of new enterprise in his blood, and he will be on a quest till the day he dies.

"Yes, sir, I'm the man who found the rich Frood ore, and don't let anyone tell you different." He nodded and tossed off a liberal shot of hot rum toddy.

This was Oscar Smith, the forgotten man of Canadian mining, not long before he died, and I had no reason to disbelieve him. The Smith & Travers Company, diamond drillers, went everywhere at the call of operators, but in Sudbury, where the main office was located, Smith performed his masterpiece. Confident from his long observation of the district that the Frood ore of International Nickel was dipping at a flat angle northwestward, he tried to obtain a drilling contract from the Mond Nickel Company, which owned the Frood Extension. Smith's plan was unusual; he wanted to drill a deep vertical hole far from developed country. Too unusual, for the Mond management considered the cost prohibitive and the chances of ore nil. In despair, Smith made a "proposition."

"I'll drill for nothing," he stated. "You don't pay unless I hit ore, and then I get $5 a foot. You can't lose."

The Mond agreed and Smith went to work. It was not easy to maintain a vertical direction; frequent wedging was necessary and progress was painfully slow.

"They said I was slipping," smiled the white-haired driller, "but I stuck to the job. Took a long time but then I hit where I expected I would, high grade and over forty feet wide. She was a lulu."

And a lulu it was, without doubt the greatest ore body in the history of mining, containing copper, nickel, platinum, and silver in immense quantities.

"They paid me $8,000, real sports they were," said Smith, sipping at his rum. "And then they merged with International Nickel which sells for over $700,000,000 today. Most of that value comes from the Frood, which has 50,000,000 tons of ore that ought to average $45 a ton. You know," and he poured himself another drink, "there's a good chance in that country northwest of the Mond, for the ore will keep going right to the contact which is still a half a mile away. Yes, sir, she's there, all right. And before I die I'd like a crack at it. Not only for the money. But to prove that those boys who're so smart with finances don't know much about the mining business."

But he died before the attempt could be made and the country still waits for another Oscar.

Another Sudbury driller, more prominent, was the late Joe Errington. Mining engineer associate of Thayer Lindsley, he remained fiercely independent. Some called Joe a professional enthusiast, but, like Hammell, he was a man of iron resolution and could not. be downed by repeated failure. He took hold of the Treadwell-Yukon and optioned it to Americans, and for a time was hailed as the founder of a lead-zinc industry in Sudbury. In the end, when fiasco came, Joe picked himself up from the floor, bruised but defiant, and continued on his way, finally to snare the Little Long Lac Mine.

"Jump in the water," he told me once. "Until you do you won't know whether it's deep or shallow. Most men waste their lives standing on the shore and wondering."

He was no dreamy twiddler. After the Little Long Lac he did what all real mine makers invariably do—he went out and grabbed another property. This time it was the MacLeod-Cockshutt. The deep taste of success after so many years of frustration made him cocky, and it was widely prophesied that he would come a cropper. But Joe was deceptive. Despite his apparent reckless abandon, he was no longer a callow youngster who had charged windmills at the drop of a hat. His engineering training came to the fore, and he picked his spots carefully. Teaming with Charles McCrea, former minister of mines, he undertook financing and development of the Negus Mines in Yellowknife.

"The biggest thing I ever landed," he enthused to Bob and me, urging us, at an early date, to acquire ground in that then-unknown field.

An exaggeration? Perhaps, but Negus is the sole dividend payer in Yellowknife today, and recent deep drilling has given justification to the hope that mine dimensions will increase appreciably. Joe did not live to see the child of his old age ripen into manhood, nor was he present when his last venture, the Steep Rock, Canada's greatest producing iron mine, dammed and pumped out a sizable lake and, after stupendous effort, made its first high-grade lump ore shipments. This is regrettable, for no one could have enjoyed the spectacle so much as Joe Errington, the man who made this dream of iron come true.

"It's the same diabase dike that crosses the Noranda," stated

Jim Norrie, the one and only. "The Stadacona will find all kinds of ore."

We smiled condescendingly. Such a statement was a cry in the dark, wishful thinking in the face of hard fact. But Jim continued to propound such farfetched theses of structure until one day his opinion became the voice of reason. A report signed by him was gospel, for was he not "King of the Muskeg," a man of faith and unswerving purpose who possessed some secret weapon which cracked open the rock and exposed ore where none was supposed to exist?

Jim Norrie

Nova Scotian and a graduate mining engineer, he drifted into Porcupine and on to Noranda. Physically rugged, with square jaw and clear blue eye, he puzzled his contemporaries by his unfailing optimism, the kind not to be expected from a man of training. He was completely unorthodox, undisciplined, but everyone admitted his insatiable drive and capacity for work, a strength which became a weakness and finally killed him. He was a crank about alcohol too; anyone on his payroll caught with a bottle was dismissed on the spot. There was no nonsense about the man. He was outwardly stolid and phlegmatic, but inwardly raged unquenchable fires of ambition. When the Stadacona became a mine, he merely smiled. This was just a warmup for him, the first inning had not even started.

His attention was directed to the Perron Mine, where Alec Perron, one-time Temagami guide, was striving to work a small high-grade gold vein. The structure was different from anything yet encountered in Quebec—massive granodiorite. But Norrie saw something more, bands of darker diorite, which convinced him that here was something which could be profitable. He took over the development, and when he announced mill construction the reaction in most mining circles was one of anger and dismay. Scandal, the worst in Quebec, was about to break. But Jim, indifferent to criticism, serenely proceeded with his plans and the expected scandal never materialized. Instead, Quebec was enriched with a new mine, which since 1936 has produced more than $12,000,000 in gold.

Next he invaded the Malartic district, which seemed a reserved province of Ventures, Ltd., then operating the only producing mine in the area. Why not diorite here too? Jim did not mull over his ideas; he went to work. And wound up with three producing mines, one of which, Malartic Goldfields, leads all others in the area.

He was beginning to feel his oats now. Backed by the powerful financial house of Nesbitt-Thompson, he ventured into Louvicourt and plucked a couple more fruits from the muskeg which seemed to bloom especially for him.

"Cross the street when the light is red," is the quaint manner he described his procedure to me. "If you wait for the green you'll never get ahead of the mob."

His untimely death in 1945, at the height of an amazing career, was the result of a heart attack. I was in Noranda at the time when poor Jim was brought into the room next to mine, there to be placed under an oxygen tent and administered to by a specialist flown in hurriedly from Montreal. A group of us collected in the lobby, anxiously awaiting the verdict of the physician.

"Very restless" was the bulletin.

"He's trying to bust out of that tent," whispered Jim De Morrest, the diamond driller. "Just like Jim."

One of the men explained that Jim had walked eighteen miles in and out of the Croinor in Pershing Township, where his latest prospect was making ready for shaft sinking. He had arrived in Noranda feeling unwell. The local doctor examined him and advised immediate hospitalization. Jim scoffed at the idea, returned to the hotel, and there collapsed.

"Hear about his job in Amos?" asked one of Jim's friends. "Well, he was having a furnace installed a few days ago and wasn't satisfied the way the boys were laying the foundation. So he whipped off his coat, rolled up his sleeves, and dug the hole himself."

"Just like him," nodded another. "Couldn't sit still. And what in hell did it all get him? A few extra oxygen tanks, that's all," and he pointed to the ceiling.

At that moment final word reached us; Jim Norrie had just taken the longest trail of them all. . . .

Pierre Beauchemin, with his brothers Joseph and Adelard of

Amos, Quebec, supplies evidence enough that mine making is confined to no one special class. Son of a one-time prosperous lumberman, the Beauchemin heir was prepared to continue the family tradition of operating sawmills, but the crash of 1929 put a stop to these plans when the Beauchemins were plunged into bankruptcy. Eventually all creditors were fully reimbursed. When Père Beauchemin died, the family decided that the Sullivan Mine offered a possible chance to recoup, and Pierre, the leader, began to familiarize himself with an entirely new kind of business. Years before, when Jim Sullivan had found a small gold-bearing vein on the mainland facing Sisco Island in Kienawisik Lake, he had interested various Amos residents in purchasing stock in Sullivan Mines. And now the Beauchemins were among the largest shareholders.

Pierre was shown through the mine. Ventures, Ltd., had taken an option on 1,700,000 shares of a once-reorganized company after having purchased 300,000 to meet costs of preliminary development. Ken Muir was the manager, and to Beauchemin he expressed confidence that the Sullivan had possibilities. But in one of the few mistakes Lindsley ever made in the direction of pulling out too early, he decided the property was a teaser and allowed his option to lapse. The directors, of whom Beauchemin was one, decided to have a report written by an independent engineer. The conclusions were negative and suggested an immediate shutdown.

"We go ahead," stated Pierre grimly, mindful, no doubt, of Muir's enthusiasm. "Easy to run a mine—just like a sawmill!"

Money was obtained in Amos and Montreal and work went forward. Raising from the 500-foot level encountered ore of surprisingly good width and grade. The structure differed entirely from that of the adjoining Sisco, but Beauchemin was confident of solving such minor problems. By April, 1934, a 50-ton mill was in operation and, in pace with startling underground developments, capacity was increased in stages to five hundred tons. The Sullivan was a huge success.

Pierre decided he liked the mining business, it beat anything lumber had to offer. And so he stepped out in a big way. As managing director of the Sullivan, he circulated about the Bourlamaque area hunting new properties for his ambitious company. He learned the business quickly, and luck was with him. Following Jim Norrie, he gathered in the first of a crop, Louvicourt Goldfields, this to be soon overshadowed by the impressive East Sullivan. Then, adding sugar to the coffee, Beauchemin obtained control of the Cournor Mine, a former producer adjoining the dividend-paying Perron. Drilling and underground work disclosed new sources of ore, and so, at the moment, the Beauchemin dynasty is faced with the comfortable prospect of managing four mines instead of one.

Joseph H. Hirshhorn leaned over his desk, talking rapidly. In a few staccato sentences he outlined terms of the financing and the ambitious development plan.

"And," he concluded, with rising inflection, "I'll put up a quarter of the money myself. That's what *I* think of the property!"

His friend smiled weakly and shifted in his chair.

"But, Joe," he protested, "I just came here to talk about this, not to make a deal."

"Okay. You want to talk." Joe's tone was now angry. "I've told you all there is to know. Now I want to tell you something. When I invite anyone to participate with me, I'm giving him a break. You understand? Not taking anything from him."

The telephone rang and he engulfed it. "Bill? Yes, yes. I told him that was my final offer. Final, absolutely. No trading. Come back to me later."

Then, turning to his visitor, who scratched his head in perplexity: "Not taking, I said. Listen to me now, I'm going to give you some advice. Keep out of the mining business, it's not for you. Why, man, I have to make a dozen decisions every day. Where would I be if I fortzed around? Now, do you want this deal or don't you?"

"Well, I—" and his friend swallowed hard—"I didn't say that I didn't want it."

"All right, you didn't, that's fine." Joe smiled infectiously. "I'll grant you that much credit. But come clean and tell me what's wrong. I don't like this holding back. Something's bothering you, I can see. What is it? Don't you think I'm putting up enough chips?"

"As long as you ask, Joe, I think you ought to put up more—a third, at least."

"It's a deal!" Joe shot out from behind his desk and pumped the hand of his new associate, at the same time gently impelling him toward the door. "I'll have my $25,000 in the bank tomorrow. You send your fifty up right away. Okay? That's fine, you'll make a killing, my boy. I'll show you how money is made," and the two passed out of the room together.

In a few minutes he was back at his desk, mouth glued to the telephone. "Jack, that you? Well, I've got $75,000 for a starter. What do you mean, fast work! I spent an hour with that guy! Of course! Get things rolling and send me down a set of maps. And don't worry, we'll have all the money we need. 'Bye. See you Monday."

There is no withstanding the man.

Joe Hirshhorn

Joe, like Al Smith, is a product of the streets of New York, training ground of so many illustrious figures who start with little save ambition and then shoot to the top rapidly. Once a Western Union messenger boy, he learned early that blistered feet were poor assets in the climb to success. Deciding that headwork was more practical than footwork, he quit his job. Out of a sense of shame and sensitive to the gibes of his companions, he never returned to receive his first pay check. Wall Street was his next stop and there for a time he was employed as a chartist on the *Magazine of Wall Street*. Having learned the fundamentals of security markets, he moved to the New York Curb, a trader in his own right. A retentive memory, a flashing mind, and an instinct for picking winners soon made him a distinguished member of that lowly outdoor mart. He soon attracted the attention of big shots who gave him special jobs to do. Among them was an assignment by participants of the Thomson-Chadbourne Syndicate to study the Toronto Mining Exchange where Noranda was first being traded. Joe performed his mission faithfully and profitably for his principals. More such Canadian commissions were given him.

"It was fascinating to watch those mining stocks," he explains in reminiscence. "They moved fast and some of them went from pennies to dollars. Pretty soon I began to think that here was just the spot for a man like me."

In 1932, when New York brokers were forming queues to jump into the Hudson, Joe took the longer and more constructive jump to Toronto. There he established his own brokerage office. In the *Northern Miner* he placed a full-page provocative advertisement reminding Canada of its mining destiny and pointing to better life in the future. Then he settled down to work. But there came an interruption even as the decorators put the final paint touches to his office walls. There were callers who had read his ad and wanted to speak with him. He asked their names. Fred MacLeod and Arthur Cockshutt. Their business? Prospectors, selling units in the Little Long Lac Syndicate.

"I bought 200 units at $10 each," related Joe. "Why? Don't ask me. For one reason, I liked their looks. And I had a hunch."

The hunch, as so many others of his proved to be, was good, for the units were exchanged for 90,000 shares of MacLeod-Cockshutt Mines which he subsequently sold for close to $500,000. Later he readily bought Macassa stock when Bob Bryce was in need of funds, and had much to do with the eventual success of that enterprise. But his largest success was the Preston East Dome. Next to the big Dome, this property had been drilled and drilled again, finally to be consigned to the ample graveyard of mining cadavers. Douglas Wright, one-time geologist for the Dome, nevertheless insisted that possibilities still remained. Valiantly he tried to persuade Dome to purchase the ground for $50,000. But Dome was not interested. In the years that followed a dogged Wright persisted in his efforts to revive a peacefully sleeping "dog." Then, hearing that Hirshhorn was a quick jumper, he made his way into the receptive New Yorker's office. Wright told his story well, and Joe, without a moment's hesitation, jumped.

The first drill hole intersected a narrow quartz vein in the lavas. Thereupon the rig was moved to cut the occurrence at a more decisive angle, but before reaching the objective a surprisingly new and more important vein was revealed where none should be—in the porphyry. The news was greeted with universal skepticism. As the stock rose sharply, squads of snipers began shooting at what was considered an easy target. Short selling was a cinch, the Bay Street "bandits" decided. But this gentry was soon smarting with wounds that still show deep scars. Joe boldly purchased almost the entire capitalization of the company, and brokers who were counting profits soon rushed in to settle their losses. And, in the interim, Preston East Dome became one of Canada's blue-chip mines.

Since those days, "Little Joe" has blossomed like a rose. A bundle of nerves and energy, ever bursting with grand plans and unfailing generous impulse, he has opened a veritable flood of money from the United States to Canda. He has had failures—and what bona fide mine maker hasn't?—but all his enterprises are characterized by substantial treasuries and continuous, well-managed development. He has learned that the big money is derived from the ground. Looked upon as a trader by those who know him only by hearsay,

Joe is a mine maker in his own right. He was among the first to enter the eastern Porcupine field almost fifteen years ago and only in recent months has this area been receiving serious development. Geophysical work on his properties helped to formulate regional geological structures and provide surer guides to ore. He cheerfully turned in all his data when the Ontario government undertook to compile a giant map of the region and so give real aid to operators. And his other properties, Anglo-Rouyn, Armistice, Aquarius and Calder-Bousquet, all of them under active development at the present time, were acquired as far back as 1933. Joe knows the full meaning of Fiorello LaGuardia's "Patience and Fortitude!"

His enthusiasm for mining never wanes.

"I love the game," he states. "There's a sense of creation about it. My family wants me to quit, but I just can't do it. I must see all my projects through, and then I guess I'm just not built to sit on the sidelines."

He is, indeed, anything but a spectator. As I write, his fieldmen and engineers are scattered from Yellowknife to distant Chibougamau in northern Quebec, hammering away at various Hirshhorn enterprises.

Like Jack Hammell, Joe is an ardent picture buyer, but his purchases are largely those of contemporary painters in whom he takes a lively personal interest. His collection has been made with taste and distinction, and in art circles he is regarded as a true connoisseur.

Several years ago, a prominent American geologist published a book on copper mining. It was an informative and entertaining work. In the course of recounting the history of various mines, however, the author found it necessary to make such remarks as "His ancestry made him a good dealer, as the trusting miners soon found out" and "True to his race, he could not resist a profit." People are much the same throughout the civilized world, and it is doubtful whether the mining industry of the United States differs from that of Canada so far as personal elements are concerned. A glance at the appended list of Canadian mine makers at once reveals the astonishing diversity of races that has made the industry the giant it is today. There are English, Scotch, Irish, Jews, Scandinavians, Levantines, French, Slavs, and even a Boston blueblood. From diversity greatness is born, and to single out one racial group for praise or dispraise is either vicious or stupid. Mine making exacts qualities and stamina almost never combined in a single individual. When such a man does appear, the unbiased observer doffs his hat in admiration and respect. One mine in a lifetime is a large enough quota for any man. And our friend, the copper authority, is a better recorder than a maker of history, for his quota is as yet unfulfilled.

CANADIAN MINE MAKERS

Name	Property	Financing Method
Thayer Lindsley	Falconbridge (D)	Promotion Ventures, Ltd.
	Sherritt-Gordon (D)	
	Coniaurum (D)	
	Beattie (D)	
	Canadian Malartic (D)	
	La Luz (D)	
	Eureka (U)	
	Giant Yellowknife (U)	
	Matachewan Consolidated (P.U.)	
	Osisko Lake (U)	
	New Calumet (P)	
	Hoyle (P.U.)	
	Lake Dufault (P.U.)	
	Joliet (U)	
	Dupresnoy (U)	
	Stadacona (P)	
	Akaitcho (U)	
	Guayana (P)	
Noah Timmins	La Rose (D)	Private
	Hollinger (D)	Hollinger
	Noranda (D)	
	Labrador Iron (U)	
	Ross (P)	
Jack Hammell	La Rose (D)	Promotion
	Howey (D)	Private
	Pickle Crow (D)	
	Hasaga (P.U.)	
	Starratt-Olsen (U)	
James P. Norrie	Perron (D)	Promotion
	East Malartic (D)	
	Malartic Goldfields (D)	
	Stadacona (P.U.)	
	Aubelle (U)	
	Croinor (U)	
	Louvicourt (U)	
	Norbenite (U)	
	Sladen (P.U.)	

Canadian Mine Makers (*continued*)

Name	Property	Financing Method
Joseph R. Delamar	International Nickel (D) Dome (D) Nipissing (D)	Promotion Private
Robert Jowsey	Keeley (D) God's Lake (D) Sherritt-Gordon (D) Kirkland Lake Gold (D) Bevcourt (U) Bobjo (U)	Promotion
Joseph Errington	Little Long Lac (D) MacLeod-Cockshutt (D) Negus (D) Steep Rock (U)	Promotion
M. J. O'Brien	O'Brien, Cobalt (D) Miller Lake O'Brien (D) O'Brien, Quebec (D)	Private
Joseph Hirshhorn	Preston (D) Anglo-Rouyn (U) Aquarius (U) Armistice (U) Andrew Yellowknife (U) Calder-Bousquet (U) Slemon Yellowknife (U)	Promotion Private
Oliver Hall	Hallnor (D) Pamour (D) Aunor (D) La India (D) Norbeau (U)	Noranda Mines
Robert Bryce	Macassa (D) Renabie (P)	Promotion Macassa Mines
Pierre Beauchemin	Sullivan (D) Cournor (P.U.) East Sullivan (U) Louvicourt (U)	Promotion
Robert Brown	Upper Canada (D) Queenston (U)	Promotion
J. H. C. Waite	Waite (D) Jerome (P.U.) Quemont (U)	Promotion Mining Corporation

CANADIAN MINE MAKERS (*continued*)

Name	Property	Financing Method
W. H. Archibald	Con (P) Ptarmigan (P) Ruth (P)	Consol. Min. & Smelt.
J. B. Streit Charles Wright	Chesterville (D) Broulan (D) Senator (P) Wright Rouyn (U)	Promotion
Charles Denison	Buffalo (D) Teck-Hughes (D)	Promotion Private
Charles Flynn (with J. P. Bickell)	McIntyre (D)	Promotion
(with H. R. Poirier)	Vipond (D)	
Fred M. Connell	Central Patricia (D) Conwest (U)	Promotion
E. L. Brown	Sachigo (D) Granville Lake (U)	Promotion Sherritt-Gordon
J. Coghlan	Heva Cadillac (U) Marlon (U)	Promotion

D. Dividend payer   P. Producer   U. Under development

On the Nature of Mineral Deposits

Editor, the *Northern Miner:*

Dear Sir:

I think it possible Pelletier Creek, 6 miles southwest of Noranda is a very important prospect, and hope the drilling operations will be carried to the bottom. If they prove a big ore there will give us a lead on Sudbury and the Centre. Another important spot, right in line and just half way. Easier to understand when turned irruptive point. There are lots of Noranda lying side by side. Divided by a barren cill three miles wide. Being a portion of the vein system extending right round the world. Its importance measured by its length. Band mine being an excellent pointed surface only in its extremity in ore. Sudbury and Oranda an echo from deep centre along a line of mines.

I have been told that the most important throw of mines would be found in the northeast and southwest. Making every place the same. Why those hard and smooth and polished walls with each deposit of mineral is not an irruptive point. Sudbury and Oranda Centre—crossed by the Wright mine. Capped with iron near New Liskeard and the centre irrupting 15 miles to the lime formations. Furnishing positive proof of its irruption. The first parallel 3 miles of lime formations Cobalt 3 acres. Material aid in its discovery. Sudbury and Oranda exactly opposite a throw at right angles. And into its thirty first side vein, each 3 miles apart, the space between them being exactly divided by a link 3 miles long. Clearly showing they are related and joined together by something. Noranda and Casey Mines exactly the same as Sudbury and Cobalt. I have also been told that the North and South vein embracing the whole world and discovered it to be a fact. The ground especially recommended directly south and at the end of a 3 mile link measured from Noranda. There I recommend a sink to the proper contact another spot geogically the same. The same minerals in its essayed content. Formations heavier, minerals sink deeper. This is written by a man who discovered the only true vein. If you see fit to print send one or two copies to Ottawa.

D. D., Ottawa

March 30, 1933

Before anyone undertakes a search for mines or attempts to appraise and value mining property, he should know something of the nature of ore deposits. Unlike "D.D." of Ottawa, I can merely touch upon fundamentals here and try to convey the fact that only an infinitesimal portion of the earth's surface contains mineral concentrations which can be extracted and marketed profitably, that

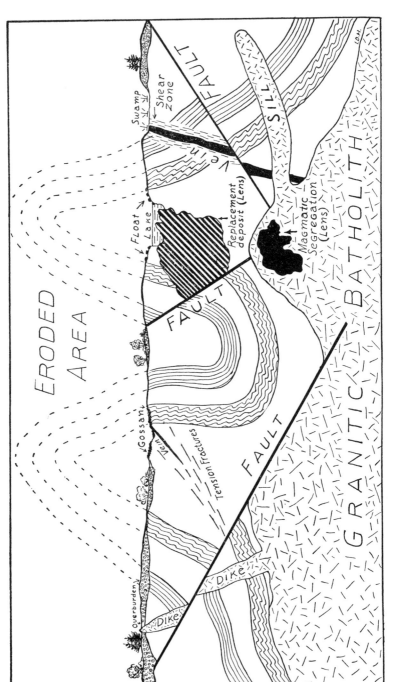

GEOLOGICAL CROSS SECTION SHOWING VARIOUS ORE DEPOSIT TYPES

is, mines. They are rare. The late Dr. Harry Berman of Harvard called them freaks. Why is this so?

For one reason, the rocks which contain ore deposits must first undergo long preparation in order to provide conditions necessary to receive them. And this may require millions of years. (But the reader need not be alarmed. All this has already happened and mankind today is reaping a harvest of minerals which were formed in the dim reaches of time.) The original strata, barren of metals and their compounds, must be broken, crushed, folded, and wrinkled in order to create apertures, fractures, and crevices where minerals can find permanent homes, much as a reservoir must be dug prior to its holding water. But nature, when left to its own devices, can be perverse and capricious. After obligingly preparing certain localities for the introduction of minerals, it often neglects to send them up. Or, if it plays the game according to man-made rules and valuable aggregations of metals are deposited in a given area, powerful forces of erosion—such as rain, heat, frost, glaciers, and the like—partly or wholly efface them. If not destroyed, the particular occurrence may remain hidden under vast gravel and detrital accumulations. Or it may be covered by later flows of lava, or thick forests and other vegetation, or lakes, rivers, swamps, and even seas.

As to the intrinsic scarcity of metals, a study of the earth's crust made by geologists is revealing. Chemical analyses indicate that 98 per cent of the surface rocks contains eight elements, of which oxygen is the most prolific, 46.59 per cent. Next, in order, come

Silicon	27.72%
Aluminum	8.13
Iron	5.01
Calcium	3.63
Magnesium	2.09
Sodium	2.85
Potassium	2.60

When we approach the end of the list and come to the metals, the percentages fall off to such fractional amounts as to become almost meaningless:

Copper	0.010%
Lead	0.002
Zinc	0.004
Tin	0.0005
Antimony	0.00025
Cadmium	0.00001
Silver	0.000004
Gold	0.0000001

Is it any wonder that mines are few and far between?

In their cloistered halls and laboratories, professors wage academic wars of their own. This is all to the good, for there is nothing more stimulating than the search for truth by means of reasoned controversy. Geology is one of the most fertile subjects for evoking differences of opinion. It is largely a deductive science and its rules and laws cannot be proved or demonstrated in the classroom. But it is a profound study which probes the very essence of life and inquires into the origin of the planet. In this there are two schools of thought: The one insisting that the earth was formed from a giant nebula which gradually changed from a hot gas to solid matter as it cooled in space. The nebula, it is said, detached itself from our sun or another very much like it in the universe. Various and ingenious are the supporting arguments for this nebular hypothesis, but the opposing school, for equally convincing reasons, champions the planetesimal theory. These adherents contend that the earth was built up by the slow accumulation of meteoric fragments—piling up, so to speak.

The controversy has not yet been settled and the chances are that it never will be. No one was on hand to observe and report what actually happened. However, most scientists now agree on one point—the earth was once a hot liquid mass which cooled imperceptibly, forming a thin crust as it did so, much like the outer skin of an onion. But, advancing further, we hear more contention. Is the earth's interior solid or fluid? Once more the definite answer is unknown and for the same reason—even the most adventurous of modern newshawks could not plumb the depths and return with an eyewitness report. The earth's crust is not extensive, probably not much more than thirty miles thick, and the deepest penetration by mechanical drilling has been little more than three miles. The layman need not lose sleep about the matter, for evidence points to a generally solid interior, but if present conclusions are faulty and the earth's interior is liquid, it is definitely as rigid as steel, due to the tremendous overhead pressure of the rocks.

Like so many geological phenomena, the original crust has never been seen, for it was covered by lava flows which broke through from the disturbed nether regions. The early period of earth building was anything but stable. Cataclysms were as common as London blitzes in 1940 and far more terrifying—and protracted. No portion of the world was exempt from this terrible succession of upheavals. Those who have seen Walt Disney's *Fantasia* will probably never forget the animated sequence that preceded the coming of life.

The violence pictured can be compared only to that of atomic bombs.

Since we are concerned with Canada (where conditions were no different from other northerly sections of the tortured globe), let us try to reconstruct this ancient activity around the shores of what we now call Hudson Bay. Fresh-water lakes were abundant and a period of quiet seemed to have at last arrived upon the young planet. But not for long. The molten interior, imprisoned below the newly formed crust, raged surfaceward, probing for weaknesses. And found them. Thrown up by irresistible pressures, these steaming magmas, like hot molasses, began to pour over the land, oblitering everything before them and piling up into great thicknesses. This mass, which is today found in Ontario and other provinces, is called Keewatin, and required millions of years to attain its final size. It was followed by a period wherein the sea advanced inland and in time produced beds of limestone. This Grenville period was comparatively gentle; new rocks were formed by the erosion of the Keewatin and laid down nicely and regularly, like frosting on a cake. Once again, however, madness shook the world. Interior forces, like a sick stomach, heaved and the already battered crust was given another savage beating. This time the rocks were thrust toward the sky and mountain ranges as high as the Himalayas were formed, only to be cut down relentlessly as erosion and decay set in later. Sand, boulders, and muds, the present Temiskaming series, accumulated in basins, and these in turn became solid strata of conglomerate and puddingstone. More infernal invasions from below, with new mountains rising, and still again the slow but effective erosion when the climate became icy and glaciated. A different type of rock was made this time, a conglomerate of one-time clay and slick boulders, which we recognize now as the Cobalt series. Not content with all this havoc, nature added fresh variety by elevating this part of the world so that the inland seas ran off, leaving a desert country with blazing sands covering the older rocks. This status endured for a few million years, a mere fleabite in terms of geological time reckoning, and then arrived another interlude of volcanic outpourings (Keweenawan), characterized by the darkish, or basic (scarcity of quartz), appearance of the lavas. And then, to complete the cycle, the region was visited by the Killarney period of mountain building, when vast intrusions of granite further buckled the rocks, giving erosion another chance to go to work.

To create some *order* out of chaos, geologists have designated this long era of unrest as "Pre-Cambrian"—before life. Certainly, no life could have existed during this time. As a native of Brooklyn would say, what happened in the Pre-Cambrian shouldn't happen to a dog. Being so venerable, these old rocks literally had the hell knocked out of them. They were broken, twisted, pushed into folds, warped and shattered into every conceivable shape. Their chemical composition was changed and rechanged by heat and pressure, and then, for good measure, compressed into layers, torn into ribbons, pulled out like dough, and crazily tilted on end. Visitors, in the shape of continental intrusions of granite, smashed everything in their path, and then themselves submitted helplessly to even greater forces of destruction. But, as we shall presently see, all this bashing and pushing around served a purpose. It gave rise to the greatest of ore deposits.

The Pre-Cambrian was followed by many later geological ages, all of them distinguished by fossil remains in the rocks, thus furnishing visible evidence of the life then existing. These ages were long, but all together they total far less than the Pre-Cambrian, which has been estimated at from eight hundred million to five billion years' duration. The younger rocks supply a field day to students of evolution, for they trace the beginnings of life from the single-celled amoeba to the vertebrates, anthropoid apes, and on to man himself. But the geologist is primarily interested in creating a kind of time-table constructed from the strata exposed in choice localities, such as the Niagara Gorge, or better, the awesome mile-deep exposures of the Grand Canyon. (It is hopeless to distinguish head or tail in the Pre-Cambrian mess, and so it is conveniently called a "basement complex," upon which everything else rests. With that we shall not quarrel.)

There are five eras in this timetable of the earth, and these are divided into systems or periods. Specialists in historical geology have subdivided these further, rendering complete classifications into brute memory tests, but it is sufficient here to enumerate the large categories, the most youthful era at the head of the list and the Pre-Cambrian, daddy of them all, at the bottom:

Era	Period or System
Quaternary [1]	Recent
	Pleistocene
Tertiary [2]	Pliocene
	Miocene
	Eocene
Mesozoic [3]	Cretaceous
	Jurassic
	Triassic

Era	*Period or System*
Palaeozoic [4]	Permian
	Carboniferous
	Devonian
	Silurian
	Ordovician
	Cambrian

Pre-Cambrian [5]	Laurentian
	Keweenawan
	Huronian
	Keewatin

Remarks

[1] These two periods represent the span of time from the Ice Age in Europe and North America to the present day. The first trace of man is found in the Pleistocene, when various mammals also reached their modern forms.

[2] The Tertiary is characterized by the rise of mammals and violent but comparatively short-lived volcanic action. Mineral deposits were laid down, some of them rich but largely of the shallow type. Gold placers were developed throughout the world.

[3] Known as the Age of Reptiles and the rise and fall of the dinosaurs. Toward the end, modern vegetation superseded the conifers and the coal beds of the West were developed.

[4] This is the great period of life development, starting with single-celled organisms and invertebrates and culminating with the introduction of fish and reptiles, some of gigantic size. Plant life became abundant. During this time much of the coal and oil deposits came into being. Toward the end, regional uplifts changed the climate into desert and caused extinction of lush animal and vegetable species.

[5] Duration probably five to ten times that of all succeeding eras. Some life toward the end seems likely, but scarcity of fossil remains makes evidence doubtful. Tremendous volcanic activity, mountain building, and the formation of most of the world's greatest ore deposits.

In Canada is found the most extensive exposure of Pre-Cambrian in the world, comprising 1,825,000 square miles.

Why is Canada so specially favored when the planet was at one time entirely composed of these ancient rocks? The explanation is supplied by prolonged erosion and the action of continental glaciers which swept down from the north, scouring the original surface,

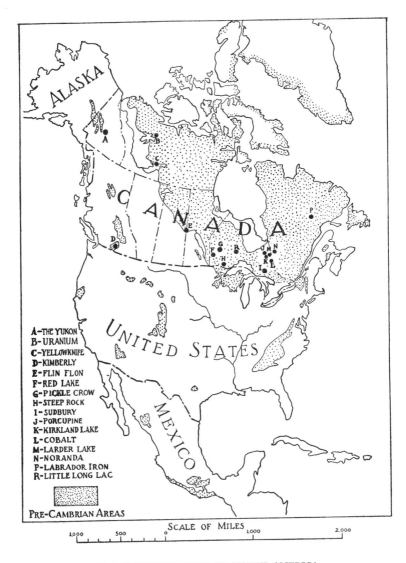

A—THE YUKON
B—URANIUM
C—YELLOWKNIFE
D—KIMBERLY
E—FLIN FLON
F—RED LAKE
G—PICKLE CROW
H—STEEP ROCK
I—SUDBURY
J—PORCUPINE
K—KIRKLAND LAKE
L—COBALT
M—LARDER LAKE
N—NORANDA
P—LABRADOR IRON
R—LITTLE LONG LAC

PRE-CAMBRIAN AREAS

SCALE OF MILES

PRE-CAMBRIAN AREAS OF NORTH AMERICA

further leveling the mountains, and biting deep into the thick beds of younger rocks. And in "retreating" these immense sheets filled the large hollows and depressions of their own making with the abundant waters streaming from the melting ice, so creating the innumerable lakes, rivers, and swamps which characterize the Canadian hinterland we recognize today.

Generally, Pre-Cambrian rocks are notable for their wealth of minerals, though the ancient rocks of Northwestern Europe are comparatively low in productive ore deposits. Canada and portions of the United States and Africa, however, have supplied famous bonanzas, large in size and persistent in depth. This is no coincidence. Pre-Cambrian rocks have undergone such a prolonged history, the rock beds are so thick, and volcanic action has been so extensive that it is reasonable to expect big results. While the later ages also introduced ore deposits, the strata were comparatively thin and the time of action relatively short in contrast to the almost endless Pre-Cambrian. It is no surprise, therefore, that younger deposits are, on the whole, superficial. This is not to suppose that all the Pre-Cambrian mines persist in depth while those of recent vintage are uniformly shallow. Exceptions in both classes are occasionally met, but in most cases the "basement complex" provides the bulk of deep-seated ore bodies. Accordingly, geologists and miners regard the Pre-Cambrian areas with more favor than those of the younger eras.

Viewing the Pre-Cambrian shield of Canada, there is little to stir the imagination. The country is low and rolling, hardly rising above a thousand feet in any one place, and the scarcity of rock outcrops suggests anything but a structurally distorted region where major ore bodies may be present. But to the trained geologist, who has learned to read the story of rocks, it is evident that huge mountain ranges once flourished in these lowlands. How does he know? Simply by mapping whatever rocks do show and correlating them on a large scale. Then it is seen that the beds are inclined or vertical, proving that at one time, before they were broken down by various weathering agencies, they towered far above the present surface. Here, therefore, is the logical spot for ore, inasmuch as mountains prove one-time intense crumpling, folding, and breaking of the rocks which slide over one another, producing faults and brecciated zones, fertile conditions for mine making. Nature has done well so to prepare the strata; the chaos of the Pre-Cambrian has, after all, been recognized as something resembling ordered purpose.

Now comes action from below. We are all familiar with volcanoes and their spectacular, and often, disastrous effects. But for each eruption to the surface there are hundreds of instances where the molten fluids we call lava never reach the crust, but cool and harden thousands of feet from the light of the sun. This cooling requires hundreds of years, even thousands, and many interesting things happen. That the molten masses, called magmas, gravitate toward mountain ranges we are fairly certain, for in such localities, as we have seen, the crust has been weakened by the pulverizing of strata, causing great openings and zones of fracturing. And so the great steaming masses of hot fluid rise to these focal points, just as steam finds valve outlets. Finally blocked by impervious barriers of rock, the hot magma begins to subside and cool. In this process the minerals and compounds begin to gravitate away from the main mass in the form of gases and liquids. The metallic contents are precipitated, under certain pressure and temperature conditions, in the apertures of overlying rocks. An ingenious geologist has compared all this to freezing cider, wherein alcohol is liberated while the bulk of liquid becomes ice. Carrying this a step further, the alcohol in the interior would naturally fill any crack in the ice. In like manner, the invading gases of ore magmas tend to take the course of least resistance, and so deposit their mineral loads in already fabricated cracks or those caused by the tremendous expansive force of the magma itself. These constitute "vein" deposits.

Sometimes these hot rock masses bore into the containing strata and literally eat their way through as they move upward. In so doing they absorb the original constituents of the material they destroy and at the same time add their own peculiar components, which sometimes—fortunately—contain mineral. If the destroyed rock itself contained some mineral, so much the better; the two added together make good ore. Such an ore body is termed a "replacement" deposit and has definite properties which make it recognizable. For example, the crust rocks are greatly changed in composition along their lower boundaries where contact with the hot "stuff" was made. This is called "alteration." And then the ore body is irregular in shape, much like a kidney or even an old shirt hanging on a clothesline. It is often called a "lens," as opposed to the sharply defined vein or sheet type of deposit which, with variations, resembles the regularity of a concrete road.

In both categories, ore is distinguished from including rock ("country" or "wall" rock) by its distinct appearance and mineral content. In the case of veins, the difference is marked, for the ore contains a filling (gangue) which is usually quartz or calcite, the color being whitish and the texture smooth. This looks entirely different from the usual drab, coarse-appearing wall rock. Replacement deposits, on the other hand, often resemble the country rock, though an experienced eye can usually detect the presence of more plentiful mineral and evidence of intense alteration. Good Canadian examples of vein deposits are furnished in the gold mines of Kirk-land Lake, Porcupine, Red Lake, Yellowknife, and Cobalt. The sulphide ores of Noranda, Sudbury, Flin Flon, and Sullivan are outstanding replacement deposits. Exactly why mines are of one or the other type is not clear. One suggestion is that vein deposits are derived from gelatinous solutions which precipitate metals easily in sheared and fractured areas while the replacement deposits are caused by more aqueous solutions which have greater penetrating power in country not readily broken up. It is also claimed that the latter were formed by reason of more chemically active and corrosive constituents in the magmatic waters.

There is no positive evidence that ore genesis is directly related to intrusive (igneous) rocks, even though observation and deduction make this conclusion logical. A convincing argument, however, is supplied by physicists who have measured the specific gravity of the earth mass and have found it thrice that of the thin crust. This at once suggests that the heavier metallic elements must be present in the deeper regions of the planet, their only egress being possible through the forces of volcanism. In any event, the geologist and the prospector have learned to work from the premise that igneous rocks were the original ore bringers, and on this basis have unearthed ore bodies and mining districts.

Rocks fall into three main divisions—igneous, sedimentary, and metamorphic. The first, as explained, are those which have solidified from a molten condition, originating in the earth's interior, later rising to lodge in overlying rocks or overflow the surface. In the latter case they are merely volcanic rocks or flows. In the former they are called "plutonic" rocks, that is, formed below the surface. There is another type of igneous rock, termed "intermediate," which occurs close to the surface or is thrown up in vertical and horizontal tongues (dikes and sills) from the more deeply embedded plutonic masses (batholiths). For example, granite, the most common of the plutonic rocks formed at 5,000- to 30,000-foot depths, becomes, in its intermediate form, "porphyry" or "felsite." It is finer grained than the granite from which it has sprung, and sometimes has large "eyes" of quartz. When the effusions keep going and spill out to the surface they become glassy from quick cooling, and then we have obsidian [which the Aztecs used to make sacrificial knives] or rhyolite, an extremely fine-grained flow. All these rocks are igneous equivalents and contain the same chemical constituents. They are "acid" too, for they are made up of 70 per cent silica. A more accurate name for such rocks would be "silicic."

As we go down the list we approach the "basic" rocks, those low in silica. To illustrate, gabbro is plutonic, coarse grained, and dark in appearance. Its intermediate phase is diabase, and when it becomes a flow it is called "basalt."

Following are some of the more common igneous rocks, familiar to mining men:

Plutonic	Intermediate	Surface
Granite	Quartz-Porphyry	Obsidian
	Felsites	Rhyolite
Aplite	Aplite dikes	Acid Rhyolite
Syenite	Lamprophyre	
	Syenite-Porphyry	Trachytes
Granodiorite		Andesite
Diorite	Quartz-Porphyry	Dacite
Gabbro	Diabase	Basalt
Dunite		

When a plutonic rock occurs as a regional mass, it is given the strange lisping name "batholith," but it is tremendously important as an ore bringer. "Stocks" and "plugs" are local in extent and are roughly circular in shape. An important flow rock is "tuff," made up of fragmental material, formed during the most violent phases of volcanic eruption when lavas were hurled into the air together with ash and dust. The cooled mass solidifies into a conglomerate-looking material. When the fragments are coarse and bouldery, the rock is called "agglomerate."

Sedimentary rocks are those derived from the erosion and disintegration of igneous rocks. Before becoming rocks they were the boulders, gravels, and silts washed down from outcrops and carried into rivers and lakes, thence to sea bottoms. As more material gathered above these deposits, the mass became compressed, and the chemical action of waters cemented the individual grains of material. In this way, the once-scattered detritus became solid rock —sandstone, conglomerate, shale, or limestone, depending upon the original character of the matter transported.

The next and final stage in rock making occurs when old beds

are exposed to heat, pressure, and intense lateral or vertical movement. In the course of this treatment, the rocks undergo significant
changes in appearance and become "metamorphic." Thus shale goes
into slate, conglomerate winds up as graywacke, a highly silicified
rock, sandstone is transformed into quartzite, limestone into marble
—all of them fine grained and much harder in texture than they
were formerly. Igneous rocks, too, are metamorphosed. Granite is
changed to a banded "gneiss," no longer a homogeneous mass but a
sheeted (schisted) rock with dark banded streaks.

The importance of this group is the evidence they provide, for
such extreme changes cannot be effected without accompanying
strong movements of the crust. The vicinity becomes sheared, as
though giant scissors had cut great swaths in the solid rock. Such
zones are called "shears," appropriately enough, and are the zones
particularly favorable to ore deposition. Rocks which shear easily—
usually the brittle varieties—and so afford excellent preliminary
conditions for the later arrival of mineral-rich solutions, are dignified by the name "competent." Or, they are "host" rocks after mineral has been introduced.

The bulk of important ore deposits in Canada occurs in the
Pre-Cambrian, which embraces most of Ontario, Quebec, and the
Northwest Territories, as well as northern Manitoba, Alberta, and
Saskatchewan. The cordilleras of the west have provided many
mines, also, the deposits being mostly of Cretaceous age. Significantly, however, British Columbia maintains its position in the
mining sun largely through the incomparable Sullivan Mine which
is found in one of the Pre-Cambrian outliers. At the present time,
more than 90 per cent of Canada's gold is won from the Pre-Cambrian, and it is in such areas that the future of mining rests.

Erosion, we have learned, can completely destroy a primary ore
deposit. But occasionally the metallic content is concentrated in the
disintegrated material and eventually finds its way to streams and
other waterways. This is particularly true of gold, silver, platinum
and tin, all of which have a high specific gravity and lag behind the
lighter rock gangue. Thus "placer" deposits are made. Often they
remain undisturbed until the eager miner comes along, but once in
a while the area is elevated by mountain building. Then the placer
deposits are lifted above the valleys, sometimes several thousand
feet, and in due course buried under lavas and other rocks. The prospector or engineer nevertheless seeks them out and mines them as
primary (lode or hard rock) deposits, by means of shafts and drifts.
Being easily recognizable, placer deposits were mined early by hand
methods, and later by improved mechanical means. Aside from pro-

viding huge quantities of precious metal in California, South America, Europe, the Yukon, the Klondike, Australia, New Zealand and Russia, they led to the more permanent and vastly more prolific lode mines upon which the world largely depends today.

Ores usually contain an amount of sulphur as well as metals, the combination being a *sulphide*. These are changed into *oxides* when oxygen and water combine to render the sulphide into a soluble sulphate. Pyrite, for example, the most common of the sulphides, contains iron and sulphur. It is a brassy-looking mineral which has deluded amateurs so much that it has been called "fool's gold." When the agents of weather get busy and work on pyrite for a time, it becomes iron oxide, a reddish-brown dusty mineral (gossan) used in making rouge and also steel. During this change sulphuric acid is formed by sulphur and water. It circulates through the rocks and dissolves whatever metal it can. Gold is insoluble, and so stays behind, sometimes resulting in an economic deposit by virtue of removal of many other elements. Or, if copper and silver are picked up in solution, they are redeposited at the level of "ground" water and superimposed on already-formed mineral deposits. This artificially created situation is given the properly descriptive label "secondary enrichment." In Canada, such monkeyshines are comparatively unknown, due to the extensive erosion which has reduced the country to approximate water level.

Authorities learnedly classify ore deposits according to depth horizons. There are deep-seated, intermediate and shallow types, say these specialists, and this leads into prolific discussion and argument about the solutions which permeate the rocks and surrender their valuable mineral content. Two general classes are recognized: Meteoric waters are those which originate along the surface, and as they percolate downward they leach out metals from the rocks and precipitate these at some lower level where conditions favor such action. Such superficial deposits are called *supergene*. In contrast are the deposits derived from hot ascending waters which emanate from deep-seated intrusives. These are *hypergene* or *hydrothermal*. In some cases the evidence to support one or the other theory is fairly conclusive, in others the issue is far from clear, and so another scientific debate results. A good example is the controversy, still unresolved, concerning the copper-nickel ores of Sudbury, Ontario. One opinion is that the great deposits were formed by magmatic segregation, that is, the differentiation of various constituents into defined and recognizable zones during the cooling of the batholith. Opponents of this idea have an explanation of their own: they favor the theory that magmatic waters rose along a contact between a basic rock (norite) and various sedimentary strata, there to yield a volume of metal. Both contenders agree on one premise—the ore is hydrothermal.

To laymen, and even students, these scientific polemics often appear useless, a tempest in a teapot. This is a mistaken idea. A fuller comprehension of ore genesis saves untold effort, time, and money, besides pointing the way to new mines. For, in a wasting industry such as mining is, metals do not grow as agricultural products, with yearly crops. Fresh sources must be constantly tapped to replace ores extracted, and as discovery becomes more difficult in time, society finds itself increasingly dependent upon the geologist to solve the growing problem of supply. And so, in a world whose material civilization is based on metals, the geologist is truly the indispensable man of the twentieth century.

The term "ore" is entirely an economic one, since it refers to an aggregation of mineral which is mined, treated, and sold at a profit under governing conditions of costs—labor, supplies, transportation, etc. In the case of base metals—copper, lead, zinc, tin, nickel—market price is an all-important factor. The precious metals are somewhat less affected, since at the moment their value in terms of currency is fixed by government statute. Gold has the advantage of stable price, but this becomes a disadvantage in times of inflation when costs rise. Thus the operator must maintain a constant awareness of economic conditions and not lose himself in the labyrinth of ore search.

Earlier in this chapter, a table of elements shows the scarcity of metals. This may be somewhat misleading. Metals are widely disseminated throughout the earth's crust, though in minute quantities. Ore deposits are the result of extreme concentration which has somehow been effected. The chance of this happening is minute, since only a relatively few intrusive magmas and batholiths contain useful metallic solutions, and, of the select number which do, not many are fortunate enough to encounter proper conditions in the overlying rocks. Mines are scarce, amazingly so, and the search for them can be likened to that for the proverbial needle in a haystack. How, then, are these rare and elusive things found?

Nature provides a good part of the answer. In areas of pronounced oxidation the landscape is reddened with patches of gossan or distinguished by greenish tinges of copper silicates and carbonates. To the prospector, these are signposts of ore, as are, also, sheared and schisted rock areas. Then, in a few favored regions, there are outcrops of easily distinguished metals in their native state or in familiar-looking compounds. Gold, in the beginning, was known to even the most primitive man. Telltale nuggets in streams and gravels were worked at the outset, then later suggested primary sources of the ore. The prospector, if he knows his business, seeks "float"—fragments of mineral and vein matter which have been detached from their original resting places by frost and other erosive forces and moved to lower topographic sections—valleys, hillsides, river beds. If the float is angular, he is positive it has not journeyed far, and so his search is confined to the immediate vicinity. If it is rounded, however, he concludes that it has come a long way, and he rambles far afield trying to find the "mother lode." Many mines have been discovered in this way. Rivers biting into the rocks have fashioned deep canyons and so disclose ore deposits in strata far below the surface. Quartz and calcite veins are invitations to the ore hunter, too, for they frequently constitute the matrix of ore bodies.

As the obvious leads are followed with more or less success, the possibility of grass-root discovery naturally dwindles. Then comes a more refined search in which there is greater dependence upon science and experience. Paradoxically, Canada, which presents enticing opportunities to the mine finder, at the same time confronts him with severe handicaps. The features of other localities—such as oxidation, river erosion, bare countryside, accessibility—are lacking or nearly so. The familiar northern bush conceals ore deposits, as do the massive accumulations of glacial debris. Then there are the glum muskegs and innumerable waterways which effectively hide the secrets of the rocks. Until recently, canoe and dog-team transportation was not conducive to widespread prospecting, but now, with the swift advance of the airplane, hitherto untouched areas of promising geology have been brought within easy reach. Operation of mines in these outposts introduces problems, but to say that the bush is entirely inhospitable would be a departure from the truth. It provides a plenitude of timber, power, and water. In the winter, heavy machinery can be moved by tractor and sleigh in any direction, despite the lack of conventional roads. The waterways permit summer travel and at the same time provide revealing geological cross sections.

An interesting feature of Canada is the difference of structure as between mining areas and even the individual deposits within the same regional sphere. Ore is seldom found in the intrusive porphyry of Porcupine, occasionally in the Temiskaming sediments, and almost entirely in the volcanic rocks (greenstone). In Kirkland Lake, only sixty miles southeast, the competent rock is a reddish syenite or porphyry, the gold occurring in its native state and in rare tellurides. In Porcupine the gold is largely admixed with pyrite, while the wall rock, highly altered and mineralized, contains important gold values. Not so in Kirkland. There the wall rock is sparsely mineralized and carries no gold. And east of Kirkland only twenty-five miles, Larder Lake has its own ore habits. The host rocks are carbonates and lavas of the vesicular variety, that is, showing the residual effects of gas vents. In the carbonates, the gold is native; in the lavas, it is found in pyrite.

Quebec shows even greater diversity. The Noranda, rich in gold and copper, obtains most of its smelter feed from the "H" ore body, hourglass in shape. The adjoining Quemont, while located in the same acid lavas, has an ore body high in zinc as well as copper and gold, and it lies flat, like a giant pancake. The Powell, adjacent to Noranda on the west, is in granite, and mines a gold quartz vein, free of base metals. The Anglo-Rouyn, just north the Powell, is exploring for both copper and gold, in the lavas and granites. On the other hand, Stadacona, only two miles south, has for years been producing gold in quartz veins enclosed by lavas exclusively. The McWatters Mine, a few miles east and entirely within the Temiskaming sediments, mined quartz lenses rich in free gold. Adjoining McWatters to the east, the Rouyn Merger, Heva Cadillac, Hosco, Normar, and Calder-Bousquet also are in the sediments, but only one mile north the Mic-Mac Mine is situated in the lavas, the mineralization being a copper sulphide with an appreciable gold content.

Proceeding eastward, the variety becomes even more bewildering. The O'Brien, only twenty-five miles from Noranda, is in the sediments. A narrow quartz vein here is famous for a short but rich ore shoot of native gold, specimens of which rival anything discovered in the history of mining. Fifteen to twenty miles southeast, the Malartic area is distinguished by pyritic gold deposits lying in silicified sediments, porphyries, and lavas. The Sisco Mine, a few miles northeast, departs strikingly from Malartic. Gold there is largely in the free state, and the host rock is a granodiorite. Where the zone dips into the greenstones, values disappear. The adjoining Sullivan, however, continues to disclose much ore in the lavas as well as granodiorite. A short distance southeast, the mighty Lamaque, Quebec's largest straight gold producer, confines its ore zone to flat-lying quartz veins in the granodiorite. But next to it the Sigma mines a nearly vertical series of quartz veins in the lavas. Neighboring the Lamaque and Sigma, the East Sullivan has drilled a gold-copper deposit of the Noranda type. This lies in the so-called greenstone. So does the producing Golden Manitou, but there the ore contains zinc with the gold instead of copper. The Bourlamaque batholith is the ore bringer, apparently, and accounts for most of the mines in the region. However, the gold deposits of Perron, Cournor, Pascalis, Resenor, and Beacon are found within the granodiorite of the batholith itself.

Other camps follow the Canadian rule: "We're all different." In Red Lake, the Howey has a network of gold-bearing quartz veinlets occurring within a wide porphyry dike. There is little resemblance to the nearby Madsen, a higher grade gold deposit of the vein type in the lavas. This, again, departs entirely from the Cochenour-Willans, where podlike quartz lenses occur in interbedded carbonates and lavas.

In far-off Yellowknife, too, the same pattern of rapid change is encountered. The Giant, Con, and Negus mines are in the lavas, but the Thompson-Lundmark, Ptarmigan, and Ruth mines are located in sedimentary belts of differing composition. The list could be extended indefinitely.

Suffice it to say that Pre-Cambrian ore deposits are complex. The study of their ramifications could well occupy the entire lifetime of an investigator, and still leave him baffled in the attempt to assign reasons for differences in structure. Surprises of both pleasant and unpleasant varieties happen so often that I have frequently been advised by older men to "never believe what you hear and only half believe what you see." That mines have been found and developed is a tribute to the Canadian operator who has avoided the common pitfall of adhering too rigidly to precedent.

Mine Development

All deposits, whether vein or lens, have a *strike,* a convenient term to denote the horizontal direction they follow. Thus a vein strikes north 40° west. The *dip* is the angle at which the occurrence is inclined from the horizontal, the measurement being taken at right angles to the strike. An 85° dip southwest is called "vertical," for it is almost at right angles to the surface plane. A "flat" deposit would be one of 50° or less, since the angle would then be pronounced.

In the American West and elsewhere, claim owners are given legal rights to follow their ore deposits underground along the dip as far as they can reasonably establish that the vein or lens is indeed theirs. This is known as "apex rights." Canada follows a simpler rule: ores are owned only within the downward vertical projections of property sidelines. This has obviated the endless litigations which have plagued miners in other countries.

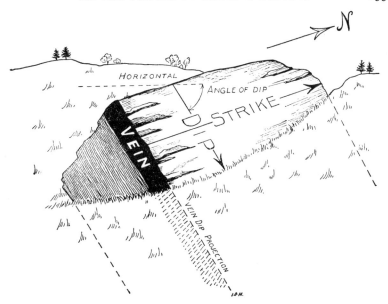

SURFACE PLAN SHOWING STRIKE AND DIP

Not only is there strike and dip, but also *rake*. Despite apparent regularity of mineralization, ore values, for no apparent reason, plunge earthward at an angle completely independent of strike and dip. This kind of behavior is disconcerting, and until understood and mastered it often leads to difficulties in drilling and underground development. When the rake is flat and vertical exploration fails to encounter the vein where expected, the ore is mistakenly considered lost, and more than one mining venture has been needlessly abandoned for this reason.

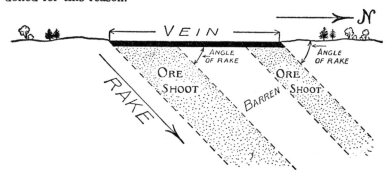

LONGITUDINAL SECTION SHOWING ORE RAKE

An ore deposit is given various names. In the American West it is a "lode" as distinguished from placer. This changes to "reef" in Africa and most of the English colonies and sometimes it becomes "blanket" locally. Canada prefers "vein," and the shear zone in which it is found is designated as a "break" or "belt." The Pre-Cambrian is noteworthy for the length of such belts along which a succession of mines occur. The Rand of South Africa is perhaps the most prolific of these zones, but Canada, from present indications, bids fair to yield comparable ones. Porcupine has been genetically linked with northwestern Quebec and these together comprise a mining belt fully 250 miles long. Sixty miles southeast of Porcupine, Kirkland Lake has been convincingly related to Quebec, thus defining a southerly break which is almost 200 miles long and includes Larder Lake in its course. Other Canadian camps are beginning to supply evidence of similar, though smaller, regional belts.

Underground work, involving heavy expenditure and painstaking organization, should not be started until the surface showings have been thoroughly investigated and considered sufficiently promising to justify the larger program. The first logical procedure is to strip the discovery of all vegetation and wherever necessary obtain fresh exposures by digging trenches and test pits. In this manner one important dimension, length, can be indicated. This done, "channel" samples of vein material are cut across the full width of the occurrence, using hammer and moil (a short piece of steel sharpened to a point or a chisel edge). Equal amounts of the detached material are gathered on a canvas sheet, thoroughly mixed, the mass halved or quartered depending upon the quantity, and then shipped to the assayer. He, in turn, reduces the sample to a powder, weighs a selected portion, and by means of chemicals and heat recovers whatever metal may be present. This is weighed on a sensitive scale and the value of gold, or the percentage of metal, per ton of rock is calculated ($8 a ton, or 2 per cent copper, etc.). This is the all-important "assay."

At this juncture a mining enterprise may show promise or appear worthless. It is here that the temptation to tamper with the sample is strong. It is common practice to include only mineralized fragments, rejecting those which are barren, and for this reason an examining engineer naturally prefers to cut his own samples. Less common, but by no means rare, is "salting." This is done before, during, or after the actual sampling operation, and is effected by surreptitiously introducing gold particles or solution into the material to be assayed.

Assuming that the assays are bona fide and return encouraging values, the third dimension, depth, must be ascertained, and for this purpose the diamond drill is employed. What is this magic tool which takes the place of X-ray eyes? It is a rotating bit, usually about an inch in diameter, whose edges are embedded with small diamonds (bort). This is attached to a hollow rod of steel and driven in a circular motion by steam, gasoline, or electric power. This device cuts freely into the rock and at certain intervals the forward motion is halted and reversed, by which process a solid core of rock, not unlike a broom handle in appearance, is hauled to the surface and slipped out of the rod sections. This is called "pulling core." A fresh length of rod is then screwed onto the first and lowered to the hole bottom, whereupon drilling is recommenced. In this way, a continuous operation soon begins to gather a considerable length of core, thus affording a cross section of the occurrence below the surface. Selected portions of core showing mineral or vein material are split in halves. One section is assayed and the other retained for further study or check sampling.

Drilling is undeniably useful but too much significance can be attached to it. After all, a one-inch section of what may be a thousand-foot-long mineralized zone can be misleading in a negative or a positive way. The size of an ore body may be easily exaggerated, too, particularly at great depths where the rods cannot be rigidly controlled. They tend to follow the easiest course through the rocks and this logically can be the direction of a vein along the strike, thus creating a false impression of width. Drilling can easily understate the true situation by intersecting an ore body properly, across the dip, but in a section which may be locally poor in mineral. Results should be closely correlated with known factors, such as surface sampling, the character of other properties in the vicinity, and good common sense. A wise operator neither throws up his hat in joy nor threatens suicide in despair; he continues to gather information. To the unscrupulous, drilling affords opportunities for chicanery, some of it crude, such as salting, and some more subtle. An old trick is to direct the drill into a known rich area from many different angles and so create the illusion of major dimensions. Honestly and intelligently employed, however, drilling can be of invaluable assistance in learning about ore behavior at depth. Despite abuse by some promoters and misinterpretation by the less informed public, which tends to regard it as an end and not a means, drilling occupies an indispensable place in Canadian mining exploration.

If the property has passed the test of drilling, it is no longer a wildcat. But neither is it a mine. Belowground only can the miner "shake hands with ore." And so a shaft must be sunk, lateral openings (drifts) driven along the ore body, and the different levels connected by raises. Sampling must be extensive, and then only can ore said to be "blocked out," ready for extraction. All the required dimensions have been delineated, and now the treatment plants are ready to be constructed. First, however, protracted estimates must be made to ensure a reasonable profit as well as return of capital. Likelihood of ore extensions must be considered, together with assurance that power, water, timber, labor, and supplies are available. At this stage, also, temptations abound: a dishonest management can announce erection of a mill when conditions actually dictate abandonment, this with the purpose of stimulating stock market quotations. An overt act of this kind is deliberate. Less culpable is bad judgment, by no means a curiosity. And dangers lie in the imponderables —fire, flood, underground caving.

Production is success, and so is achieved all too seldom. But even here risks remain. Extraction methods devised in the laboratory can be found wanting in the field where large tonnages of ore are treated. Or the ore may pose complicated metallurgical problems. In the case of most Canadian gold ores, however, difficulties are not serious. Usually the material is crushed to one-inch size and then ground to a slime in ball mills (closed rotating receptacles filled with steel balls). When the slimes are allowed to escape after reaching desired fineness, they are collected in large vats and treated with a cyanide solution and agitated until the gold is absorbed. Then the "pregnant" solution is treated by a special chemical process to liberate the gold from its compound state. In special ores there is an intervening stage of "flotation" whereby the slimes are conducted to containers saturated with reagents (special oils which have affinity for metal). A froth, much like soap bubbles, is thrown surfaceward by a device similar to an egg beater, swept into conduits and dumped into tanks and treated with cyanide. When the ore is "free milling" (native gold), cyanide may be dispensed with altogether. Mercury, spread on slightly inclined copper plates, receives the slimes directly. This liquid metal has the strange ability to pick up gold particles and in due time assumes a gummy consistency. Then the "cleanup" is made. Operations stop while the plates are scraped of amalgam, which then is placed in chamois bags. Vigorous pressure is exerted until most of the mercury exudes through the pores of the chamois, leaving a residue rich with gold. This is subjected to furnace heat and the residual quicksilver quickly expelled as a vapor. Frequently amalgamation is used in conjunction with flotation or cyaniding, or both.

In gold ores trouble is caused by "cyanicides." These are certain sulphides, chiefly chalcopyrite (copper) and arsenopyrite (arsenic), which render the cyanide innocuous or cause it to be used in pro-hibitively high amounts. Flotation sometimes removes this hazard, also finer grinding in the ball mills, but roasting will always expel the culprits. In all such cases the costs must never be neglected, for the cure may be as harmful to the pocketbook as the disease.

Base metals, unless they are found in the form of massive sul-phides which can be shipped direct to the smelter, are handled by flotation. The concentrated material (concentrates) is then put through the smelter and crude metal (matte, or blister) produced. The final process is electrolysis and refined metal.

Mine making, the reader will agree, is a long, grueling, expen-sive business. Rich surface discoveries are not enough; they must run the gantlet of the various development stages. Until they do, they are merely prospects. And, in Canada, they cost money: $1,000,-000 for a 100-ton daily producer is the average. There are no time-and moneysavers, no short cuts or royal roads to success. The same extended and dogged program of labor confronts anyone, commoner or king, who has the temerity to venture into the precarious, though stimulating, adventure of mining.

Operators have their individual methods of approach to the problem of obtaining new mines, but Fred W. Schumacker devised a workable formula which has justifiably created the expression "Schumackering." This venerable American, a native of Cincinnati, became interested in Canadian mining shortly after Cobalt, and dis-patched Shirley Cragg and Morgan Millen to investigate possibilities of the new country. Millen was not impressed, but Cragg was en-thusiastic. In glowing terms he outlined to Schumacker the discovery of gold in Porcupine and the sagacious American, who had married the daughter of the wealthy inventor and manufacturer of "Peruna," a patent medicine, decided to plunge. He purchased a number of Veteran Lots, which were given to veterans of the Boer War, among them 160 acres adjoining the Dome Mine, for which he paid $8,000. Another of his Vets adjoined the Hollinger, and this he incorporated into the Schumacker Mines, later sold to Hollinger for $2,000,000. But the Dome situation, he decided, was one requiring nothing more than patience. So he waited.

In 1911 he optioned the property to Archie Fuller for $50,000 and advised him to approach the Dome officials. This Fuller did, asking $75,000 for the ground. The figure was ridiculed and Fuller returned to Schumacker with a sad tale of refusal. The American listened patiently and then requested Fuller to return to the Dome offices.

"Tell them," he said, "that if they ever decide they want the ground and come back, the price will be $150,000."

Fuller delivered the message, which was greeted with derision and laughter. But Schumacker was not disheartened; he could wait.

Twenty years passed. In 1931 Dome, sensing the growing importance of the Schumacker ground which abutted its own, decided the time was ripe to purchase. Word was sent to Schumacker that $75,000 would be paid for the Vet.

"I told you," was the bland answer, "that if you came back the price would be $150,000. And if you don't pay that now, the ante rises to $300,000 next time."

Jules Bache, Wall Street banker, collector of $500,000 paintings and president of Dome, was apprised of the situation. Indignant, he advised his directors to forget the matter. But underground, developments were moving uncomfortably near the man from Cincinnati. Conferences were held at Dome, and long-distance calls made to New York. Bache, in a grim mood, finally agreed to pay $150,000. Schumacker, listening to the Dome spokesman, shook his head.

"But I said the price would be $300,000 this time," he explained naïvely. "And if you don't take that figure now the price goes up to $600,000."

Deciding the aging Schumacker had lost his reason, Dome broke off all negotiations. But in the cooler atmosphere of reflection, worried officials decided to approach their tormentor once more. To their astonishment, Schumacker, stroking his white mustache, repeated his price formula, warning that unless $600,000 was paid him the figure would be automatically doubled on the next occasion. Like one of John L. Lewis's coal conferences, discussion ended without result.

Meanwhile, engineers were working underground, ever closer to the Schumacker. The grapevine news had it that operations were actually being carried on across the boundaries of the forbidden ground. If true, Schumacker would recover enormous damages, for the law is strict on claim encroachments. Denials were indignantly made; the Dome was merely drilling close to the line. But Bache stopped buying old masters long enough to give de Pencier, the manager, new instructions. A fresh attempt to break down the refractory exponent of the unearned increment was made.

Schumacker proved to be as excellent a trader as he was a patient campaigner, for in 1936 an official Dome announcement was made to the effect that the Vet claim had been purchased for $1,125,-000 cash plus 20,000 shares of Dome, worth approximately $600,000. The course of arithmetical progression had been halted, but at a price somewhat above the original $75,000.

In the past ten years, it has been variously estimated that $20,000,000 to $40,000,000 in gold has been taken from Schumacker ground. Prospects for additional ore continue excellent.

Does Schumacker feel cheated? Probably not, for twisting the lion's tail into knots must have given him untold satisfaction. And almost $2,000,000 for an $8,000 investment is not, after all, a bagatelle.

The field is wide open for newcomers to repeat Schumacker's performance. All that one needs is another Porcupine, expert advisers, wealthy in-laws, longevity, an increased price of gold, overcautious and somewhat parsimonious mining executives, and a hatful of luck.

Jump in, the water's fine!

The Age of Science

Editor, *Northern Miner:*

    I have a natiral born gift i can locate mineral by going over the top of the grond and can tell ware the ore is and give how wide the vaine is and how long or wather it is a true long vaine and wather it is a leane vaine or a rich one and also can locate oil can pick out a pool of oil ware there is one wen i go over the grond and i pay my owe expencess if i cant do the work as i say a company wood not be out a cent for my expencess my work will be garentted or no pay but the company wood have to drill or go down ware i tell them but want free board and expencess while goying over the grond of the company i can test out a q of sec per day and if you get me oney work true The Miner i will give you ten per cent on wath i make net less outh of my railroad and expencess wile going to Canada and returned hoping hear from you if you think there wood be wark of that kind for me it doesn't make no diffrence how much over burden there is nare no rock in sight i can tell ware the vaine is and the company wood not need to make trances to locate a vaine can safe them thosand of dollars in wark triing to find a vaine all they need to do put a drill doon ware i tell them ware to drill and if the company have any drill hole on there land

i will tell them ever hole ware they strock ore or a blank one and
if i fall down on one of them i am no good if i fall down on one
of them ware they have any drill hole down i will give them a test free
of charge to test me outh to wath i can do wen i do this wark it
should be warm wather wood not go outh on less it from 30 to 40
above z.

—William Walter, Hurley, Wis.
January 2, 1930

The big man wrinkled his brow in perplexity. His engineer sat
before him, detailing the results of a geophysical survey which had
just been completed.

"And I'm glad to inform you, Spud," he concluded, "there are
four anomalies."

"Amon . . . anom . . ." the big man sputtered. "What in hell you
talkin' about?"

"Anomalies," repeated the engineer firmly.

"Can you put 'em through the mill?"

The engineer smiled condescendingly. "No, Spud," he replied
smoothly, "you can't run anomalies through a mill. They're just
indications of something projected below the surface by a magnetometer."

"To hell with indications!" Spud pounded his desk as he judged
an executive should. "I want ore!"

The young man laughed appropriately and then, between telephone calls, proceeded to explain that the day of rich surface bonanzas had passed. The search for ore bodies had now resolved itself
largely into extending known favorable structures along the strike
and dip, closing gaps which still existed between separated ore deposits. One couldn't look below the surface, through a hundred feet
of glacial overburden or muskeg or lake, but by the use of a magnetometer and electromagnetic devices underground rock structures
could be outlined together with possible mineralized zones.

"But these amon . . . anom . . . whatever you call 'em," interjected Spud, "do they mean ore?"

"Not necessarily. They may denote many things: water, a contact between different rock types, or disseminated magnetite in the
greenstone, or massive pyrite which is worthless up here, or sec—"

"Ore?" interrupted Spud, his face expanded into a smile of
expectancy.

"Could be," was the reply, "but the only way to know definitely
is to drill, and that takes money."

"Money." Spud inhaled deeply. "Always money, and I'm the
guy who's dishing it out."

He assumed an attitude of profound thought which lasted about ten seconds. Then his huge fist crashed down upon the desktop.

"Okay! Make your estimates and hand 'em in. I'll put up the dough and we'll knock 'em dead with our publicity."

And so, in the year 1945, another mining exploration effort is born in Quebec, the property containing 1,000 acres of mineral land on which there is not a single outcrop. The reader may well inquire as to the success of the drilling, which began when the geophysical survey was completed. Well, it is too early to say. No ore as yet, but then the drill is still working and anything can happen. . . .

The use of a doodlebug as an aid to ore search is far from new. Indeed, Georgius Agricola, in his classic work *De Re Metallica,* first published in 1556 and translated from the Latin by Herbert Hoover and his talented wife, Lou Henry Hoover, almost three hundred fifty years later, has much to say about divining rods, dear to the hearts of the lunatic fringe.

> There are many great contentions between miners concerning the forked twig, for some say it is of the greatest use in discovering veins, and others deny it. Some of those who . . . use the twig, first cut a fork from a hazel bush with a knife. . . . Others use a different kind of twig for each metal. . . . All alike grasp the forks of the twig with their hands, clenching their fists, it being necessary that the clenched fingers should be held towards the sky in order that the twig should be raised where the two branches meet. Then they wander hither and thither at random through mountainous regions. . . . The moment they place their feet on a vein the twig immediately turns and twists and so by its action discloses the vein; when they move their feet again and go away from that spot the twig becomes once more immobile. The truth is, they assert, the movement of the twig is caused by the power of veins. . . . On the other hand, those who say that the twig is of no use to good and serious men, also deny that the motion is due to the power of the veins, because the twigs will not move for everybody, but only for those who employ incantations and craft. . . .

Today, more than ever, the mining industry depends upon the trained geologist and the use of modern scientific devices, specifically geophysical instruments of the magnetic and electric types which have slowly come into general use after a bad beginning. Stated simply, geophysics endeavors to point the way to buried ore bodies, or, more accurately, conditions favorable to their occurrence. The range is limited to depths of about five hundred feet. Methods vary. There is the magnetometer, which registers the different magnetic intensities of underlying rock strata. Attraction readings are plotted to scale and an approximation of the unseen geology thus obtained. Occasionally, in areas of intense mineralization, actual deposits of sulphides are detected. (Thomas Edison spotted the Falconbridge Nickel Mine with a magnetometer as far back as 1906.) "Anomalies" are those loci which depart sharply from normal and so are classified as possible zones of mineral concentration. In the course of years more refined instruments have been introduced, utilizing seismic and gravimetric principles. During World War II the advance of electronics pointed the way to more exact determinations and if the scope of this modern magic can be broadened and related to geophysical prospecting a revolutionary change in mining is to be expected.

The Pre-Cambrian of Canada is an intriguing arena for the geophysicist because of the scarcity of outcrops, which limits surface prospecting. Shortly after the discovery of Noranda, doodlebugging became an obsession. Lines were feverishly cut in the bush and the demand for geophysicists almost reached hysteria. Promoters hailed the new wizardy which could transform worthless muskeg and moose pasture into mines. But the wave passed and mining men, sadder and wiser, began to appraise geophysics in the cooler light of reason. It is realized now that in this earlier day too much weight was placed on science and too little on geology and simple intelligence. Investigating anomalies was expensive and uncertain, especially in "Indian country," far from proved mineral deposits. "Indications" could be variously interpreted, and this added up to more perplexity than ore. If drilling was attempted it invariably gave negative results and more than one geologist, ordinarily temperate, became blasphemous and inarticulate when the touchy subject of geophysics was mentioned.

A revival of interest, however, followed carefully improved techniques and more modest representations by geophysicists. It was emphasized that geophysics and geology overlapped; results could be effectively applied only by men able to correlate readings with recognized conditions in the particular area. Structure, and not ore, was accentuated. Maps were simplified in order to facilitate interpretation and enable the engineer to render geophysical data into terms of understandable geology. In this way areas of potential mineralization were sketched, removing exploration from the realm of complete guesswork. Not unimportant of late has been the almost routine application of geophysics to the extension of established mineral areas, where maps can be read and interpreted in conjunction with a growing mass of valuable data obtained from actual underground operations.

The era of flush production seems nearly over in Canada, as should be expected after a generation of easy surface discoveries. A study of mining camps reveals these startling truths:

Fifty-five per cent of production is currently derived from areas discovered before 1910.

Twenty-eight per cent comes from discoveries made between 1910 and 1920.

Eleven per cent is credited to discoveries made between 1920 and 1930.

Only six per cent comes from operating mines found since 1930.

Under these circumstances, complete reliance upon the prospector is no longer practical if production is to be maintained or increased. While the sourdough still roams the bush and renders valuable service, the technical man, by painstaking geological study and rational application of geophysics, has been slowly winning the battle for ore. This is a costly procedure, admittedly, but one which pays worthy dividends and will continue to do so as more detailed knowledge of ore deposits is compiled and the search for extensions closely localized. And so, a new scientific trend in prospecting is manifesting itself in Canada and will be increasingly felt in coming years.

An early sign of the change from the old to the new came in Quebec when geologist J. G. "Jock" MacGregor applied himself to the Waite-Amulet district, a few miles north of Noranda. There he noted the presence of a highly altered lava bed which had been given the name "dalmatianite" by H. C. Cooke, a government geologist who had mapped the district. This rock, containing rounded inclusions of a highly chloritized (altered) material, was locally referred to as "spotted dog." To MacGregor, this chloritization was highly significant; he was convinced that it evidenced close proximity of ore. But where was it to be found? Certainly not on surface, where only desultory patches of mineralization, far from ore grade or extent, were to be seen. He concluded that the logical possibility was along the bedding planes between rhyolite and andesite strata far belowground. He examined the small flat-lying ore bodies on the old Amulet property, which had given early hope only to fizzle out after providing a few thousand tons of gold-copper-zinc sulphides. He noted that the beds were dipping gently to the southeast and decided that an accurate geological section should be made and tied into the surface expression which, he was convinced, was a sign of buried ore. This was done.

Lake Dufault Mines was a consolidation of several earlier companies formed by Thayer Lindsley and later absorbed by his Ventures, Ltd. The ambitious MacGregor now went to Lindsley in Toronto, his maps in order and his mind brimming with ideas. Himself a geologist of no mean ability, Lindsley hearkened to the eager words of his young colleague with rising interest. Few others, perhaps, would have been sympathetic to a plan involving large expenditures with only remote chances of success, but Lindsley always responded to a situation of this kind.

"Go right ahead," he said, "we'll drill."

MacGregor, overjoyed, hastened back to Quebec. Almost a half mile from the Amulet ore bodies he set up a drill rig and began to test his as yet purely theoretical deduction of a hidden ore deposit. Each section of core was examined under the glass for evidence of mineral. At first the rock appeared "hungry," but as the drill cut deeper, significant changes began to appear. Alteration became more pronounced and an occasional smattering of pyrite, zinc blende, and copper sulphides heightened expectations of better things to come. Nor was MacGregor to be disappointed. At approximately 1,200 feet below the surface, a goodly intersection of gold-copper-zinc sulphides showed in the core.

Thereupon efforts were redoubled, with several machines placed in operation. The mining world buzzed with excited comment, for this was a novel kind of prospecting for Quebec. Interest became astonishment when it was learned that almost 3,000,000 tons of ore had been outlined, with a grade of more than $17 per ton. Lindsley, it appeared, captured another of what he soberly referred to as "plums." But God, in supplying ore, did not fix claim boundaries. Upon examination, it was found that the $50,000,000 deposit straddled the line between Lake Dufault Mines and the Waite-Amulet, with the bulk of the ore lying well within the latter property. Furthermore, the Waite, a producing mine, was equipped with a plant and underground workings from which the ore could be quickly and effectively mined.

With rising misgivings a chagrined MacGregor followed negotiations. Noranda, in control of the Waite, was insistent. Engineers had appraised the situation and determined that almost all of the ore rested in their grounds. Accordingly, Noranda proposed the formation of the Amulet-Dufault Mines to extract and treat the ore and sell the metals derived therefrom, they to receive 90 per cent of the stock and the Lindsley group 10 per cent. It was a bitter pill to swallow, especially for Jock, who had snared the ore body. Under the circumstances, however, no other alternative could be found. The agreement was signed and Noranda began to mine a deposit which had been discovered for them gratuitously.

Lake Dufault Mines, retaining most of its property, promptly undertook to locate another deposit. For some reason these efforts, to date, have been negative. But the persistent MacGregor still continues the search and if ore is present, he will find it.

In British Columbia, Paul Billingsly, a gifted American geologist, performed the miracle of the Nickel Plate Mine. The Hedley district, two hundred miles east of Vancouver, was visited by placer miners as early as 1860. Lode mining was slow to start, and it was not until 1902 that the Marcus Daly interests of Butte, Montana, brought the Nickel Plate into production. Operations ended in 1909 when ore supply failed, and in that same year the property passed into the newly formed Hedley Gold Mining Company. In 1910, Charles Camsell published a *Memoir of Nickel Plate Mountain,* a remarkably keen paper which furnished valuable suggestions to Billingsly in his later rehabilitation efforts. Meanwhile, the Hedley company was able to find enough ore to keep the mill functioning, but in 1931 reserves were finally exhausted, and once again the property shut down. Billingsly, who had made an examination in 1927, now saw an opportunity to study the situation calmly, without the pressure of ore demands. Accordingly, he obtained the assistance of New Yorkers who, in 1932, advanced a substantial development fund through the Kelowna Exploration Company. Assisted by Augustus Locke of San Francisco, Billingsly worked out the tangled structure, with the result that plentiful ore was disclosed. In 1934 the mine began to produce once again, and since that time has added well over $21,000,000 to Canada's gold pile.

The geology of Nickel Plate is so complicated that only an exceptional talent could unravel its minutiae. The area consists of Mesozoic rocks related to the great Coast Range batholith. At Nickel Mountain the rocks are largely sedimentary, closely interbedded, folded intensely, and intruded by dikes and sills of gabbro-diorite. Ore-bearing solutions apparently followed the bedding planes upward, and Billingsly, contrary to popular belief, proved that the favorable structure continued, notably in relation to the sills, which acted as barriers to the spreading solutions. At the contacts flat platelike ore masses were formed. Other ore types were successfully delineated, and a once dead property, thanks to the geologist, proved the old saying: "A good mine dies hard."

In the Sheep Creek district, the Gold Belt Mine is another high-water achievement of useful geology. The claims were staked as early as 1905 but no serious development was done until 1932. Then the Lakes brothers, encouraged by developments in the adjoining mines, drove tunnels into the mountainside to intersect the downward projection of several veins which outcropped on surface. None of these carried commercial gold values, but it was hoped that there would be improvement in depth. A few encouraging spots were found underground, but funds were low. Outside help was needed. Now came H. G. Lynch, a geologist familiar with the area. Lynch had worked for North American Mines in Lower California some years before, and he was convinced that the Gold Belt was just the kind of property that would interest his former employers. So he journeyed to Boston and sat in conference with Q. A. Shaw, Jr., and Robert Livermore, engineers both. Lynch explained that good ore had been found in a series of short quartz veins lying athwart a quartzite bed which occurred on both the Reno and Sheep Creek mines adjoining Gold Belt on the east and west. It was reasonable to suppose, therefore, that the same favorable stratum traversed the Gold Belt. The Lakes team had worked in the slates above the quartzite, and this accounted for their failure to find ore. Lynch now proposed a long tunnel at the base of the mountain, this to crosscut the entire length of quartzite. In the course of this work any promising veins would be investigated by raises.

Lynch must have been convincing, for the two Bostonians agreed to provide the money for his ambitious program. A visit to British Columbia convinced them that the chances for ore were reasonably good.

With Lynch in charge, work started in 1935. As anticipated, the quartzite was found together with a number of quartz veins. Values were negligible at first, but later picked up briskly. And in the course of time several of the veins yielded excellent, though small, ore shoots. By the latter part of 1938 a respectable ore reserve had been built up and a 150-ton mill began to operate. Since that time Gold Belt has produced close to $5,000,000. The effort was a geological triumph, particularly gratifying to Shaw. As grandson of Quincy Adams Shaw, who sponsored the Calumet & Hecla Mines in Michigan, he proved himself a worthy scion of a distinguished forebear.

Farther east, in the blue of northern Manitoba, Eldon Brown, manager of the Sheritt-Gordon Mine which had seen its best days, tried repeatedly to present his needful company with a property of merit. After many attempts, success finally came in the Granville Lake area, where a geophysical survey returned several pronounced anomalies. Brown, quicker in action than speech, rushed a drill north. The first cores yielded interesting quantities of copper and nickel. Brown ordered more claims staked, and laid out an ambitious program of work. As drilling continued, it was realized that sizable tonnages of ore were possible and an entirely new mining district might be in the offing. While I write, more results are being announced, all of them decidedly bullish, and "Brownie," thanks to the once ridiculed doodlebug, is preparing for one of the largest developments in Canada.

In Quebec, where it seemed that Noranda was destined to be the only important mine in Rouyn Township and so justify the "I told you so's" of professional croakers, the work of Jock MacGregor inspired others. Stewart Troop, a mining engineer who had clung to Rouyn for years, teamed with Colonel Thain McDowell of Montreal to patiently acquire a group of long-neglected and seemingly worthless claims east of the Noranda. Attempts to engage the support of mining companies met with refusal or indifference. Donalda was a raw wildcat from which respectable money automatically shied, and so money was raised through Toronto promoters. To map the ground, Troop engaged Howard Butterfield, former chief geologist of the Noranda. There was little to be seen on the stark overburdened surface, but the low relief and hypothetical presence of fault zones justified Butterfield's recommendation of a geophysical survey. This was followed, and drilling commenced in the autumn of 1943.

At the outset the drill, after penetrating more than a hundred feet of bouldery clay, intersected a wide quartz vein rich in gold. Entirely different from the Noranda sulphide ore, Donalda created a sensation. At long last, apparently, the environs of Noranda were giving up their secrets. There ensued a mad scramble for claims which, through the passage of years, had been staked and restaked dozens of times, then dropped by discouraged prospectors and impecunious companies. Indeed, one of the first of our own early stakings included a goodly part of the Donalda itself, but our misfortune is so widely duplicated in Canada as to be entirely commonplace. Comfort came from the spectacle of revival. Drills began to clatter cheerfully, troubling habitants who had settled the district with expectations of transforming it into farming country. But mining was coming into its own again.

Subsequent drilling at Donalda did not repeat the results of the first hole. Various interpretations were placed on this failure, but again the geologist came to the fore and advanced the interesting idea that the ore was flat, much like a plate. More drilling confirmed this hypothesis, and while the eventual ore body as outlined was not so large as at first calculated, Donalda was well justified in sinking a shaft. Final results must await future underground work. The geologist can point the way but it remains for the miner to bring home the bacon.

Parenthetically, it must be said that Canada here offers a welcome contrast to other mining countries. Seldom is a mill built before ore has been developed underground. In some cases remotely located prospects have jumped the gun a bit in order to obviate unduly large capital outlays, but the industry has generally adhered to the maxim: "Develop ore before you mine it." This policy is so ingrained that any deviation from it generates immediate unfavorable comment. Whatever the reasons for this, Canada can be justly proud of a tradition that assures integrity in mining development.

Bill Martin, of Ventures, Ltd., is a geologist of the progressive school. When the first suggestion connecting the occurrences of Quebec with those of Porcupine, Ontario, was made, Bill showed interest, for he had arrived at this conclusion himself. It was a simpler matter for him to obtain the support of Thayer Lindsley in a project which had long been forming in his mind. From eastern Porcupine to the Quebec border stretched sixty miles of country buried beneath a mantle of sand, clay, gravel, and muskeg. Here and there small rock outcrops showed. One of them, in Hislop Township, was uncovered by a farmer who thought it a large boulder. The Hollinger learned differently when it purchased the farm and brought in the Ross Mine, a healthy and growing gold producer. But it was impossible to drill miles of clay indiscriminately; a program of geologizing was first required as a guide. Martin, accordingly, became a familiar figure among the settlers in this predominantly agricultural area, compiling data methodically over a period of years. His work was augmented by geophysical surveys along the gently rolling "clay belt" and then the ponderous mass of information was incorporated into a regional map. Two distinct fault zones, cutting through the region north and south of the Temiskaming sediments, were plotted. Unobtrusively, thousands of acres were acquired by purchase and staking. By 1943 Bill was ready for drilling.

But in the midst of this crucial work, he was stricken ill and forced into the hospital for a long period. His associate, J. M. "Jack" Cunningham-Dunlop, manager of the Hoyle Mines and graduate of the Haileybury Mining School, took over and proved that his training and experience were equal to the formidable job of exploring a small empire. In Michaud and Guibord townships painfully slow drilling was carried out—slow because of the deep overburden and abundance of boulders. And the indifferent results when bedrock was finally reached caused little surprise, for this was like shooting at the moon. However, Jack continued doggedly, guided by his colleague's elaborate maps and accumulation of drill core. Then, in 1945, holes with economic gold values and excellent widths began to appear, and in two widely separated locations. Mines? It is far too early to say, but working almost in the dark, Martin and Dunlop have unearthed all the essentials of gold mines—quartz veins with length, width, gold, and all the geology anyone could desire.

The secret was an open one and long before the promising drilling was encountered farseeing companies and prospectors picked up all the ground possible. Kelwren, north of the Ross, is obtaining encouragement in its drilling. In Garrison Township, Wright-Hargreaves is reported to have "clicked" in the first of a series of drill holes. The clay belt, comparatively untouched since the Porcupine discoveries of 1909, is receiving the kind of attention that may net a crop of mines worthy of the main Porcupine camp, thanks to the farseeing efforts of constructive geologists.

Let us return to Quebec, one of the younger mining areas of Canada and in many respects the most difficult from the viewpoint of exploration. The varying complexities of deposits seemed at first to have no definite design or relationship. For this reason early prospecting was haphazard. Men rushed in all directions at the slightest rumor of a find, constantly in fear that they had located in the wrong spot. But as government geologists widened their mapping over a period of twenty years and checked information furnished by operators and producers in the district, certain rational features began to suggest themselves. The Temiskaming sedimentary bands were recognized as zones of weakness and several belts outlined. These, we have seen, were linked to the distant Kirkland Lake and Porcupine fields. To the south, an important regional phenomenon, termed the "Bouzan Lake Fault," was established, and this, together with smaller subsidiary northeasterly faults, was designated as a presumed channelway for the circulation of ore-bearing solutions. Stressed, also, was the significance of granitic batholiths, such as those in Duprat, Rouyn, Bourlamaque and other townships. Even the surface was made to yield clues, for geologists were aware that glaciation was more effective wherever structural weakness in the rocks, such as faults, shearings, veins, and massive mineralization were present. Erosion was more active in these areas and formed significant draws and depressions as compared to the monotony and flatness of the surrounding topography. While admitting that such evidence was not a guarantee of ore deposits, the geologist did not equivocate in recommending investigation.

The story of the Sisco Gold Mine, with a production exceeding $25,000,000, would have been vastly different without geologist Jack Forbes. The property was among the earliest found in Quebec, having been discovered in 1914 by Stanley Sisco, a Pole, who had "taken to the bush" when war broke out. He settled with a few friends on a small island in Lake Kienawisik into which the Harricanaw River flows. Having had some mining experience in Cobalt, the men killed time by lazily prospecting. They found a small quartz vein containing rich sections of gold, but war years were not conducive to mining exploration. The Rouyn rush, which spread to the east, in due time caught up with Sisco, however, but then most engineers considered the geology—quartz veins in granodiorite—unfavorable and the vein too narrow to be of economic importance. One of the few who saw some promise in the occurrence was Jack Baragwanath, but his employers, the American Smelting & Refining Company, decided the Sisco was too small for an organization of their magnitude. It remained for Toronto brokers, alert for just such an opportunity, to provide the first funds.

Work was not encouraging. Though values were good, tonnage possibilities were decidedly poor; the promoters bowed themselves out of the picture. But Thayer Lindsley, ever on the prowl for such situations, headed a syndicate to advance the requisite money for continued operations. Jack Forbes was then given the task of unraveling what appeared to be a hopeless geological puzzle. That he solved it is yet another tribute to the profession he so ably represented. At once he observed a regularity of fracturing in the granodiorite which he considered hopeful. Accordingly, he modified the plan from that of lateral work to one of crosscuts and winzes, much in the fashion of a stairway. This disclosed what no one else had suspected, namely, that the ore consisted of smallish high-grade quartz lenses occurring successively in a zone dipping toward the greenstone contact. This was later given the name "ladder structure." Once understood, the Sisco Mine was opened up at a rapid rate, and changed from a wilting prospect to one of Quebec's major mines.

In 1944, sagacious Ike Waite, whose Mining Corporation controlled Quemont Mines adjoining Noranda, looked with growing interest at the doings of Donalda. True, the ore was a fleabite when compared to Noranda, but Butterfield's theory that mineralization was associated with the Horne Creek Fault had produced results. This same fault traversed Quemont, and though United Verde Extension had spent almost $1,000,000 on the Quemont during the 'twenties in a futile attempt to duplicate the luck it had in Arizona, Ike began to think of another try. He moved cautiously, obtained funds outside the fold of Mining Corporation before ordering a geophysical survey. It was a happy time, for the freezeup had come and readings could be taken from the surface of Lake Osisko, a

decided advantage of Canadian winter. No struggling through the
muskeg; pickets thrust into the ice were better than blazed lines
and posts in the bush. And, anyway, this was about the only part of
Quemont still untouched. In an interval of weeks the map was completed and two anomalies in an east-west line plotted. Drilling began
at the eastern end. First results were negative. Trouble then came in
driving casing through the silt on lake bottom, and inasmuch as
such work is added to the footage charge, the contractor, fearing
objections might be raised later, decided to telephone the Mining
Corporation office in Toronto and explain.

Waite was not on hand and so conversation was held with a sub-
ordinate official. At once he insisted that work should be stopped,
for, after all, drilling had shown nothing to date and the added cost
of piping was not justified. The driller, however, used his best persuasion, even volunteered to assume the expense if bedrock was not
reached within a reasonable time. With this promise, he was given
permission to continue the hole. The casing was successfully driven
and the drill began to function once more. Within 150 feet a wide
section of sulphides was intersected. Quemont stock jumped from a
few cents to almost $2 a share, nor was enthusiasm dampened when
the assays were found to be below ore grade. For, reasoned speculators, was there not a bonanza only a few hundred feet away? This
Quemont might be as good, or better. Mining men, recalling the
past, shook their heads pityingly, but the foolish public rushed in.
A second hole was spotted a hundred feet from the first and results
were no different—plentiful pyrite but not enough gold and copper.
The stock churned about uncertainly, then held steadfast when more
drilling went forward. But now came a change in the form of an
unexpectedly early breakup. The rotting ice could no longer safely
sustain the weight of the drills, and so a hurried move to the mainland was made.

Here drilling was resumed from the fringe of the golf links, this
time directed at the western anomaly. The holes were necessarily
longer now and the mining world debated chances as the tiny bits
sunk deeper toward a theoretical ore deposit. Was it there? And if
so, would the values be commercial? Excited drill runners knew the
answer when the first familiar bronzy-looking sulphides appeared in
the core. This was the stuff to feed the troops. Noranda and Rouyn
buzzed with anticipation. In Toronto the news was flashed that Quemont had "hit big," and by the time the rumor reached the Stock
Exchange the Quemont post was literally engulfed. The public was
receiving a handsome premium for its ignorance; Quemont shares
rose like a rocket. Up to $5, then $8, $10, $12. Official word added

fuel to the flames, and as new drill holes punctured the ore the stock climbed to $20 a share and higher. Donalda, which had pointed the way, was now forgotten in the excitement. By all the rules, Quemont should not have had ore, but there it was! Stock salesmen attempting to "peddle" Quemont shares at 15 cents a year before would have received short shrift from the SEC.

This is mining in Canada.

Out of the chaos came sober bulletins from the Mining Corporation office. Values were excellent, somewhat above Noranda in gold, about the same in copper, but with an extra "sweetener" of zinc. Unlike Noranda, however, the ore appeared to be of flat pancake shape some 200 feet under the lake bottom. The old United Verde shaft, which had gone to 900 feet, was to be rehabilitated, and coincident with the drilling, lateral work would commence at once.

By May, 1946, sufficient drilling and underground work had been completed to assure at least 6,000,000 tons of high-grade ore, with possibilities of much greater tonnage. And how far will it go? Judging by the price of the stock, the public believes Quemont will rival Noranda, but engineers are generally more guarded in their opinion. It was their duty to direct the search for ore, but evaluating this kind of a property under development is quite another matter.

Quemont, undoubtedly in the "big elephant" class, held but did not monopolize interest in the revitalized camp. More drilling was being conducted in the "sneer" zones of the district. For years men had been stressing the regional extension of shearing through the eastern townships, but their prognostications were taken lightly and even derisively. Now Bill Hosking and his associates, Jack Coghlan and Bobby Cockeram, acted upon what they considered a logical assumption, and acquired ground in Joannes Township adjoining Rouyn to the east. It was a rather nondescript section, noted for its dreary muskeg and hellish flies which even depressed the not very impressionable settlers who were attempting to farm there. Hosking, manager of the now defunct McWatters Mine from the start to the finish, had familiarized himself with the region, and decided that it offered a good geological bet, more so as the Bouzan Lake Fault had been projected through the southern half of the township. Accordingly, Heva Cadillac and Hosco Gold Mines were formed to incorporate several miles of moose pasture and with funds supplied by Bryant Newkirk, a Toronto promoter and broker, drilling started.

It was not long before the Temiskaming sediments began to yield interesting gold values over substantial widths. Both properties, developed simultaneously, showed similar characteristics, with the Heva indicating somewhat better values than the Hosco but over lesser widths. It was difficult to accept the fact that this despised muskeg, which so many of us had staked and abandoned scores of times, and then finally handed back to the Indians with curses and imprecations, was actually the carrier of important gold mines. True, underground work has not yet substantiated the promising drilling results, but the regularity of the occurrences and excellence of values provide good reason to expect producers. In any event, the work of Hosking and his associates has naturally encouraged others, and efforts along this part of the belt are being redoubled after a 20-year period of neglect.

Adjacent to the Bourlamaque batholith, mines which have produced an aggregate of more than $125,000,000 provide two essential elements for successful mining exploration, incentive and proper geology. "Doc" H. C. Wilson, who as geologist at the Lamaque Mine had much to do with developing that bit of muskeg into one of the great gold mines of the Dominion, began to inspect outlying areas. His attention was arrested by the suggestion of another granite plug several miles east of Lamaque in adjoining Louvicourt Township. Satisfied by his investigation that here were present much the same conditions as those at Lamaque, he interested Bev Jowsey in a program of geophysical work to be followed by diamond drilling if the results warranted. Jowsey, brother of the famous Bob, had been struggling with the property for years. Encouraged by Wilson, he enlisted the aid of his brother and the Bevcourt Gold Mines, Ltd., was formed. Wilson's magnetometer survey then outlined an intrusive granite and the ensuing drilling encountered ore.

After a long slumber, the adjoining property to the west woke up abruptly. A consolidation of this and other ground became the Buffadison Mines. With an alacrity which was almost amusing, several large companies, including the ponderous Newmont Mines, placed ample funds in the Buffadison treasury, and drills were soon in cheerful operation. The first row of holes produced little resembling ore, but new holes were pointed to deeper horizon, and, as hoped, the rake of the Bevcourt deposit was squarely encountered on Buffadison. Another geological bull's-eye! Of course, both enterprises are still in the prospect class and will remain so until they pass the acid test of underground development. Doc Wilson, nevertheless, has opened new vistas to the gold hungry, and growing interest now characterizes a section of Quebec which had scant appeal only a few years ago.

More than any other area, Quebec has demonstrated the value of geological planning. In the feverish years from 1943 to 1946 approximately 5,400,000 feet of diamond drilling were completed, or a total of 1,021 miles. Sidney Norman, who computed these astonishing figures, calculates the cost of such work around $14,000,000. He estimates that to date about 20,000,000 tons of ore have been indicated and developed, with a gross value of $156,000,000, exceeding the cost of drilling by more than 1,000 per cent. And the score continues to mount.

The reader, I hope, has not concluded that modern mining follows a simple rule of thumb—geological mapping, geophysical survey, drilling, and presto! a mine. Would that it were so! In presenting the geologist's case, I have not listed the failures, which vastly outnumber the successes. But in mining only the plums in the pudding are counted, and a camp is evaluated entirely on production and dividends. Exploration losses are inevitable, and while adding up to a respectable aggregate sum, they are individually small in a relative sense. No effort is a waste, however, for negative results do supply information and help eliminate unfavorable areas. Frequently, as has been shown, fresh knowledge has been effectively supplied in the revival of dead herrings.

Giant Yellowknife is a significant illustration of a new approach to an old situation. Troubled by lack of funds and a remote property, the Bear Company was glad to transfer a headache to Ventures, Ltd. A. S. Dadson and Hugh Fraser, the Ventures geologists, decided to forgo operation of the high-grade but small Brock Vein. Encouraged and advised by Thayer Lindsley, they raised their sights toward bigger game. Plotting the regional West Bay Fault, whose escarpment formed a conspicuous landmark against the somber flatness of muskeg, they followed a plan to investigate depressed ground areas. Clearly, ore was deposited before the fault occurred, so there was nothing to be gained by tracing the many fractures subsidiary to such a post-ore faulting. Hope rested in meeting conditions similar to those obtaining at the Con and Negus mines five miles to the south, where, it was calculated, the Giant originally abutted.

The successful results achieved by geologists Dadson and Fraser will be discussed in some detail in a later chapter. Had their mine-finding efforts been negative, Yellowknife would still be a comparatively quiet camp awaiting an uncertain future and the winning of the last frontier would have been indefinitely postponed. Aside from providing a major gold deposit, the Giant has induced bolder concepts and aspirations among technical men and has also made speculative money less hesitant. The effects of this most unprecedented development will long be felt in Canada.

A justifiable criticism is that the mining industry has been too slow and cautious in following the recommendations of its technicians. Oil companies, with their wildcat drilling upon the slightest provocation, have been known to risk $500,000 on a single well. This kind of plunging is almost unknown in mining, and to many of us such financial prudence is often exasperating. In their defense, mining executives point out the hundreds and even thousands of enterprises which are offered to them each year and the impossibility of investigating more than a few with their limited staffs and treasuries. But the time will come when the approaching exhaustion of ore reserves and the evolution of surer exploration techniques will force the adoption of more daring exploration. The personal factor, however, will remain the deciding one. A Noah Timmins or Thayer Lindsley will always balance the scales in favor of courageous enterprise.

The geologist has redeemed himself lately, but it cannot be denied that in the early years he was not free of deficiencies. Hasty condemnations, a fear of recommending what was too readily considered a long shot, and slavish devotion to precedence and textbooks had undoubted influence in retarding the march of Canadian mining. For every engineer who saw hope in a discovery there were dozens who had well-considered reasons for turning in negative reports. Hardly a single mine was recommended, even the "big elephants" which are today the pride and joy of Canada. Knowledge, it seemed then, was more dangerous than helpful. There is no better example of this than the case of a noted scientist who compiled an able and comprehensive report on the ore deposits and geology of Cobalt, a work which has since become the bible of the district. He proved that intrusive diabase sills had introduced the rich native silver, and described the competent rocks as largely conglomerate (graywacke) and the diabase itself to a minor degree. But the old Keewatin lavas, he declared, were impervious to ore solutions, and hence could not contain silver.

For a time these conclusions were substantiated by camp experience. But it remained for E. V. "Ernie" Neelands, engineer at one of the large mines, to wreck an excellent thesis. Ernie, probably the outstanding operator in Canada, was not circumscribed by any preconceived notions of ore genesis. His job was to find silver, and he overlooked no chances. When, therefore, he encountered a vein in the despised Keewatin, he ordered his miners to follow it along an exploration drift, with the result that they soon opened a major silver deposit. Word circulated through the camp, and the learned Ph.D. received the news which spoiled his carefully propounded theory.

"It can't be!" he exclaimed. "There's no silver in the Keewatin!"

But seeing was believing, and in a supplementary report he was obliged to include the enigmatic Keewatin as a host rock.

There is little doubt, however, that the earlier mistakes of geologists have been given too much prominence. An erring diagnosis is accorded much publicity, especially by disgruntled claim owners and promoters who are wont to capitalize the experience of Kerr Addison, which was turned down by a small army of technical men and later went on to become a mighty producer. Conveniently forgotten are the melancholy properties which brought ruin to stockholders and sponsors who bullheadedly insisted upon ignoring the voice of reason. No man is infallible, and in all fairness to the man of science who expressed honest doubt of the future of the Canadian picture, the increased gold price had much to do with confounding his conclusions. We all realize now that most of the Quebec mines, and a number in other provinces, would be questionable ventures with gold at $20.67 an ounce instead of $35.

The technician has performed with esteem in the selection of entirely new mineral areas. There is no mining camp since Cobalt which was not first pointed up by diligent government geologists. In the early days Ottawa and the provinces were handicapped by limited resources and could employ only a handful of faithful men, but even these small groups supplied the clues which led to major developments later, such as the fateful trip of Mackintosh Bell and Charles Camsell in Great Bear Lake. With more parties in the field as the country expanded, prospecting resolved itself into following the suggestions contained in the ever-swelling numbers of government reports. Quebec, Red Lake, Little Long Lac, Pickle Crow, northern Manitoba, Yellowknife, and even remote Labrador first heard the sound of the geologist's pick before the prospector appeared on the scene.

Granting that the book-versed engineer has at times adhered too rigidly to his academic background, or has forgotten that field observation is, after all, the valuable teacher, he still has been a vital contributor to Canadian mining. For he has shown the way to new camps and extended dimensions of the old. With time he has shaken off provincialism, broadened his vision, and taken firmer hold of himself. This is true in greater measure among the younger crop of men who have grown with the country and have learned most of their geology in the bush. Reason dictates that the study of rocks is not a library science; in the rolling hills and muskegs alone are Canada's mining treasures to be found. While post-mortem examinations of already established mines and districts have definite value and application in projecting and expanding structures into wider spheres, salvation for the economic geologist lies in the direction of penetrating the veil of the as yet unknown.

Between the prospector and the engineer exists a curious relationship of quarrelsome interdependence. This is, in a way, to be expected. A man who makes a discovery looks with suspicion and hostility at anyone who passes judgment on the apple of his eye. Few properties make mines, and so most of them are examined with a justifiably critical attitude. The prospector objects; like a fond parent he is sure that his baby will someday become president. He remembers the disdain with which the blue-chip mines were once regarded, and never fails to speak of the famous geologists who scorned the Lake Shore, Hollinger, or Noranda. Much is made of these incidents in the bush evaluation of university degrees.

I recall an episode in Noranda which exemplifies the proverbial belligerence of prospectors toward engineers. It happened long before the productive stage of the camp was reached when few technicians were blessed with optimism. One of the large American mining organizations had obtained an option on a gold prospect which had already been sampled by their fieldmen, and now the chief engineer was sent north to pronounce final judgment. Anticipating his arrival, the prospector diligently cleaned out the trail to his claims so there would be no turndown because of unpleasant travel. The vein was cleanly stripped and all trenches and samples neatly marked with identifying numbers. A special supply of moose meat was in readiness to tickle the palate of the expert, on whose opinion so much rested.

The great man duly arrived and was escorted to the property. All went well. The flies were not bad, the food excellent, and above all, the vein beautifully exposed. The engineer went to work with unexpected energy and in a few days silently gathered enough information to write his report. Never once did he give any indication of his conclusions, however. When he prepared to depart, the anxious prospector decided to ask a question.

"Well, what do you think of 'er?" he inquired.

"Interesting, interesting," came the reply. "The geology is good, the vein is long and wide and it contains gold, apparently." Then he paused and shook his head dolefully. "But . . ."

"But what?"

"But will it go down?"

"Will it go down?" the prospector repeated, his anger rising.

He scratched his cheek and assumed a mocking pose of thoughtfulness. Then: "Wal, I can't say it will an' I can't say it won't. But one thing I kin tell you, Mr. Jones. The God-damned vein ain't going up in the air!"

The contemporary prospector, while still pugnacious, has mellowed somewhat. He remembers Lake Dufault, the Giant, East Sullivan, Quemont, and so many other properties which owe their success to the superior craft of the "man who taps the rocks." The change has come grudgingly and imperceptibly, but it has come. The truth is, prospector and engineer are much like man and wife, contentious, accusing, suspicious, but at the same time indispensable to each other.

CHAPTER VIII

Meet Clary Dixon

Diminutive in stature but large in heart, Clary Dixon stepped across the tiny cabin, lifted the cover of the simmering pot, and looked inside.

"Coming along nicely," he said. "The only way to cook rice is on a slow fire. Too much water and stirring with a spoon's no good —the rice burns."

He pushed a stick of birch into the wood stove and opened the draft. Sniffing at his heels was Pete, his inseparable spaniel, who could do almost anything but talk. Pete had been taught to sleep at the foot of our bunk, beneath the eiderdown, so we could rest our toes on his thick furry back. There was an affinity between dog and master which would have melted even a professional animal hater.

"The rice may be coming along nicely," I said, glumly, "but the weather's getting worse."

"Don't worry," replied Clary, filling his pipe, "it's too early in the season for the snow to stay. In a day or two there'll be a thaw and then we pull out."

I looked through the window, studied the snow which was now falling in great leaden flakes. The sky was gray and low, but no more than my morale. I was unhappy; our position appeared hopeless, despite Clary's reassurances. It was freezeup time, when sensible men should have been out of the bush. Anything could happen. I had come into Matachewan with Clary to map his claims, sample the vein occurrences, and report to my "principals." We canoed into

Moyneur's on the Montreal River from Elk Lake, the end of steel, stored most of our duffel, and walked to the claims, a six-hour trek. Since the trip was to be of short duration, three or four days at most, we left our snowshoes at Moyneur's and packed only a week's grub. At the end of the fourth day, just as we were prepared to leave, a fierce blizzard swept in from the northeast. Now, on the following morning, the wind had abated, but the snow continued to fall thickly. It would be a cruel, dangerous trip to Moyneur's.

"Cheer up, bucko," he said, as if he had divined my thoughts. "If we run out of chuck and the snow's still bad, I'll make snowshoes out of some rope and old wood."

Legs spread in a Napoleon attitude, eyes twinkling, chin elevated aggressively, this cherubic little man, not yet thirty-five, was already a legend in the North Country. Staker of a large portion of the Hollinger Mine while yet in his 'teens, he had played a vital role in the history of Porcupine. I now studied him reflectively, called to my mind's eye the image of his partner, lean Tom Middleton. The two were a familiar sight in Swastika where Tom shacked in Jack Miller's cabin alongside the railroad and Clary lived with his petite wife, Irene, near the banks of the river. Mutt and Jeff they were called, Middleton well over six feet and Clary, with his broad-brimmed cowboy hat, almost a foot shorter. Tom had long since dissipated whatever share of the winnings Jack Miller vouchsafed him while Clary had succumbed to connubial bliss, fortified by two thousand shares of Hollinger which he had purchased from his "cut."

"Brings us $1600 a year," he explained, "which is enough for us, I guess."

"And Jack Miller?" I asked.

"Jack!" Clary sucked his pipe deeply. "He's making a trip round the world. Cruise, I believe. If it ain't that, it's Florida. He's got over a million."

"And you and Tom did the staking?"

"Jack did some and he put up the money, you know." He grinned. "About $100—big transaction."

Clary set the table expertly and we sat facing each other, Pete sniffing at our heels. "You hear so many stories, Clary," I said, "it's difficult to decide what really happened."

"That's right." He tasted the rice and nodded approvingly. "Try some of this," passing the bowl. We ate silently. It was so still in the cabin that the candle flame was motionless. Pete gulped a handful of rice Clary threw him and then looked his gratitude.

"Lots of stories, you bet, lots of 'em." Clary shook his head slowly. "People forget quickly, don't they? It's Benny Hollinger and Noah Timmins mostly, but there were many more, I can tell you, many more." He paused to fill his pipe. "Only sixteen years ago when it started—1909, to be exact—when you were just getting out of the cradle."

"You weren't so old yourself, Clary," I reminded him.

"That's right," he agreed, "I wasn't. Not quite eighteen. Too young to stake but nobody knew that at the time, and I guess it's too late now to tell and have 'em unscramble the eggs." He smiled mischievously. "Once in a while, whenever I want to throw a scare into Jack, I remind him that part of the Miller-Middleton claims were never legally staked. Just about kills him."

"You don't seem to like him, Clary."

"Oh, Jack's all right, I guess, if you understand him. Not very generous, that's all, and his memory's awful short, like most Heinies'. Sure, didn't you know he was German? Why, his mother could hardly talk English; she used to call him 'mine poy.'"

"Nothing to be held against him," I murmured.

"Suppose not, but somehow I could never get to like the man, probably because he married my mother when I was a grown kid. And then the way poor old Tom is treated after what he did to make Jack wealthy—that doesn't sit with me."

I mentioned genial Tom's fondness for the bottle.

"So what!" Clary was almost explosive. "It's enough to drive any man to drink, to be broke after staking part of the Hollinger. Another thing; when it came to doing the first assessment work on our Porcupine claims, Jack reduced our interest one half 'cause we had no money to pay our share. My own father too!"

"Stepfather," I corrected.

"Right you are." His good nature returned swiftly. "Stepfather. Well, I was able to take care of myself, but Tom was free and easy, you know how he is, and today he's flat. All Jack does is let him live in the shack while he takes sun baths in Florida, picks up a new wife, or goes on one of those damned world cruises of his. Say this for Jack, though, he was always a good miner and knew his minerals." Then, quickly: "But he should have been, he was born in Leadville, Colorado, and kicked around the West for years. At the time he married my mother he was a shift boss in the Morning Mine, the Coeur d' Alenes, you know.

"There was that trip to Alaska, now. Did I ever tell you about it? I didn't? That was really something. My mother had earned a bit of money in Spokane real estate, nothing much, but enough to make Jack want to go prospecting. He was never lazy, and he had big ideas. This time, nothing would satisfy him but a trip through northern British Columbia and on up to Alaska. Well, my mother could never refuse him anything. We bought an outfit in Seattle and the two of us went by boat up to Skagway. There we bought a pack horse and started overland for Fairbanks. Someone had told Jack there was gold in the back country and now he was going to find the biggest mine in the world. I was only fourteen at the time, but he gave me an equal share of the work, which was plenty, I can tell you. We covered sixteen hundred miles in four months, part of it by boat, and ended the season with one bearskin—you've seen it in the living room at Swastika—no money, and no mine. It was one hell of a trip; I could sit here telling about it for days.

"One time we camped with some Chinook Indians who had never seen a white boy in their lives. Made quite a fuss over me; one squaw offered to buy me from Jack for two dollars. Guess he would've sold if the price was high enough! And then there was a day, on the return trip, when we came to a river and the ferryman refused to take our pack horse over, said he was too heavy and might upset the raft. So Jack ordered me to ride upstream where there was a shallow ford, cross, and then return downstream on the other side where I would meet him. He takes the ferry over and away I go. But things didn't turn out as he said. The ford was almost a hundred miles upstream, and so I was on the trail almost a week."

"Didn't he worry about your being away so long?" I inquired.

"Dunno." Clary shrugged. "He told me what a tough little runt I was and all that. You can never tell what Jack thinks; he hides everything behind his loud manner."

"When did you leave for Canada?"

"Oh, about a year after the Alaska experience. Mother had made another little stake, she was always busy as a beaver, getting into those little real estate deals, and this time Jack says Canada was the place for a mining man. He had some relatives in Toronto and they had been writing to him about Cobalt. There was no stopping Jack once he made up his mind. We pulled up stakes in Spokane and headed east. It wasn't easy to go. I have a sister, you know, Margie, and we both hated to leave our childhood friends. The trip was expensive too, but we managed, somehow, thanks to my mother who was a wonderful woman, the best." He desisted a moment, patted his dog with fierce affection, and continued. "It was no picnic for us in Cobalt. The boom was on, you see, and living quarters were impossible to find. Right away Jack heard about silver discoveries in Gowganda, and would listen to no arguments about staying in Cobalt—we had to go to Gowganda. The jumping-off place was Charlton in those days, a rugged trip, but we were used to moving and didn't mind a bit, especially with the way things were situated in Cobalt."

He described the arrival in Gowganda, then in the throes of the wildest kind of boom. People lived in tents and improvised shacks and traded for lots at fantastic prices. The Millers were unhappy, but with Clary's mother providing the leadership, they dug in resolutely and soon acclimated themselves to their new and overcrowded surroundings. When word of silver came in from Elk Lake, however, they needed little persuasion to leave Gowganda, and were among the first to settle in the new townsite. Here fate was kinder. Jack Miller found immediate occupation contracting for assessment work and operating a ferry service across the Montreal River, and at frequent intervals he and Clary staked claims, all of which were sold at modest prices. Clary received little, except a growing reputation for his resourcefulness and bushmanship. As he talked, I recalled numerous conversations with Jack Munroe and others who described the Clary of those days as the "Elk Lake Wonder," a boy in his 'teens who performed a man's work, his Stetson perched on his head at a rakish angle and his mind quick to react to the sudden opportunities which only a mining camp provides.

Clary Dixon

A fortuitous meeting between Jack Miller and Jack Wilson, the man later responsible for the discovery of Dome Mines, provided the first germ of thought about Porcupine. Later, when the news of George Bannerman and Harry Preston making gold finds in the new district reached Elk Lake, Jack Miller decided that the time had come to act. He summoned Tom Middleton, who was working for him, and Clary, and ordered them to proceed north immediately where they were to locate claims in Porcupine. Jack was too busy to go himself, and promised to divide interests with them. Actually, Miller did not advance any funds. He did, however, provide groceries, a canoe, and supplies for the trip, all of which, in Clary's opinion, did not exceed $100 in value.

Tom and Clary paddled out to Charlton and there caught the train which let them off at Kelso, then the end of steel. Resuming canoe travel, they headed into Nellie Lake and thence up Porcupine Creek to Porcupine Lake. There they met Tom Geddes, George Bannerman, and Bert Hotchkiss, the last-named subsequently the staker of the West Dome Mine. Bannerman had already staked the Scottish-Ontario, several miles north of the lake, and there Tom and Clary went to inspect the showing.

"It looked good," Clary declared, "lots of high grade, though it didn't amount to much when they finally went underground. Anyway, Tom and I agreed we were in the right country. We returned to Porcupine Lake and visited Jack Wilson's camp. The boys had found a nice-looking vein—the Ida Maud, they called it."

Clary and Tom prospected farther west and staked two claim groups, one north of Jarvis (Pearl) Lake and the other west of Porcupine Lake. A month had now passed, and it was time to leave.

"The night before we left for Kelso to head south and meet Jack Miller in Haileybury," resumed Clary, "we were camped on Porcupine Creek. It had turned cold and we had a big fire going to keep out the chill. I heard a splashing sound which I took to be a moose, so I ran to the tent for my rifle. But old Tom hollers, 'Don't shoot, Clary, it's a man.' I looked down the creek where the reflection from our fire carried and sure enough I saw a canoe sliding through the horsetails. In a minute, Harry Preston steps out and shakes hands with us."

"You knew him?"

"Sure, we met him in Gowganda a few years before. Tom reminded him of the time we told him about a muskeg which would be a likely spot for game. He followed our advice and got three moose, something he never did forget. And now he was in Porcupine, hunting for the Wilson party and taking care of supplies. The other boys had told him we were in the country, and he was anxious to see us.

" 'You fellows was good to me,' he said, 'and now I want to do something for you. I ain't much on this gold stuff, but I know everyone is looking for them white rocks. Quartz, is it? Well, there's plenty of it west of here, along the portage between the long lake (that was Gillies Lake, we found out later) and a small lake southwest. Stake that, boys, and you'll have something.'

"We had quite a discussion after he left. Tom wanted to go back and have a look, but I was against it. We were short of food and had already used up our licenses in staking. I could argue better than Tom and so he agreed to follow our original plan and pull out for Kelso the next day. As things turned out, I made a bad mistake. Know what those 'white rocks' were?"

I shook my head.

"Just the Hollinger Mine, that's all." Clary laughed shortly. "We could've had the whole works—Gillies and Hollinger didn't get in there for another month.

"Well, we went out and met Jack Miller in Haileybury. He was fit to be tied when we explained our staking. Called us 'damned wildcatters.' Refused to let us record the claims, said he wanted us to find gold before we staked. We had quite a time with him and finally he said he was going back north with us for another try. But things began to happen, and the whole damned situation changed."

Clary sat on the bunk and rolled the eiderdown into a comfortable back rest. Pete leaped beside him. It was growing cold. I placed more wood in the stove, pushed a chair close to the bunk, and lit my pipe.

"Before you go on, Clary," I said, "I'd like to know what eventually happened to the claims you staked but did not record."

"They became a part of the McIntyre and West Dome mines," he answered, adding airily, "just a matter of a few million dollars, that's all, but we didn't know it until some years later. Such is life, live in hope and die in despair. But let me tell you how the fireworks started. Jack was going back to Elk Lake and then on to Porcupine with us. Lucky for him the train was late, and who does he meet but Alec Gillies at the railroad station. Alec was carrying a telegram which bore sad news. His grubstaker, an engineer in Philadelphia, had just died, and so Alec and his partner, Benny Hollinger, were left without backing for the rest of the season. Jack did some quick thinking, handed Alec $100 and told him to go up to Porcupine at once. Fifty-fifty agreement it was, and verbal. One thing about Jack, his word was always good.

"While Alec was making his arrangements with Jack, Benny Hollinger was wheedling a little money from Jack McMahon, the bartender at the Matabanick Hotel. Benny gave Jack half interest in anything he was to stake for $60. McMahon turned around and sold half this to Jim Labine for $50. Not bad, eh? Funny, ain't it, that Alec and Benny didn't stick to their old partnership, but I guess it was a case of everyone for himself when the heat was on. Anyway, the pair of 'em visited Tom and me, and we gave them all the dope we had about the area, including the story about Preston's 'white rocks.'

"Get this straight, though. There were plenty of men in the area before us, Harry Preston for one, and A. G. Hunter, the first staker in Night Hawk in 1907, and Reube D'Aigle, who worked the

Alex Gillies

Benny Hollinger

Hollinger ground even before the Night Hawk finds were made. Why, Tom and I saw one of the pits that Reube had sunk, even found his anvil and blacksmith outfit lying about. Say, that was something; the way D'Aigle was all over the place before the rest. He had a crew with him too, Billy Moore, Bob Mustard, and a couple of boys he picked up in Matheson. They packed in from Night Hawk Lake and sank those pits. D'Aigle was an old Yukoner and had placer gold on the brain; never took any assays because he couldn't see any gold in the quartz. And so he quit cold. Later, Jack Miller took a grab sample of some of the dump material, and the stuff ran almost an ounce."

"Poor D'Aigle," I said. "To have been so near and yet so far. What became of him?"

"Still looking for a mine, I guess." Clary was not sympathetic, for near misses were common in the life of a prospector. "But he wasn't the only one. Charlie Camsell was in Porcupine as early as 1901, scouting for the Algoma Central Railroad. Then there was Ken Murray who prospected the area a few years after that, even dug a few pits. So did Jock MacGregor, Harry Lemon and Tom Geddes. Why, man, the Hollinger ground was cut by an old Hudson Bay portage that had been traveled for a period of almost 250 years! Sure! Jack Dwyer sunk a number of pits near Porcupine Lake in 1907. Joe Vipond and Bill Davidson were prospecting

around before Tom and I first went into the place, months before
the Hollinger and Dome discoveries. That's what I mean when I say
there were plenty of forgotten men who had much to do with the
camp."

Clary told how he, Tom Middleton, and Jack Miller followed
Alec Gillies and Benny Hollinger, who, for convenience, were traveling together, though representing different interests. The Miller
party met Sandy McIntyre and Hans Buttner in Kelso, and both
canoes proceeded together into Porcupine Lake. The summer was
waning, and the men, in their anxiety to reach the gold area in good
time, pushed along rapidly. Rumors of finds were already circulating, and prospectors were beginning to stir themselves. Clary described Jack Miller as "nervous as a cat."

Arriving at Jack Wilson's camp, they stopped to make lunch.
No one was on hand to receive them, but as they finished their meal
Harry Preston and George Burns, members of the Wilson gang, appeared. Both of them appeared highly agitated, but all they would
say was that Gillies and Hollinger had stopped by several days before and pushed on immediately. They both insisted that ground
around their camp was solidly staked and advised looking elsewhere.

"There was something about those men that looked suspicious,"
said Clary. "I got Preston off to one side and tried to pump him.
The old boy was carrying a gun and looked kind of wild, but I knew
how to handle him even though he was bushed. He repeated the
story about the white rocks and then kept saying we ought to beat
it further west before Hollinger and Gillies gobbled up everything.
Later I'll tell you why he was particularly anxious to see us go."

Preston's advice seemed reasonable, and both canoes departed
for Jarvis Lake forthwith. Before nightfall, they encountered Hollinger and Gillies, who had just completed staking twelve claims
northeast of the lake on four sides of the Platt and Schumacker
Veteran Lots.

"They were half crazy with excitement," Clary recounted. "It
took quite a while to get their story, and when we heard it we
couldn't blame 'em for feeling so high. Seems like they found one
of Reube D'Aigle's old pits, I think the very one we had discovered
earlier that summer, and like us, they began to stake. All of a sudden Benny Hollinger went nuts; Alec could hear him yelling like
a stuck pig. So he cut through the bush, thinking Christ knows
what, and there was Benny dancing a jig and throwing his hat in
the air. 'Gold, gold!' he yelled. Alec looked down where the moss
had been pulled up and saw as rich a showing of free gold as has
ever been seen in the north. Well, you can imagine they didn't waste

any time after that. Later, we were told they tossed a coin to divide the ground, and Benny won the discovery claims, Alec taking the six to the east.

"We didn't hang around to watch them flip a coin, you can bet. Sandy McIntyre and Buttner went north, and Jack, Tom and I staked west, tying on to the Gillies claims, which were half Jack's, remember. Well, sir, it was unbelievable. Almost every time I cut a claim post I'd find visible gold. Tom and Jack had the same experience. It was hard to believe we weren't dreaming. Poor old Tom kept saying we were all millionaires and wouldn't ever have to work again. Great moments in history, bucko."

He paused and stroked Pete's glossy back. In the detached quiet of the cabin, I pictured the succession of events which had stimulated this northern land to a realization of its mightiness.

After a long interval of reflection, I asked Clary what had caused Hollinger and Gillies to investigate the Pearl Lake vicinity.

"Told you," said my friend shortly. "Tom and I had a session with them before they left Haileybury and gave 'em the dope about Preston's white rocks. Harry may have also said something about it when they stopped at the Wilson camp. Alec said afterwards that Charlie McInnis and Billy Hughes advised him to look over Tisdale Township because Whitney was already solidly staked. I've also heard it said that Al Reading was the guy who gave Alec the first tip, but I'll let you decide where the first information came from. Say this, though; Alec found D'Aigle's old test pit himself. We forgot to mention it to him. Incidentally, Benny Hollinger's first find was made right on one of D'Aigle's old work trails.

"Well, anyway, we staked six claims," said Clary, resuming the narrative. "The Miller-Middleton the group was called, most people thinking I was really Jack's son. Later, when Noah Timmins bought the ground he named it the Millerton."

We discussed the vagaries of chance, the unpredictable twists of fate arising from seemingly inconsequential incidents.

"That's the way it is, you never can tell what may be important." Clary's face lighted in sudden memory. "There was the freeze-up that year, did I tell you about it? No? Well, it was a screwy one and had much to do with the history of Porcupine. It froze solid, just about the time we were returning from Matheson after having recorded our claims, and Jack, Tom, Alec Gillies and I were caught with our pants down on Porcupine Creek. We had two canoes loaded with supplies; Jack almost had a nervous breakdown. As a matter of fact, he had to go out for a long rest when the thing was over. Anyway, he was all for packing into the claims, but Tom and I wanted to wait a bit, the weather looked as though a change was coming. But Jack raised hell, as usual, said we'd be stuck all winter if we didn't move in right away. Finally, it was agreed that he and Alec would pack in whatever they could, and Tom and I would stay with the canoes. If the ice went in a day or so, we'd paddle in; otherwise we'd start packing.

"As soon as Jack and Alec left, it began to rain and continued for three days. The creek opened, and then the fun commenced. Hundreds of canoes began to arrive, packed so closely together that many of 'em swamped. It was a Wild West show, I tell you—nothing like it ever happened before. You could hear men cursing as they fell into the drink. Lost paddles and supplies drifted by us. Whoever wasn't upset wanted to fight the guy next to him. It was the big Porcupine rush, that, and Tom and I had all we could do to keep ahead of the pack. We each handled a canoe, and if it wasn't for the congestion we'd never have reached Jack and Alec with the stuff."

A thought struck me as Clary paused for a moment, and I reminded him that he was to tell me exactly why Preston was so anxious to get rid of the Miller party that fateful day.

"Oh, yes." Clary grinned. "But I'll have to go back, to Jack Wilson, Edwards and the rest. It all started in 1907, when gold was discovered at Nighthawk Lake. Wilson told me this story himself. He was living in Massey then, still is, I guess. Anyway, Jack had met W. S. Edwards of Chicago and Dr. T. N. Jamison and got them excited about the Gold Island find. They agreed to grubstake him in 1908 but he didn't hear a word from them. Wilson wrote them early in 1909, and this time they came through with $1,000. A party of five was organized, Harry Preston, who knew the section, Cliff and Frank Campbell, George Burns, and Jack Wilson himself. They met in Kelso before the breakup and hired Tom Fox, an Indian, to help them bring supplies into Frederickhouse Lake by dog team. When water opened, they paddled into Porcupine Lake and started prospecting. Edwards was supposed to join them, but instead he met Wilson at Matheson. Edwards wanted to stake as soon as possible. But Wilson had heard about a silver find in Sudbury and pulled out the gang, leaving Preston alone in Porcupine. It was just about that time that Tom Geddes and George Bannerman came in and made their Scottish-Ontario find north of Porcupine Lake. Meanwhile, Preston, a real worker, and don't let anyone tell you different, he goes out and finds a quartz vein in Tisdale Township. That was the Ida Maud which Tom and I first saw. Wilson comes back with the rest of the boys, for there wasn't any silver near Sudbury, it turned out. The gang staked fifteen claims near Bannerman, but they couldn't find any gold. There was only one thing left to do and that was work on the Ida Maud vein.

"Shows you what mining is. Wilson didn't like the vein but he took a few grab samples and went out. When the assay showed about a third of an ounce, Wilson beat it for Chicago to give Edwards the good news firsthand. Meanwhile, Cliff Campbell had got bushed and quit the job and Bert Rheault was taken on as blacksmith. Phil Mecklenberg, who wandered into camp looking for a lost dog, was also hired. That dog was more valuable lost than found, 'cause Phil received an interest in the Dome from the other boys.

"While Wilson was on his way to Chicago, Preston found the 'Golden Sidewalk' near the Ida Maud. It was a terrific show, gold stuck in the quartz all over the place, like candle drippings. The big dome, they called it, and that's how the Dome Mine got its name. That was in October, before we went outside to record our claims. Well, the Wilson-Edwards crowd was in a hell of a mess. The story might get out, even if they covered up the discovery, and Harry Preston stood guard with his rifle. Yup, that's why he was sporting a gun that day—not because he was going hunting, as he told me."

"But why were they in a mess, Clary?"

"Don't you see? They had staked fifteen claims in Whitney Township and having recorded them they had used up their licenses for the year. You know, only three claims per license is the law."

"So they actually couldn't stake the 'Golden Sidewalk'? Was that it, Clary?"

"Correct. When we came along the boys had just blanketed the ground, staked it on licenses which were invalid, but hoped no one would get wise and stake while Wilson was still away, for he was supposed to return with a new bunch of licenses."

"And did he?"

"He did. When the news of the find got out all the papers in Canada printed the story and it was repeated in Chicago. Edwards, Jamison and Wilson read it in Chicago and grabbed the first train north. Wilson wired to Jack Campbell, the head fire ranger in Matheson, to have canoes ready and so everything was set when they arrived. They had a terrible trip. Edwards was hog fat and I suppose wasn't used to a canoe. Anyway, the damned thing upset and it was a miracle everyone wasn't drowned. They pulled ashore, dried themselves before a fire, and then went on. This time they got through, but Edwards twisted his ankle and they didn't get him into camp until the next morning, carrying him on a stretcher made out of spruce boughs. They all went out to see the show and everything was fine and lovely until it came to settling the matter of staking the claims with the new licenses and figuring who was to get what interest and how much.

"Wilson assembled the men and reminded them the Dome claims were not yet staked and recorded, but he had brought in the necessary licenses. The original agreement with Edwards called for staking fifteen claims for the syndicate; anything staked after that would be divided 75 per cent to the prospectors and 25 per cent to Edwards. Now, then, which claims would be the syndicate's and which would go to the Wilson crowd? That was a question! Edwards was called in and an agreement was finally worked out. First of all, the Dome claims were to be properly staked and recorded; Edwards and Jamison would get 50 per cent interest, Wilson 10 per cent, and the prospectors 40 per cent. Edwards also was to pay the boys $1,000 each for their interest in the discovery claim."

"If you people had staked the claims," I suggested, "things would have been different."

"If a bunch of things," he rejoined tartly. "First of all, I doubt we'd've staked if we knew what the situation was; not cricket, you know. And then, Harry Preston's rifle was handy, remember, and he was the sort of man who would use it. But as it turned out, we did all right, that is, Jack did, for the Hollinger was a good swap for the Dome."

He proceeded to tell how Johnny Sauvé sent out word to Alphonse Paré that a big gold discovery had been made. Paré quickly went into Porcupine, examined and sampled the Hollinger claims, and then tried to work out a contract of purchase with Benny Hollinger and Jim Labine. Nothing tangible resulting, Paré hurried to Matheson and there telephoned his uncle, Noah Timmins, in Montreal. Shortly afterwards the Timmins brothers managed to negotiate a deal with Jack McMahon, calling for an immediate $2,000 cash payment with large following monthly payments, totaling $330,000 in all. With so large a commitment overhanging, Noah Timmins rushed plans of work; Paré assembled a working crew and arrived on the property New Year's Day, 1910.

Jack Miller's fortunes were rising. Through the services of A. T. Budd, a druggist turned mining promoter, the Gillies claims, now called the Acme, were optioned to M. J. O'Brien of Cobalt. There was no cash consideration, but the agreement provided for $50,000 to be paid within two months, and a balance of $200,000. O'Brien instructed Culbertson, his engineer, to speed drilling so that results would be in hand before the payment fell due.

"That was a mistake," said Clary, "giving those hurry-up orders. There was a hell of a pile of drill core to be packed out by dog team, and Culbertson had to cut down the load somehow if he wanted to make the deadline. So he went over the stuff and threw out anything that didn't show quartz. He reached the steel in time that way and ran his assays. The results weren't any hell, $3 and $4, so O'Brien dropped the option when Jack refused to extend the time on that $50,000. Later, it turned out that the wall rock with the quartz stringers carried the real values. Culbertson had assayed the main quartz vein which was low grade in that particular place. What a boner that was!

"Jack wasn't caught napping. Budd had already been talking to Noah Timmins about the Acme and Noah wanted the ground. Jack told Budd the price was $350,000, but that didn't stop a man like Noah Timmins. He gave the word and Budd, all excited, went to see Jack with the good news that $50,000 would be paid on the line. But Jack was careful; he called at the bank in Haileybury to find out whether Timmins was able to write that size check. The answer was satisfactory, and the deal went through.

"They say that O'Brien was furious, accused Noah of ruining the mining business by paying outrageous prices for claims. But Noah was a big leaguer all through. I happen to know that while O'Brien held the Acme option, Paré was told to give every co-operation to Culbertson and show him the Hollinger results. Noah wanted the country to go ahead, you see. But O'Brien had given orders for his men to keep away from the Timmins outfit, on account of those old lawsuits in Cobalt, I guess. I understand that O'Brien and Timmins never met personally, though they were neighbors in Cobalt and in Porcupine. Human interest," added Clary, with a roguish smile.

He now related the circumstances under which Timmins purchased the Miller-Middleton claims, Jack Miller agreeing, at length, to sell for $250,000.

"When it came to getting our cut," explained Clary, "there was a row. I was cut down, as you know. Jack claimed my mother would get the whole business when he died, anyway, but that man will never die. He outlived my poor mother and has had several wives since. I was so damned sick of the whole business, I accepted 2,000 shares of Hollinger which Jack bought for me plus $8,000 cash. Tom, he took the $28,000 Jack handed him and then blew it all in a few years."

Clary remembered the successive steps through which Timmins arrived at the Hollinger Consolidated Gold Mines. The Acme was incorporated separately, also the Miller-Middleton which became the Millerton. Came the consolidation in 1916, in which the Hollinger Gold Mines, Noah Timmins' first purchase, received 2,400,-000 shares, the Acme 2,100,000, and the Millerton 200,000.

"At that time, the Acme and Millerton had most of the ore," stated Clary, "and Noah, whose syndicate owned them, would have been justified in taking most of the new stock. But he didn't; he played the game with the old Hollinger stockholders, and now the ore's all over the place. There's only one Noah Timmins, I can tell you, and the city that bears his name today ought to be proud."

An unusual man, I agreed.

"You bet he is, smart, honest, and plenty of guts. Why, just a few years ago he got the Hollinger to pay almost $2,000,000 for the Schumacker ground. That took courage, bucko, but the old man knows his business. They're talking 8,000 tons for the Hollinger now." He wagged his head incredulously. "And to think the mine started with only a two-ton stamp mill in 1910. And then the fire . . . that was something."

Clary was in Porcupine at the time, mid-July, 1911, and at my urging he described the disaster which laid the district bare. The weather for some days had been unseasonable, dry and windy, with small fires burning in the vicinity. The wind suddenly whipped into a gale and the Hollinger was completely burned out.

"By that time we were busy, trying to save the towns and mining plants," said Clary. "But it was no use. The wind was roaring something fierce; flames and smoke rose a mile high. Nothing could stop that fire, bucko. Most of us who could make it ran down to Porcupine Lake, and lived through the worst of it by standing in water up to our necks and holding wet blankets over our heads. When a trainload of dynamite went up, a tidal wave swept over us. Some of the boys were drowned. It was hell. The fire jumped across Gillies Lake. All the wood piles, headframes, and houses were caught. Then there were those poor devils who went down the West Dome shaft and suffocated to a man. Tracey, the bookkeeper, was afraid to go underground and thereby saved his life.

"All we could do was tough it out and hope for the best, and when the fire swept on to destroy Cochrane and God knows what else, we survivors went through the ruins and gathered up the bodies, or what was left of 'em. Over seventy lives were lost. One thing I'll never forget—not important, but unusual. That was the ice lying around in the open where icehouses had once been. Seems like the fire came through so fast the ice didn't melt completely, although everything else was destroyed."

Clary, who had risen to his feet and was pacing the cabin restlessly, now returned to his bunk, followed by Pete who at once assumed a restful attitude of attention. A short interlude for pipe filling, and Clary continued.

"The fire threatened to kill the boom, but Noah Timmins was not the man to be stopped. There was no production to speak of that year, but a 200-ton mill was operating on the Hollinger by the end of 1912, and then we received our first dividend."

"How about the Dome?" I asked, curious to know what had happened after Edwards had made his "deal" with the prospectors.

"The Dome? Well, there was a merry time while everyone and his dog came to see the Golden Sidewalk. Wilson interested a New York crowd, the McCormicks, I think, but they got cold feet. Ontario had a bad mining record, you see. Then this man Captain Delamar pops into the situation after Charley Denson decided not to follow the recommendation of Sam Singlehurst, his engineer. Delamar went ahead full steam. Big boy Edwards did fine, thank you. His bunch received $12,000 down for the six claims containing the Golden Sidewalk. There were three time extensions before the balance of the deal finally went through, Edwards hiking the purchase price from $350,000 to $750,000. Yes, those boys had no kick coming."

He reviewed the early underground history of the Dome, told how the Golden Sidewalk disappeared by the time the 200-foot horizon was reached.

"Had the glacier eroded another 150 feet of country," observed Clary, "there probably wouldn't have been a Dome Mine. If it wasn't for Cap Anchor, your brother Bob's old partner, feeding Delamar with optimism, the others would have quit."

"What others?" I asked.

"Well, Denison had a small participation. And there was that Nickel fellow, Monell, who came in the deal. Delamar had a large chunk, but not all. Anyway, it was during that time, when the shaft was going below the 200-foot level, that Edwards was asked for the extensions on payments, and they were obtained, as the lawyers say, for a consideration. Old Cap Anchor, God rest his bones, was right all the time. He did a job for his boss—hit a jewelry shop below the 200. You should have seen that stock perk up. I know, 'cause I bought some at 50 cents and sold at $3. That was the money I used to pay for a couple of years at the University of Idaho." He laughed a moment. "Rather expensive education, that was, for Dome kept going until it hit $40 or more. Well, never mind, I've stuck with my Hollinger, and it's doing all right by me."

"Amen," I said. I then asked him how the Dome fared in the big fire.

"Burned out like the rest of 'em, but Delamar was just as hard to kill as Noah Timmins. He built all over again and had a 300-ton mill turning over in 1912. Produced almost $1,000,000 that year. The rest was easy sailing; Dome bought the Extension claims from Edwards and worked up to a $4,000,000 production last year."

"The McIntyre," I said, "had a different kind of history, I hear."

"You said it! It was the stepchild of Porcupine. I remember going up to the McIntyre claims when Sandy first started to prospect them. He found some gold, you know, but it wasn't much, a quartz stringer in the porphyry. However, being next to the Hollinger meant something, but Sandy threw away his chances for a stake. Weldon Young got a half interest in the three claims for $300, I think it was, and Jim Hughes got a quarter for $25. Seems screwy, doesn't it, but you know Sandy, easy come, easy go. He did manage to get about $8,000 or $9,000 on his remaining quarter interest, only a part of what he was promised, but hell, what's the difference? He'd've blown a million or more if he had it. Sported a team of spirited horses for a while, made a trip to Europe and all that, and then had to start from scratch again. He'll always be broke."

"Anyway, the Flynns finally obtained control of the Buttner and McIntyre ground and the company was formed."

"Which Flynns?" I asked.

"Oh, Charlie, who was so close to Noah Timmins in Cobalt. Then there were his brothers Tom and John, and John's sons Milton and Miles. A regular tribe, they were, scattered all over Porcupine. They had the Vipond too, which they optioned from Bill Davidson and built the first mill in Porcupine there. Charlie was the leader, and he was some guy, I want to tell you. A real plunger. Fine-looking man, aristocratic, and a big spender."

The Flynns, it appeared, experienced difficulties in promoting the McIntyre, but help came when Albert Freeman, a New York broker, fortuitously appeared. Freeman, it seemed, was in something of a "hot spot," due to an ill-fated Cobalt promotion, in which his associates were none other than Julian Hawthorne and E. Morton, son and grandson respectively of America's illustrious man of letters and the first American surgeon to use chloroform. The McIntyre, by comparison, was a "respectable" venture, and Freeman eagerly accepted Flynn's offer of a $250,000 option. The then governor of New York, Nathan Miller, was a large purchaser of stock, and altogether Freeman accounted for 80,000 shares sold. The Flynns, after calling in R. J. "Dick" Ennis from Colorado to supervise milling and mining operations, retired from the enterprise. It was then that J. P. Bickell made his entrance and became McIntyre's guiding director and president, a position he has since occupied with distinction. But the early period of development was plagued with so many tribulations that for a time it seemed there was little hope in avoiding bankruptcy.

Clary explained how Bickell had become interested. He was a stockbroker in Toronto who numbered Alec Gillies among his clients.

"Alec persuaded him to buy the Pearl Lake water claims, and Bickell later turned these into McIntyre for $100,000 cash and 70,-000 shares of stock. The company kept acquiring ground to the east until Sandy's original claims were only a small part of the acreage. Bickell always listened to Dick Ennis, and Dick knew his stuff. The rest of Pearl Lake was bought up and then the Extension and Jupiter ground. Later the Plenaurum and Platt Vet became a part of the McIntyre, too.

"The early days were something, a regular circus. The first stock was sold in the States, you know, at about $2 a share. Damned company was reorganized and stockholders cut down 80 per cent. It was a case of tough titty and no teeth. Company always in debt. No doubt you've heard the story many times, it's getting to be an old chestnut—how the gold bricks were shipped while they were hot and Dick Ennis used to hide underground whenever creditors came to the mine howling about unpaid bills. When the steel came into Porcupine, there was new hope of pulling through, but then the miners' strike of 1913 broke out and that looked like the end of McIntyre. The company tried to sell stock to the Hollinger at 35 cents, but the price was considered too high. That was the time Bickell was made a director. Then Bickell put out a $250,000 bond issue, or tried to, in order to finance a 300-ton mill. A bonus of 1,000 shares was offered free with every $1,000 bond purchased, but the public just wouldn't bite. Desperate days, those. Some of the machinery companies were talked into taking bonds for equipment. Ennis even persuaded the mine doctor to accept 550 shares instead of a cash fee. All the insurance policies were in hock. Yes, sir, McIntyre was the biggest joke in Porcupine."

Bickell, however, stuck to the ship, loaned the company money whenever particularly pressing bills could not be avoided, and if a commitment was made, he guaranteed notes personally. And during this period of trial, the shaft was gradually approaching the favorable greenstone horizon. The ore situation began to improve slowly, then more perceptibly, and finally with an aplomb that gave Mc-

Intyre a place in the "Big Three" of Porcupine. By 1916, all liabilities were discharged, and Ennis was able to parade the surface a free and proud man when the first dividend was paid in 1917.

"The Platt Vet," said Clary, "didn't have a thing on surface, and now it's the best bet McIntyre has. They're sinking a 4,000-foot shaft through the porphyry into the greenstone, proving how right Ennis always was when he talked about that eastern ore rake. All the big shots talk about it now, but I don't remember any of them saying a good word about McIntyre when the boys needed encouragement."

"Do you remember who the bigwigs were, Clary?"

"A few." He pondered for a moment. "There was that big English engineer, McClaren, the fellow who tackled the Scottish-Ontario but refused a chance to get into the Hollinger and McIntyre. John Hays Hammond was up, too, but guess he didn't like the look of things, for he never came back. Then there was Augustus Heinze; did you know he had the West Dome for a while? Sure. It was just after his bank failure in New York. Charlie Mentzel was his engineer. Caught in the big fire, he was, but came out fine, except the maps he carried in his hand were burned when he ran down to Porcupine Lake.

"It was a great place in the early days." Clary sighed. "Never meet fellows like Bill Davidson and Billy Cooper today. Know Billy? He shipped the first high-grade ore out of the Hollinger by dog team. Mine captain at the McIntyre now. And then Bert Poirier, who took over when the Flynns sold the Vipod to his New York crowd. Old 'Cranberry' Jack Callinan was quite a character, too."

"Where did he get the name Cranberry?" I asked.

"By staking claims in the sand plains which the boys said were only good for raising cranberries. But Jack had a chance, finally, to make a stake in the West Dome, and he muffed it. So did plenty of the others. You know Harry Heine?" he asked suddenly.

"Met him in Rouyn a few years ago," I answered. "He broke a leg going over the Lake Olier portage."

"Heard about that." Clary nodded. "Guess he'll stick to Timmins now. Grew up with it, anyway. There was something about that camp, right from the start. We had characters you never see now, like that prospector who used to travel the bush wearing one of those hard-boiled miners' hats, and 'Whispering' Bill Smith who staked the Booth-Armstrong. And the girls! Say, they were something. I remember a time going out to Kelso in the dead of winter. There were about a half dozen of us who left Golden City, all men except for one sporting girl. Cold, it was, about thirty below, but we were comfortable under rabbitskin robes. Well, the lady decided to do a spot of business en route, and spoke to each one of us in turn whenever we stopped to pick up mail. No results at first, and then one guy—he was in the lumber business—said he guessed he might. So she bundled up with him in the back seat, under a robe, while the driver was cursing hell out of the horses." He brightened at the recollection of the scene. "Yup, Porcupine was the one and only."

"What became of the prospectors?" I asked. "Benny Hollinger and the rest."

"Well, Benny didn't last very long after the money came in. Died a few years later. High living, I'd say, though he always had a bad heart. Alec Gillies is still buggering around but he hasn't much luck since he lost out on that wheat corner of his. Sure, he tried to be a wheat king, trading in Bickell's office. You know about Jack Miller. Guess he's the only prospector in the north who has more money today than he started with. Bill Davidson is still around with not much to show for the Vipond. Harry Preston is broke and more bushed than ever. Tom Middleton is just where he was years before Porcupine, only older. Let's see. Oh, yes, Sandy McIntyre, he's around Larder Lake now. Poor old Sandy, he just can't keep away from the booze. And Jack Wilson went broke—on wheat, like Alec Gillies. The Flynns lost most of their stake, too. And so it goes."

He yawned sleepily. "Most of the early Porcupine fellows have damn little to show for it today. Guess I've done about as well as most of 'em and you know I didn't exactly come out a millionaire."

To console him, I remarked that the discoveries in Porcupine had done much for Canada and the north. The trails he and Tom and the others had cut were now roads, the old campsites were towns and cities. Clary made a gesture of hopelessness with his hand.

"Suppose you're right, but that doesn't help us much. The trouble was that none of us, even Noah Timmins himself, realized how important the camp was going to be, so we took the cash and let the credit go. The people who came along later, when we had made things easy, they were the buzzards who made the big money. But I'm afraid that's the way it will always be."

The fire was almost out now. The bright glow which had warmed the cabin had died to a faint lingering spot of light which barely showed through the cracks of the tin stove. Pete huddled closer to Clary; even the candlelight seemed to droop in the coldness which had begun to envelop us.

Clary rose, stretched noisily, and began to unbutton his shirt. "Getting late," he said; "time to turn in, bucko."

He unrolled the eiderdown, spread it over the bunk. Pete

eagerly watched him and then took his accustomed place, spread himself comfortably to make the usual footrest for us. Clary extinguished the candles and slipped into the bunk, rolled over to make space for me.

"G'night," he murmured and in a few minutes his deep breathing indicated that he was sound asleep. But for me slumber was impossible just then. The stirring events which Clary had related began to flood my mind, and try as I did to compose myself, thoughts of the gold of Porcupine and the men who had found it kept me fully awake. Hours passed before I dropped off. . . .

"Bean on the tab!" sang Clary.

It was morning. The sun was just rising and as I rolled from the bunk I could see through the window long blue shadows taking shape on the spotless snow.

"Be out of here in three shakes," promised Clary, pouring the coffee. "C'mon, bucko, there's no time to lose. Don't want to walk through slush, do you? The sun's coming up."

We ate hurriedly. Pete, sensing our departure, barked happily, ran to the door and made a series of sharp sallies outside. Each time he returned he found us busily packing and putting the cabin to rights. We were ready, at length; Clary boarded the window and placed a heavy padlock on the door.

"Let's go!"

With his peculiar abbreviated gait, rolling slightly like a small bear, Clary broke trail ahead of me. He was a veritable Indian in the woods, taking his direction instinctively. We were well into the thick bush before the sun rose and while the snow was deep Clary considered our progress satisfactory. I plodded behind him, Pete trotting between us obediently. For more than an hour we pressed forward, neither of us speaking. Suddenly Clary halted, sat on a fallen log and wiped his glistening forehead.

"We're taking a fiver," he announced. "The worst is over; from now on it's high ground and the thaw won't bother us."

The bush was coming alive. Canada birds sang dolefully against the deep-throated messages of chickadees near at hand. At intervals the faint drumming of partridge, like distant motors, was audible. Rills of water gurgled cheerfully under our feet as the day warmed and the snow began to melt. Trees nodded and shook with the lessening weight of snow among the boughs. A rabbit, its fur not yet white with the season, plowed across our trail within a stone's throw. Pete, held in hand, barked with frustration.

"Pretty, ain't it?" observed Clary, when Pete had quieted. "The bush sort of gets you on a morning like this."

I could only nod in acquiescence. It was one of those rare times when even the dullest nature responds to the primordial beauty of the woods.

In later years I have often thought of that quiet moment and the joy of good and tried companions who are, alas, no more. For poor Clary died in a hospital that winter and Pete did not survive him long.

Today, visitors at the great Hollinger Mine stare in awe at the old two-stamp mill which rests on the lawn facing the office building —a unique memento of a historic event. Few, however, see the Dixon shaft through which millions in gold have passed. It is only one of many, a gray, bleak structure silhouetted against the northern sky. Year in and year out, in all seasons, it faithfully serves the miners who toil a mile underground, just as its doughty namesake served Canada. It is a novel monument for any man, and knowing Clary as I did, I am sure it is the kind he would have chosen, if the choice had been his to make.

Production and Dividends of Major Porcupine Gold Mines 1910 to 1945

Name	Year First Production	Total Production	Dividends
Hollinger	1910	$362,893,687	$120,812,800
Dome	1910	144,185,037	60,877,874
McIntyre	1912	162,756,426	38,384,146
Hallnor	1938	16,226,000	6,100,000
Preston E. Dome	1939	16,456,411	3,840,000
Pamour	1936	22,025,000	3,550,000
Coniaurum	1928	21,379,063	3,227,751
Buffalo-Ankerite	1932	27,686,831	2,763,000
Aunor	1940	10,892,054	1,800,000
Delnite	1937	6,726,602	625,541
Broulan	1940	5,937,570	1,091,072

Entire Porcupine Area, 1910 to 1945

Total Production	$846,000,000
Total Dividends	$246,322,932

CHAPTER IX

Who Killed Sir Harry?

Many readers will recall how the salubrious indolence of the Bahamas was rudely shattered by the mysterious murder of Sir Harry Oakes. The war was still in progress when the tragedy was announced to a startled world and Sir Harry enjoyed a posthumous fame which, from the point of view of newspaper space, rivaled the headlines blaring forth the dizzy tides of war. It was a juicy story of crime mingled with the best rags-to-riches tradition. The mining tycoon, once a penniless prospector and later considered to be among the world's wealthiest men, was found murdered and partially burned in his bed. Few clues were in evidence to guide the police. Suspicion, however, pointed strongly to Oakes's son-in-law as the killer and the luckless young man was promptly indicted. Special reporters at the trial kept the world informed in the manner of a blow-by-blow description of a prize fight and a wealth of "human interest" material flooded the press. But in the end the accused man was acquitted by a jury of his peers—Sir Harry had gone to his grave, the victim of a celebrated and unsolved crime.

It was a bizarre ending to a career which has few equals in the annals of mining. . . .

I first met him in the commodious private car of a railroad executive. The time: October, 1925. We are quietly parked at a siding near Kirkland Lake. Sundry gentlemen, pink with food and good living, sit in the rococo salon. The air is thick with the smoke of rich Havanas and an obsequious colored attendant arranges fresh cigars on the mahogany table while removing the stumps of old ones. His movements are noiseless and deferential.

"As Steel goes, so goes the market," sagely observes one of the Buffalo magnates.

"Yup. The strikes seem to be on the wane," says another.

Snatches of unrelated conversation rise and fall.

"Where did you catch those fish?" suddenly asks the man beside me, waving his cigar dangerously close.

While I answer, Harry Oakes, seated vis-à-vis, regards me fixedly. He is a small man, but the square face and jutting chin give a sense of largeness and power. He appears ill at ease, and there is a definite note of contempt in his glance as he surveys the men about him. As I speak I wonder whether he senses my feelings, the strangeness of luxury after a spartan existence in the bush, the overpowering numbness of a sycophant existence embedded like a thorn in this land of timbered silence. My thoughts, like the shifting colors of northern lights, range wide and far, but out of the chaos arises the conviction—youthful, I admit now—that only a few of us in the car had discovered Canada. The others, despite their acumen and undoubted financial substance, do not know this land and never could; to them, it merely represents speculative possibilities. I seem to read confirmation in the eyes of Harry Oakes.

"Harry," says the cadaverous man, "I could never understand why you didn't turn in that fractional claim to us. After all, you only gave those prospectors your personal note for the ground. Lake Shore didn't need it. You could have transferred it to Wright-Hargreaves for a handsome consideration."

"I couldn't do that." He shakes his head vigorously. "Don't do business that way."

"You think a lot of Lake Shore, don't you?"—banteringly.

"The biggest gold mine on the continent," comes the ready answer, cutting, pugnacious. "Bigger than the Hollinger, someday."

"I hope you're right, Harry," injects the white-haired lawyer. "We have the mine next to yours, you know."

"I know. And I want to tell you that Kirkland Lake will be one of the greatest camps in the world, better than Cripple Creek or the Comstock."

His voice, that of an assertive self-made man, breathes defiance and conviction. There is an intense humorless quality about him, as though he has a mission in life which must be performed, a destiny that is almost a burden. I recognize the sharpness of his outlines: he hates fiercely as he loves; men are either good or bad, he has no compassion for human frailties. He is no ordinary prospector, this

Oakes. Born in Sangerville, Maine, in 1874, the son of a prosperous land surveyor, he was a graduate of Bowdoin College in 1896. He was bitten deeply with wanderlust at an early age and roamed the far places of the globe, seeking, but never finding. Relentless, inevitable, he wandered into Kirkland Lake, a tiny section of primeval Canada, and here, like a homing pigeon finding its haven at last, he has stayed. He could not have seen gold under the lake, but with an instinct he himself probably did not understand, he was convinced this was to be his El Dorado. And so he pitched his tent on the lake shore, among the sighing birch, with never a moment's hesitation. We can visualize him, a pygmy in a country of nature's giants, grimly determined to wrest fortune from the lonely and enigmatic wilderness. Nor could he be lured away by stories of gold finds elsewhere; his wanderings were over, this was to be a last fling of the dice.

"You noticed we have no stopes in the Lake Shore?" He is speaking to me now, oblivious of the others, as if they were incapable of understanding. "You were underground with Coffey. The only muck going to the mill comes from development drifts."

I remember that Bob Coffey, the manager, had been quick to point this out a few days previously. It was my first experience underground, and my impressions are indelible.

"Very interesting, very interesting," says the lawyer doubtfully, for he is not familiar with the strangeness of underground. "I'm sure the Lake Shore is going to be everything you think it is."

"You will see," replies Oakes, with the air of a prophet. "I know gold mines. I've been in the Philippines, Australia, the Yukon, Alaska, and the American West. There's nothing, nothing to compare with Lake Shore and Kirkland Lake."

"Well, we bought some of your stock," drawls the man beside me, "so it won't make us mad if you turn out to be right." A deep puff of cigar, and then: "What I want to know, Harry, if you don't mind the question, is this. Were you really broke when you landed in Swastika?"

"I wasn't exactly flush," replies Oakes, with the faintest suggestion of a smile. "Matter of fact, I had to outrun rabbits, otherwise I wouldn't have eaten."

"And is it true that the conductor put you off the train when you weren't able to pay for a ticket?" persists the other. "And that a Chinese told you about Kirkland Lake when you ate at his restaurant?"

"No, it isn't!" Oakes's face turns a brick red and he pounds the arm of his chair. "Damn the man who started those canards! I planned my trip north after hearing stories of Cobalt and Porcupine. And in Toronto I made it a point to visit the Department of Mines where I obtained literature on the country as well as a miner's license. I also visited the office of the Swastika Mining Company and examined some of their ore specimens. That decided me. I figured this was a gold country well worth investigating. What I liked particularly was that the area was new and uncrowded since the Larder Lake rush in 1906, and a man like me would have a chance. So, you see, that story about the Chinaman who told me at the restaurant there was gold in Kirkland Lake is just another fairy tale! As I said, I planned the trip and got my information from government reports, at the recorder's office, from Jim Labine in Haileybury and men who had been in Larder Lake and had staked in Lebel Township. I have never taken potluck anywhere. I plan my work, then work my plan. I realized at once that if there was gold around Swastika and in Larder Lake there was every reason to suppose there was gold in the intervening townships! And I was right! I can tell you here and now, gentlemen, that the structure in Kirkland Lake is as near perfect as it can be—sediments, intrusives, and lavas. And the break in the syenite is a major one, long and wide. It's what I call regional. That syenite is competent rock, brittle and easily fractured. I've traced it for miles, gentlemen, miles. The quartz veins are there and with high gold values.

"My early investigations of the district," he continues, with evident relish, "convinced me that the lake offered the best opportunity for development of a large mine. Why did I think so?" he asks rhetorically. "Because porphyry, or syenite, intrusions were most numerous there. For a time I thought I could have been mistaken, but the disappointing results at Tough-Oakes at the east end of the camp, after an exciting discovery, convinced me that the intrusives to the west offered the best chance. So I began to prospect intensively—that was in 1911. I had four different camps, just small lean-to's of tarpaulin under which I could sleep of nights. This saved me the trouble of always having to return to my main base. And then I found a quartz vein along the south shore and concentrated my work there. With hand steel I began to sink a small shaft right in the quartz. Values were spotty, being mostly confined to a narrow band of grayish rock. This streak persisted downward and so I was encouraged in spite of the pessimism expressed by visiting engineers. You all know what a difficult time I had to get finances, but I managed, I managed."

He stops suddenly, realizing that the attention of the others has wandered. But I have a question to ask.

"How did you find the Number Two vein under the lake? Were you trying to obtain the extension of the Wright-Hargreaves vein?"

"Where did you hear that?" he retorts pugnaciously.

"Oh, around town somewhere," I reply evasively.

"Well, those people don't know what in hell they're talking about! I put out a flat drill hole north from a drift on Number One vein. At about 400 feet we intersected eight feet of $2 stuff. Not ore, mind you, but the break was there. So I ordered a crosscut to follow the hole and hit big—ounce ore over 12 feet and only a step from where the drill cut the low-grade material. Why, I knew the break was there all the time! I could see it at the west end of the lake where my ground adjoins Teck-Hughes and I traced it east myself, across the Wright-Hargreaves and on to the Tough-Oakes. No, son, there was no guessing there. Knowledge did the trick, not luck. Remember that always. You are just starting in this business and should know that men like myself don't just stumble on bonanzas. They study mineral deposits and learn to recognize the conditions that make for ore. When they see the right country it's only because they know from observation and experience. Then comes work, hard work; don't think those underground workings at the Lake Shore were put there by nature. *I* had to do that. It wasn't easy, and yet people call me lucky." His voice betrays intense bitterness, as though his qualities as a mine maker are not properly understood and appreciated.

"Is it true," I ask, "that Toronto newspapers refused to carry your first advertisement offering Lake Shore for sale?"

"Just one." He shakes his head. "I only tried a few. You see, I financed Lake Shore myself and sold the odd stock when I needed money for something special, such as the mill, for example."

"That's right," agrees the man beside me, with unexpected interest, "bought 20,000 shares myself at 35 cents. Still have the stock, too; it's close to $8 now."

"And going much higher, much," says Harry Oakes. "On earnings and dividends too. No stock rigging. When I sold shares I told the truth. Did you ever see a copy of my original ad in the *Northern Miner*? No? Well, I have it here, I believe." He reaches for his wallet with a quick movement and draws forth a wad of assorted papers. Selecting one of these, he passes it to me. It is a faded clipping, neatly folded.

"So you can see I never overstated my case," he remarks. "Always know what I'm talking about before I say anything. That's the way to be, young man."

The men from New York are bored. Someone rings for Swinton,

Lake Shore Mines, Limited

(No Personal Liability).

Incorporated Under the Ontario Companies Act

Authorized Capital : $2,000,000

Divided into 2,000,000 Shares of the Par Value of $1.00 each

Issued about 1,300,000

Prospectus dated September 14th, 1916,
and filed in the Office of the Provincial Secretary of Ontario.

DIRECTORS

Harry Oakes, Kirkland Lake, Ontario, Mine Owner.
Ernest Martin, Swastika, Ontario, Prospector.
William H. Wright, Haileybury, Ontario, Mine Owner.
John W. Morrison, Kirkland Lake, Ontario, Mine Manager.
Arthur G. Slaght, Haileybury, Ontario, Barrister.

OFFICERS

Harry Oakes, Kirkland Lake, Ontario, President.
Ernest Martin, Swastika, Ontario, Vice-President.
John W. Morrison, Kirkland Lake, Ontario, Secretary.

BANKERS
THE ROYAL BANK OF CANADA

SOLICITORS
Slaght & Slaght, Haileybury, Ontario.

HEAD OFFICE
Kirkland Lake, Ontario.

The company now offers for sale 150,000 treasury shares of $1.00 each at 40 cents per share.

PROPERTY.—About 160 acres, patented in the centre of Kirkland Lake area, on the line of strike between Tough-Oakes, Wright-Hargreaves and Teck-Hughes properties.

DEVELOPMENT.—Mainly on 100-foot and 300-foot levels, the best values being hitherto found on the latter, where the drifts have developed about 260 feet of good ore, which still continues. Diamond drilling has disclosed promising leads under the lake to the north.

EQUIPMENT.—Seven drill compressor and hoist and all necessary buildings. The present issue is to provide funds for a 100-ton mill, which development fully warrants.

FINANCE.—The Company is entirely free from debts, bonds or charges. One million shares issued to vendors are under pool at not less than $1.00 until 1918.

PROSPECTUS.—Dated 1916, on which this issue is based, and all other information can be obtained at the Company's office, Kirkland Lake, Ontario.

PROGRESS REPORT.—Will be issued quarterly to shareholders.

BROKERAGE.—Will be paid on applications received thro bers of any recognized stock exchange, with whom orders shou

the flunky, and he appears with glasses, ice, White Rock, and Scotch in fat bottles. Drinks are quickly poured and slowly imbibed, for prohibition in the States has taught us all to appreciate good liquor. The president of Lake Shore pushes his heels deep into the carpeted floor and regards his tan Oxfords with smug satisfaction.

"Made to order," he announces to no one in particular. "Just like my suit." He runs a hand along his sleeve, a brown herringbone. "Every bit of clothes I have is made to measure, even my shirts and neckties."

Our hosts exchange glances of sly understanding.

"You look quite well, Harry," nods one, "quite well, indeed. But I think my man in New York might suggest a few improvements here and there, of a cosmopolitan nature. Small things, you know, but they add up to what a gentleman should wear."

The lurking irony of the words seems to be lost on Oakes. He is a good talker, but a poor listener, utterly absorbed in himself. Apropos of nothing, he suddenly launches into a surprising tirade against those in the past who derided his ideas. It is clear he is laboring under a mild persecution complex, not unusual in self-made men who are incapable of viewing their fellows objectively, absorbed as they are in their own prodigious efforts. His close-set eyes burn with a fierce light as he recounts his wanderings. He has been misunderstood and ridiculed everywhere and as he speaks of his detractors his hands twitch nervously as though he would destroy anyone with the temerity to oppose him. He is impressive in his strength but obviously riddled with fixations, a mixture of the rare and the common, bright hues matched against the dullest gray.

He is finding it difficult to hold his listeners. One of them nods over his newspaper and the drowsy silence of the others accentuates the strident tones of the mine maker. But the situation is saved by the arrival of Robert who has at last come in from Larder Lake. Older than I, he is still young, and the lawyer, signaling his friends, fills his glass and rises.

"A toast, gentlemen." They all rise, glass in hand, happy at the interruption. "To youth! And success!"

They drink while the husky bushwhacker stands bewildered. He has come straight from the world of muskeg and tag alder and black flies into a padded nook of security held to the larger one outside by thin miles of steel rail. The transition is too sudden.

"Sit down. Have a drink. Care for a cigar?" There is a perfect babel now. Oakes rises. He is surprisingly short, well below middle height, and he carries himself with the dignity of a bantam rooster. He shakes hands all around, lingering with Robert a few moments, and then departs.

"What a tiresome man that is," says a plumpish young man, eying Oakes's departing figure.

"Henry, I resent that remark." It is the cadaverous man speaking. "I want you to know that Oakes is one of my dearest friends."

"But not a gentleman," retorts the other, refilling his glass.

"You're quite wrong, Harry is a college man. And I must ask that you treat him with more respect. He's my friend, an old friend too. When you get accustomed to his ways he's not at all dull. And besides"—he hesitates and clears his throat—"he's worth several million dollars."

"You became acquainted with Harry Oakes when he was in the money," said my friend Barney in the snug warmth of his home. "But I knew him when the arse was sticking out of his pants, and I mean literally so."

And Barney described meeting Oakes in the fall of 1911. It was close to the freezeup. Barney, one of the engineers at the Buffalo Mine in Cobalt, was sent into Kirkland Lake to examine the Tough-Oakes Mine which had been staked less than a year previously. Barney was selected because he had already visited the area and acquired some claims for his company. He approached Kirkland from the north, following the Teck and Lebel Township line; there were few trails in those days. There were two bushmen with Barney and they became vastly discouraged when the camp was not found where anticipated. But Barney had heard the faint sound of a hammer against rock and steered toward it. In a few minutes the travelers came upon two of the Tough brothers and Harry Oakes.

"Harry was all curled up in a shallow rock trench. His overalls were patched like an Indian's and he sat on some old gunny sack as he sampled a narrow quartz vein. Wouldn't some of his fancy friends in the Bahamas rub their eyes at the sight! Well, we watched him swinging a hammer against the moil. He complained that the steel wasn't sharp, but the Tough boys paid little attention. When I explained that my crowd was interested in the property, Oakes dropped his hammer and offered to show us the layout. It was an instructive trip. He talked well and had definite reasons to support his ideas of structure. But I didn't like the show; the veins were too small. However, I was impressed with the amount of work done."

"He wasn't lazy, then."

"Anything but." Barney was emphatic. "That was his trouble, I think. He overdid the work and it made him one-sided. He wasn't like most of the boys here, ready for a joke, handy with a bottle."

"But he was considered a heavy drinker," I reminded.

"Not at first." Barney shook his head. "That came later, when the Lake Shore put him in the big money."

"Just how much stock did he have? There are so many different stories."

"Not easy to figure." Barney was thoughtful. "I know for a fact he was prepared to sell 800,000 shares to New Yorkers in 1923, but they turned him down. Whether or not that was all his stock, I can't say. It may have included his sister's, too; she had a flock of it."

I expressed surprise that Oakes ever attempted to sell, since he had always been represented as tenaciously holding on to his stock. Barney laughed, and remarked that, tenacious or not, there were few opportunities to sell in the early days. Later, when Lake Shore paid a $5 dividend, there was little reason to do so.

"Did you ever hear about that Buffalo affair? Well, let me tell you what happened. Not long after my visit to Kirkland, Harry came down to Cobalt and tried to interest Tommy Jones, our manager, in buying his Tough-Oakes stock. It came about this way. On that first visit, I stayed overnight at Harry's camp and quite a place it was, tent all patched up and looking like Joseph's coat of many colors. Only a couple of cots and a tin stove inside; we had to sleep on the floor. Anyway, Harry questioned me closely about the chances of my crowd buying into Tough-Oakes. I was frank with him, said I wasn't going to recommend it, but just the same he persisted in asking all about my Cobalt principals. In the end I advanced him the price of a railroad ticket, and that's how he happened to turn up as he did. Little Tommy called Denison and the answer was no. So Harry returned to Kirkland a disappointed man."

"But he did sell the stock, did he not?"

"That's right, but a lot of water flowed over the dam first. I don't know all the details. It was a long drawn-out affair and Clem Foster came into it. I think he had an interest in the Tough-Oakes through an earlier connection with the Tough brothers. Anyway, Bob Fennell formed the first Tough-Oakes company in Haileybury and Clem went off to London to raise some money. In his pocket he had powers of attorney signed by Harry Oakes and the Tough boys, and the first thing he did was to option 1,000,000 shares of stock at 40 cents a share to an Englishman named H. G. Latilla. This chap and his brother, who went by the name of Burt, assigned their option to a company they formed, the Kirkland Lake Propriety Mines. Just about that time the Tough-Oakes came into production and the stock went to over $1 a share. Naturally, there was hell to pay back in Kirkland where Harry and his partners felt they were getting the short end of the stick. Just to warm matters, Clem Foster became involved in a lawsuit with his Englishmen. It was a mess. When war broke out, Clem enlisted at once and so the litigation was held over until after the Armistice. When that was settled, Clem returned to Canada and there were more squabbles. Oakes fought him in court,

I believe, but the Tough family made a settlement. In the end Harry obtained the release of stock and sold it for about $250,000, less solicitor fees."

"I see. But how about Lake Shore, Barney? And the Buffalo Mines?"

"I'm coming to that. But you must know something about the background."

He described Oakes's problems after Arthur Slaght formed the company. There was, at the outset, the perplexing one of securing the Cockeram and Wright claims, so that the mine would be amply protected on the strike and dip. Then, of course, came the question of money, partly resolved by help from the family. When the Number One shaft reached the 100-foot level, however, Oakes was without means of continuing.

"That was in 1913," said Barney. "I went to Kirkland to examine Harry's show and a poor one it was even though he insisted that he had a mine."

"Number One never amounted to much, did it?" I interrupted.

"Not at first, but later it was fine. Of course, Number Two under the lake was the main cheese for years, but when the price of gold stepped up Harry returned to Number One and developed all kinds of stuff which would've made ore even at $20 per ounce."

I asked again how the Buffalo Mines entered the situation.

"That's just the point, we didn't. Harry went to Cobalt for the second time and interviewed 'Handsome' Charley Denison himself. This time he wanted to sell the Lake Shore outright for $85,000. There was plenty of talking, but in the end the answer was no as before, and Harry returned to Kirkland more sour than ever, the lucky stiff," and Barney reviewed the years of plenty that followed. For the darkness was that before dawn, and once the fabulous Number Two Vein was found and developed, Harry Oakes was safe in harbor.

"But our crowd got into Kirkland after all," finished Barney. "Tommy Jones remembered what Oakes had said about the structure and went up to examine the Teck, next to Lake Shore, just after Nipissing had spent $40,000 and dropped their option. Tommy liked the situation and persuaded Denison to take over. Miller and Pomeroy were in, of course; Charley always dragged them into his deals. Well, it was a shaky kind of business at first. So much stock was passed around that it traded like cigar coupons for a cent or two a share. The first crowd that had the property paid the men in stock. The cook got 25,000 shares and the bookkeepers 50,000. Nip thought so little of the mine that they shipped their stock down to Cobalt in an ordinary packing case and didn't take the trouble to insure it. But don't think my crowd had an easy time. Far from it. Denison and the rest had to make loans up to $600,000. Then, instead of foreclosing, they reorganized the company, bought the Orr ground next to them and let Doc Forbes do the rest. Interesting, don't you think, that Oakes and Denison became neighbors, after all?"

"It is, Barney. At least all those talks weren't wasted. I take it Denison was quite a man in his time."

"He was." Barney smiled. "Homely as hell; that's why we called him 'Handsome.' In the coal business originally and was sued by some railroad or other on a delayed freight payment charge.

Harry Oakes
1915

Seems like Charley was accused of getting free storage of coal cars in the yards, then selling the coal when prices were high. There was a lawsuit and Miller defended him successfully. Years later, some-one accused Miller of being such a rotten lawyer he only had one good client in his life, Denison. 'But that one is enough,' replied Miller. And he was. When the Buffalo was purchased for $8,000 Charley carried Miller for a third; took his note. Not bad for a mine that paid almost $3,000,000 in dividends, eh?"

When he stopped to light a fresh cigarette, I asked for an opinion of Harry Oakes.

"Harry?" Barney inhaled deeply. "Fundamentally, I'd say he was all right; he knew his business and worked hard. Most people disliked him because of an unfortunate personality. But he was generous. He did much more for Kirkland Lake and Canada than many of the people who criticize him. Read just the other day he maintained a fleet of buses in Nassau to provide badly needed trans-portation for the natives, as well as three or four airplanes for emergency cases of illness. He employed almost half the population on various public projects, too. He spoke with too much authority maybe, especially after he was a success, and this offended listeners.

Oh, he had his share of weakness, but, after all, who hasn't? Just because he was an uncompromising kind of gent is no reason why those of us who knew him well shouldn't remember his constructive qualities."

Did Barney have any thoughts on who might have killed him? Anyone from the north who went south nursing an old grudge?

Sir Harry
1939

"Forget that idea." Barney tossed his cigarette into the blazing fireplace and rose. "It was someone he met in Nassau, I'm sure. May have been an affair of money. Harry had a genius for making unnecessary enemies. But one thing I do know. He never should have left Canada. That was the biggest mistake he ever made, for it was a fatal one."

Into our office drift northern friends, who come on business and pleasure bent. With them we are always free to sit and discuss the country, which never tires us. One such visitor, an elderly mine seeker who has prospered and mellowed with time, had much to say about the riddle of Sir Harry, whom he had known intimately since 1912.

"I kind've lost track of him while I was overseas," he explained, "but I saw him a great deal before and after that. He was a hard man, hard." He made a clucking sound with his tongue. "Too bloody serious all the time. Never once did I see him enjoy a belly laugh, and a man like that ain't right. No balance. He had his points; worked like a horse and helped a lot of people. But he had too much hate in him." He nodded sorrowfully.

He portrayed Lake Shore when mining operations were just beginning. Jack Morrison was manager, but Oakes dominated the situation completely. No detail escaped him. He was everywhere, underground as well as surface, and the men resented his constant presence.

"Just about the time Harry left for Australia to marry that McIntyre girl—the schoolteacher, you know—I met one of his old shaft men in Timmins who told me that Harry could only get a woman by trapping her on an island where she couldn't run away. There you have it; no one seemed to have a good word for 'im, and I'd say it was his own fault. Pigheaded, he was. Now you take that lawsuit with Clem Foster. I advised him against it, but he was just burning up to get revenge. And what happened? He tied up his money for years and almost lost the Lake Shore in the bargain."

"Did his family help him much before he sold his Tough-Oakes stock?"

"Plenty, plenty. There was the brother in Maine who had a nice lumber business and his sister, Gertrude, the one who was drowned. I believe she worked for the government in Washington and saved a tidy penny. They both helped, especially the sister. And she didn't lose out, either; ended up with 200,000 shares of Lake Shore."

I asked about the grudges which Sir Harry nursed so close to his heart. Could he remember any? Yes, a few, little things which most men would normally forget.

"Like that row with Jimmy Doige, the storekeeper. For a while he carried Harry on the books but as times got tougher he began to worry. One day Harry walks into the store, fiddles around the counter, picks up a pair of overalls and sticks 'em in his packsack.

" 'Put 'em on the account, Jimmy,' he says.

" 'Just a minute, Harry,' says Doige. 'Can't you pay now?'

"Harry explained that he couldn't until some money he was expecting from down below arrived. But Jimmy wouldn't listen to the story, said he had heard it too many times already. And then he ordered Harry to put the overalls back where he found 'em. There were several of the boys hanging around and they had quite a laugh. Well, sir, Harry never did forget Jimmy after that. The miners at the Lake Shore were ordered to keep away from Jimmy's store. If they traded there they were fired. Harry hounded that man until he had to get out of Kirkland. Moved to Swastika, he did. That's what I mean when I say Harry had too much hate in 'im. He made too much of the little things which most of us don't even notice. It was his nature, I guess. A born bellyacher. Even when he smiled he looked sour. But his bark was worse than his bite, I think. Helped the Kaplans, you know that. Like an elephant, he was, never forgetting enemies or friends. Even his generosity became a fault; he set himself up as a kind of Solomon, rewarding or punishing, you might say.

"Remember the château he built in Kirkland over the tailings dump?" My friend chuckled. "And that famous nine-hole golf course? Now, that was a strange sight in a mining camp. Harry wasn't much of a golfer—shovel work ain't good training for the links. Anyway, there was one trap he could never get over. It was too much for 'im, so what does he do finally? Calls in the surface crew at the mine and has the trap filled with muck so's he could reach the green. That was Harry Oakes, my lad. He couldn't accept failure, not even in a stupid game of golf. And when the Lake Shore manager wanted to sink a new shaft Harry said no, 'cause it'd interfere with that damned golf course."

He told another characteristic Oakes story. When Sir Harry, then a plebeian, built his much-talked-of estate at Niagara Falls, the grounds were elaborately landscaped. Among other things, an artificial hill was made with steam shovels, thus providing a view in otherwise flat country. While Oakes was away, his wife is supposed to have had the hill removed to another part of the grounds. Upon returning home, Oakes, in a rage, ordered the hill transported to its original site.

"This happened a few more times, until finally Harry made sure the hill would stay put by taking the gardener with 'im when he went north again."

"Sounds farfetched," I said.

"Maybe. But if you knew the man as I did you wouldn't think so. He was that kind; must have his own way, come hell or high water.

"When I read about him being killed, I was sorry but not surprised. Always had the feeling something like that'd happen. You wonder who killed him? Probably someone who didn't amount to much, like a servant who resented the way he was treated. Harry was a poor judge of people. He didn't know how to make friends, tried to buy 'em all the time."

"Why did he leave Canada, Jack?" I asked.

"Different reasons. Most people say it was because of the high income taxes. But I heard different."

According to Jack, a smooth-talking politician promised to make Oakes a senator, the Canadian equivalent of a member of the English House of Lords, if he contributed substantially to the party. The mining magnate dug into his pocket for a substantial donation and then purchased a large Ottawa residence, which was remodeled extensively in a style commensurate with the glory of office. But the election went wrong somehow, and Oakes became long of a mansion and short of a senatorship. He was resentful, naturally, and decided he had been willfully tricked.

"He was game, though. Next thing he does is present the government with a large section of land in Ottawa to be converted into a national park, a gesture that must've set him back near $250,000. And what do you think? The government boys turn around and soak him a gift tax. He couldn't take that, and the next thing you know he's out of Canada once and for all."

"Then it was taxes."

"No, not exactly; more his protest at being pushed around. For all his bluster, Harry was very sensitive. Figured he was in a position where he didn't have to take anything from the government or anyone else. Of course, income taxes were high and going higher and that may've preyed on his mind. Who can tell for sure? What ruined the man was too much gold, like that ancient king with the touch of gold which he wanted so badly. But it finally killed 'im."

Reader, I give you Hyman Kaplan, not the lovable mangler of English who delights subscribers of the *New Yorker* magazine, but an old resident of Kirkland Lake. This round little man with brown eyes had much to do with the rise of Harry Oakes, and now that his benefactor is dead his genuine grief is real proof that the late baronet was not without some appreciative friends.

How many times, since Bob and I first met him in 1922, did we listen to his quaintly worded version of the early days, when, fresh from Poland, he made his way north and staked *his* claim, a tiny grocery store which grew into a Kirkland Lake institution! And now, as I conversed with him in the office above one of his cinemas, he pressed his knuckles into both cheeks and groaned.

"He wanted always I should take Lake Shore stock at 30 cents a share for bacon and flour and all kinds things. But what do I know from stocks with mines and this business? I was a greenhorn, a first-class schlamazel, you'll forgive me the expression. He was poor, he had no money, he worked from morning till night and no one else gives him credit. So what I did? I give him credit, all he wants. And when I'm seeing Lake Shore the stock is going in up, up"—he waved his hands in rising circles—"I could tear mineself in liddle pieces. Charlie Chow is more smart. The miners is taking to him Lake Shore stock they get for pay, so he gives them credit at 50 cents. T'ousands he gets like that, so today he is a millionaire."

"Never think it," I replied. "His hotel hasn't changed since the early days."

"So what is that? Lake Shore stock he has, dividends is coming. His hotel needs painting, a few new boards on the floors, maybe? He shall worry. Me, I'm painting mine theayter, everything is so clean you can eat dinner on the floor. But Lake Shore stock I don't have." He groaned and rocked in his chair.

"But Oakes didn't forget you," I reminded.

"Forget?" He looked at me with a comical expression of incredulity. "I shall say not! Whenever he is coming here to Kirkland Lake he is first seeing me. Bet your life! He is sitting many times on the same chair you are and I always have a bottle of schnapps for him. And does he drink! Glug, glug, glug," he intoned, holding an imaginary bottle to his lips, "glug, glug." He wagged his head sadly. "Only afterwards when he is rich, he did this. Why, you're asking me? I ain't sure, but I think the reason is because he's no more a happy man. And why he's not happy? Because he ain't working. Who can be happy, tell me, please, if he's doing nothing, unless maybe a bum who is never doing anything in his whole life? But Harry is busy in the old days, all the time he's working. Also he is making too much money. So what happens? He stops working and begins to loaf and then starts his troubles, and what troubles!"

"You may be right," I said, "but what I'd like to know is how much he actually helped you."

"Enough! He was a perfect gentleman. When we wanted money for our real estate and theayters, where could we get it, from the air, I ask you? Of course not! Harry Oakes, who then? He even gives us the idea; he is always talking about how Kirkland Lake becomes a big city someday and he wants the old-timers should stay and do business. Sure thing! Of course we paid him back everything, to the penny. He didn't want it but when I tell him we are doing good business and don't need money it's all right by him. We start in 1921, without cash. By us it was never like with Mr. Rockefeller. I go to see Harry Oakes and I'm telling him Kirkland must have it a movie for the miners and their families. Two lots I have picked, real diamonds of locations, but I have a headache, there is a big rock in the middle, twenty feet it comes over the sidewalk. Money it costs to remove such things, and that's why I'm talking to Harry. He is polite—he is always a gentleman—and then he is very agreeable I should go ahead, he will advance the money so soon he shall get settled with his wife, he was just married.

"I'm waiting one year, two years, it is taking a long time he should be settled, but you know how it is. Do I have to explain? Finally it comes 1923 and he's calling me up to go ahead with the work, he's paying for everything. We make a contract with two Scotchmen for $1,800 so they will take away the rock. All summer they are working like dogs to make ready the cellar and then they're telling me they have lost $700 on the work. What could I do? Harry Oakes is paying for everything. So I'm advising them make up a statement and go see Harry, he is a gentleman. And that's what they are doing."

"Did Oakes pay?" I asked.

"Of course!" Kaplan was surprised at the question. "He gives a look at the statement and says he doesn't want anybody shall work without a fair profit—not too much, but enough, you know how it is. The contractors named it a price but Harry says this ain't enough— bare wages, they should get something more. This I'm telling you is facts, not fairy tales.

"I'm coming now to the theayter. We are buying the lots in 1924, but there is only a cellar without a building. So again I'm talking with Harry Oakes. He listens to mine story, then he says, 'What plans did you make and what kind agreement you want?' So I am answering him, I don't know anything from plans and agreements, he can write the ticket, why not? By me it would be all right. This makes him laugh and he says I shall go to see O'Mara, the lawyer, and he will give me $35,000 which will be a mortgage. So it was done, and we are building the first movie in Kirkland Lake. But there is more headaches—we are losing money. I am ashamed to speak with Harry again, so I went to someone else—never mind who, a gentleman. He says, 'I'll give you $5,000, Kaplan. The interest will be 18 per cent, that's all.' That's all! Pfui! Like a knife in mine heart.

"By this time I'm a nuisance, but I went once more to see Harry. Mine brother is sure he won't bother no more with a little Jew, he is now a rich man. But I am going to the mine just the same.

Harry is on the golf links and yells I should come over—his wife is not with him. I am sitting down and he talks. That day he feels good, thanks God. He speaks of all the improvements he is making, new bunkhouse, a hot house for all kinds vegetables, a curling rink. Everything. He doesn't like the way Wright-Hargreaves is not doing these things; their money goes, he says, to Buffalo and New York instead some of it is spent in Kirkland. Then, when he findishes, I tell him about $5,000 I need. He jumps up, first he is sore, then he is laughing. 'You're the limit,' he says. 'Don't you know you can go to the bank for loans? You're a businessman now.' But what I know about these things? 'It's time you learn,' he says, and then he tells me I should have made an audit of mine condition and send it to him. This I do, and he sends a letter with introduction to Mr. Goddard from the Royal Bank of Canada, he should take good care of us and he'll guarantee we are 100 per cent good risk. So we got the $5,000 like that." He snapped his fingers.

"Then comes another time I must see him. Someone is trying to buy a lot near us to build another theayter, it should ruin us. I cannot sleep, mine appetite is disappearing. Mine brother this time is smarter from me, he says, 'Schlemiel, stop crying. Go like a man to Niagry Falls and get money from Harry Oakes.' I will not tell you a lie I didn't think of it mineself, I'm half crazy. So I leave right away. Did you ever see that house in Niagry? House, did I say? A palace, better, with fountains, with servants, with carpets and all kinds things. Harry is sitting like a king in the middle of a big room and he pours me out a drink. He won't let me talk, I must see all the plants, the furniture, it's like in the movies. Two days I am staying—he won't see no one else. Finally, I tell him mine troubles, but this time he ain't so pleasant like before. He says we are already getting too greedy and why don't I take it mine problems to Mr. Goddard?

"A few days later I am in the bank with mine brother and the manager says, 'Hello, boys, have a seat,' and is shaking hands like we are old friends and landsmen. Then he says, 'It's all right, gentlemen. Mr. Oakes just called me by the telephone and now your credit is good up to twenty-five thousand.'"

"Oakes changed his mind, then."

"Yes, by him it was a joke or maybe he wanted he should warn us not to be so smart the next time, we are going too fast ahead. But he forgets himself. Dividends! Pfui! Every minute I figure the mine it pays him eight dollars. What he wants it for, I ask you? He cannot spend so fast. So it drives him crazy, building palaces for a king, with a title in England so he's a sir, living fancy-shmancy where he doesn't belong there. He helps people, he helps us, but it ain't enough. What he should do? He doesn't know. Better he stayed here in Kirkland and paid taxes."

"So you think taxes drove him from Canada."

"What else? When a man has eight dollars a minute it is becoming a disease with him, no? He has dividends, but he hasn't. Taxes he must pay. So he thinks and thinks and pretty soon he is no longer a man, he is a machine from money, God forbid! He wants money in the early days? Yes, but only for work, to make a mine, to prove he is right in the first place. Somewhere else he should have tried again, yes, a t'ousand times he should have tried."

"I wonder," I said after a pause, "I wonder who could have killed him."

"Who knows that?" The little man's eyes glistened with honest emotion. "But whoever it is, he should die a bad death, like Hitler, because he killed a good man, a man with a heart."

The bus to Swastika started jerkily, gathered momentum and cruised easily along the main street of Kirkland Lake. Behind the clusters of shops and buildings the lowering sun caught the tops of headframes and transformed sullen darkness into warm spots of light. It was truly a Golden Mile. Busy citizens walked about unconcernedly; to them this was a town like any other town. But to me those headframes told a story of their own, of men like Harry Oakes, Bill Wright, Al Wende, and the Tough brothers. Gold was being taken from the earth and buried again in guarded vaults, but in the process of this apparently useless transformation, the fingers of destiny were writing a strange and fascinating human drama.

"Swastika!"

We tumbled out of the bus and climbed wooden steps to the station platform. Nothing had changed, not even the name which, for an interval during the war, had been called "Winston," in honor of a beloved English statesman. But old habits die hard and often come to life again, and even so it was with "Swastika," a name rich in Canadian mining tradition, which once more adorned the eaves above the ticket office.

Old Eagle was on hand to greet me as of yore, white haired now but still sprightly, scanning arrivals for familiar faces. His eyes gleamed when he spotted me, but his greeting was the usual one of studied casualness.

"Hi, there."

We shook hands gravely and then he fell into his accustomed role, pumping for news. It was his contention that the best mining information could be obtained through meeting trains and engaging prospectors and others in friendly conversations.

"What's new?" he asked.

It was something old and not new that I wanted. Perhaps he could enlighten me on one or two controversial matters concerning Harry Oakes?

"Oh, that's it! Well, I knew him, sure. Who didn't around here? He was all over the place at one time." Old Eagle seemed pleased with the strangeness of his position, that of supplying information instead of extracting it from others. "And he was a good guy. Helped a lot of people round here. Take Jimmy Doige, now."

"Just a minute, Eagle," and I told him the story I had heard about the overalls.

"May have happened," he admitted, "but the ending was different. Jimmy got help from Harry when it was needed. In the old days there was trouble, sure. Jimmy was carrying Harry on the books for plenty. Well, Jimmy was having a spot of worry himself, the wholesalers were after him for payments on account. So he went after Harry. Well, sir, Harry himself was waiting for money his brother was supposed to send up from Maine, so he goes to Jimmy and explains the situation about the check he's expecting. It's no dice. There's a hell of a squawk; Harry curses Jimmy and vicey versey. But Harry ends up by signing a note for the amount due, and Jimmy takes the note to his creditors. They go to the bank and come back with the story the note's worthless, Harry's credit is flat. So back Jimmy goes to Harry, but by that time Harry has the money from his brother which he gives to Jimmy and demands the return of the note. The wholesalers has the note, though, and there's another to-do about that—a real mess, you see. Jimmy had to pay out the money Harry give him before he could get the note which he had signed too. Anyway, when Harry finally had the note, he cussed out Jimmy real good, and he could cuss, I tell you. Said he'd ruin him and all that. Well, Joe Boisvert, the hotel feller, claims he fixed things by explaining to Harry that it wasn't Jimmy's fault if creditors were after him, he had to protect himself. And Jimmy and Harry were supposed to have shook hands and made up their quarrel."

The train south was late, and we paced the platform leisurely. Eagle continued to enjoy himself; the break in his accustomed routine was pleasant.

"Not long before Jimmy died he was in bad trouble. Some kind of mining deal, I don't know exactly, but I do know he had to get $10,000 fast or he'd be a goner. Harry Oakes is his only bet and he ain't so sure the old boy will come across. But he goes down to

Niagra Falls just the same and when he gets to the house he takes
off his shoes and enters like he was praying in church. Yes, sure,
that's a fact. Everyone in Swastika heard about it."

"And did Jimmy get the money, Eagle?"

"You bet he did! And you should have heard him carrying on
about Harry Oakes after that! He'd knock you down if you said
anything against 'im. And I don't blame 'im. There ain't many men
that pass out $10,000 the way Harry Oakes did. Do you know any?"

"No," I admitted. "You're quite right, Eagle. He certainly had
his points. But why do you think he pulled out of Canada?"

"Don't you know?" His astonishment was unfeigned. "It was
asthma! Sure! Had to get into a warm climate, the doctors advised
him. Niagra Falls was too damp. And so he packed up and left;
the mine was running itself by that time."

The whistle of the approaching train hurried our conversation.
There was one more question to ask, the old one, and I had to shout
above the rising hubbub of departure.

"Who killed Harry?" cried Old Eagle. The train was grinding
to a stop now. "Say, you been reading detective stories or something?
Harry was a gambler. He took a chance on that title stuff and went
to the islands and he lost out, that's all. His last spec was a dud."

"And you're sure it was asthma?" I was on the steps of the
train already in motion.

"Sure as my own rheumatism," he panted, trotting heavily.
"That tax idea is all bunk."

The train was gathering speed but I remained where I was, waving to the diminishing figure of Old Eagle. He stood motionless, like
a solitary statue. . . .

A Bay Street acquaintance desisted from telephoning long
enough to expound his views of Harry Oakes.

"Did I know him? Sure did! Come from Niagra Falls myself,
y'see, and folks down there never stop talking about Oakes. Nifty
place he built for himself, right near the Falls. Must've cost millions.
Popular? Not on your life! When he gave anything to the town, his
name had to appear. Like the 'Oakes Garden Theatre' and 'Oakes
Baseball Park' and the 'Lady Oakes Wing' at the hospital. Always
'Oakes,' you see."

"But he gave," I said.

"Sure, who says he didn't? But never anonymously; the world
had to know. If it happened to be a charity or something he couldn't
tie his name to, then he wasn't interested. He was that type. I met
him back in '26 it was, when I was selling bonds." He smiled guiltily

as though making a confession. "I knocked on the big front door and a little guy dressed in old clothes and high boots with large buttons on the side opened up for me. He was a dirty-looking runt as I remember him standing on a carpet a foot thick. I said something about seeing the boss."

" 'I'm Harry Oakes,' he said, looking funny. 'What do you want, young man?'

"Trying not to show my surprise, I said that I had some nice bonds to sell. He smiled, if you call it a smile, and I thought I had a sale when he invited me inside. But all he did was tell me that he had a regular manager who took care of his investments. In another room about the size of Madison Square Garden his wife was entertaining some fancy lady friends. Well, I figured there was nothing more to say, and got up to leave, thanking him for his courtesy. He must have been proud, or lonesome or something, for he said, 'Not at all. Before you go I want you to see my new swimming pool,' and he took my arm. While we walked through the house he explained that he had been working on the rosebushes, not trusting his gardener to do things right. Quite a gripe he had, I remember. And then I looked at the pool all decked out with colored lights underwater. I said the right stuff, how wonderful it all was, and he was pleased as Punch. When the tour was over, he rang for his chauffeur.

" 'Take this gentleman (get that!) to town,' he ordered. 'Anywhere he wants to go,' and off I went in great style."

"Did you see him again?" I asked.

"Sure, several times, but he was always with a crowd of people and I had no chance to talk to him. To tell the truth, I never gave a thought to Harry Oakes until he was bumped off. Nasty mess, that," he confided, "and from the gossip you hear that case could stand more looking into. It was a hot potato, some big shots mixed up and all that, and the authorities rushed the case along to get it out of the way. But, what the hell—" he shrugged—"something was bound to happen to a guy like that. Always told my wife that. Everything I knew and heard about the man pointed to one thing—he always led with his chin. So why, tell me, shouldn't he expect a K.O.?"

About five years ago there was considerable local excitement in Cobalt and vicinity. The occasion was the arrival of two enormous oil paintings of Sir Harry and Lady Oakes which had been executed in London and shipped to Canada, bound for the commodious Lake Shore office. For customs purposes, the crates were opened for inspection at the Cobalt station, and amused and astonished citizens gazed at the prospector who had been created a baronet. The artist had gone to considerable pains in detailing the traditional costume of royalty, and a slick Sir Harry appeared in a sea of lace and ribbons and satin knee pants, his full and resplendent figure looking at the world with uneasy elegance.

Various and biting were the comments evoked by this spectacle, for a prophet fares badly with those who knew him when. More contemptuous than the rest was Andy Sommers, one of Harry Oakes's early intimates. Remembering this, I dropped in at Andy's shack at Haileybury, there to be greeted warmly. Above the noisy banter of friendship we exchanged news of latest developments in the various mining camps, and then I steered the conversation to Kirkland Lake and Harry Oakes. Andy peered at me over his glasses.

"What do you want to know about him?" he asked. "Harry's old hat around here. Many's the time he came in this shack to get a good square meal and talk his head off about that mine of his. He really wasn't much, my boy, just lucky as hell."

"But he fought for his success, Andy."

"All of us work up here," he replied. "Only damned few of us happen to locate in the right place, that's all. Harry might've chose a thousand other places and all he'd've had to show for his trouble was a bruised rear end and calloused hands, like me. Yes, yes," he said impatiently, "he was always blowing about how he knew the break was under the lake all the time, but that's plain hot air. Did he have a diver's outfit or something? If he had underwater eyes, then why didn't he stake Bill Wright's claims? He had the west end of the camp to himself. But that was Harry every time; he'd rather be right than regular."

Andy found discussing Sir Harry distasteful and it required considerable urging on my part to make him continue.

"All right, what you want to know? I admit he was a hustler. Was he good company? No, sir, he was not. I remember one time I was in Kirkland selling supplies and called in at the Lake Shore. Harry was running the whole show then; his word was law. First thing I ask for a drink—I was quite a boozer in them days, but I ain't touched a drop since I turned sixty. Anyway, Harry says, 'Shush, Andy, the men might hear you.' And I says, 'So what? Is that a crime?' Well, he goes to a cupboard and takes out a half empty crock. 'What's that?' I ask, and he says, 'Your drink, Andy,' and I says, 'Well, guess it'll do for me. But what'll you drink, Harry?' He says, 'I'll have one with you,' and he does and then he places the cork in the bottle and puts it back in the closet. 'That's enough,' he says, 'one drink's enough for any man.' Can you beat it?

And that's the way he was at a bar too; he'd never treat the gang to more than one shot but he'd take all the drinks they give him. We called 'im 'One-Treat Harry.'

"That title of his, now, he bought it like everything else. Gave St. George's Hospital in London something like a half million. That was his life's ambition, an empty piece of paper with a red ribbon around it. He went after it like a billy goat, head down and charging straight ahead. Generous? The money he passed out was like me giving a buck to a hungry prospector. He couldn't spend the income on his income for his own needs. Which reminds me of a little story."

He began by relating his return from overseas in World War I. The transport docked in New York, and Andy, hungry for life after so much death, put up in the old Waldorf on 34th Street and 5th Avenue. Harry Oakes maintained an apartment in New York at that time and came at once to see his old friend.

"I was glad to see him," related Andy, "for, after all, he was from the north. I had him to dinner and a leg show with all the trimmings. You know me, I was always a big spender when I had money. Well, Harry got a big kick out of it all. He must've called on me more'n a dozen times before I left. But not once did he invite me to his place or stand treat for an evening. I was in New York almost a month, too."

I asked, then, whether he considered Sir Harry parsimonious.

"No, not that; he just wasn't a regular guy. Never fit in with people. What do you call those men who are only interested in themselves and what they do?"

"Egotist?"

"That's the word. Harry was one of them in a big way. If he had married earlier in life, he could've been made over a bit, but he was fifty or so when he lit out for Australia and became a squaw man at last. Harry was too far gone by that time for his wife—and she's a fine woman, I want you to know—to do any changing."

Andy assigned tax burdens as the reason for Sir Harry's exodus from Canada.

"He was always beefing about what he had to pay, forgetting that it was tougher for us little men who gave till it really hurt. The country was good to him and he shows his gratitude by leaving it cold. He tried to be bigger than Canada, and even he couldn't make a go of it. No, my boy, he just wasn't right in the first place. Maybe it was the Yankee in 'im, I don't know. Anyway, I wasn't surprised at the end, not a bit. He always had a chip on his shoulder and someone knocked it off. When a man's as rich as Harry was, he don't have to go round treating people with kid gloves any more. He's solid and he shows his real character. That's where trouble starts. If Harry had properties like mine, real dogs, instead of that bloody Lake Shore, he'd be alive and kicking today."

Before I departed, Andy gave me his version of the murder.

"Harry never learned to play around. I know that 'cause I went out with 'im a great deal. Well, what happens to man like that? In his old age he gets to thinking and decides he's missed something. Hears all them wasters he used to entertain talking about women. So he has a fling or two but he doesn't know the ropes; no training, you see. He makes a false move with some dame and along comes her husband or lover, and bang, bang, Sir Harry's no more and his son Sydney wears the handle now. It's like the French used to say when I was overseas, 'Chercher the femme.' "

To those of an inquiring mind, enough has been written to suggest further investigation into the life and death of a man of destiny. To others, of a philosophical bent, who know that mining will continue in the hands of others and the bush will grow in Kirkland Lake again, the inquiry is sufficient as far as it goes. For them, the saga of Sir Harry Oakes was aptly characterized long ago by Shakespeare through the lips of Macbeth:

> "To-morrow, and to-morrow, and to-morrow,
> Creeps in this petty pace from day to day,
> To the last syllable of recorded time;
> And all our yesterdays have lighted fools
> The way to dusty death. Out, out, brief candle!
> Life's but a walking shadow, a poor player
> That struts and frets his hour upon the stage
> And then is heard no more: it is a tale
> Told by an idiot, full of sound and fury,
> Signifying nothing."

KIRKLAND LAKE

Production and Dividends from three mile "break."
1917–1945

	First Production	Total Production	Total Dividends
Lake Shore	1913	$201,013,382	$94,020,000
Wright-Hargreaves	1921	107,450,658	45,532,500
Teck-Hughes	1917	80,512,198	40,931,038 *
Kirkland Lake Gold	1919	20,188,431	4,360,011
Sylvanite	1927	31,012,821	8,743,675
Macassa	1933	20,580,786	7,129,551
Toburn	1932	13,782,758 **	2,711,125

* Includes dividends received from Lamaque Mines
** Includes production of predecessor Tough-Oakes-Burnside

ENTIRE KIRKLAND LAKE DISTRICT

1917–1945

Total Production	$488,043,621
Total Dividends	202,187,443

CHAPTER X

Flinotin Flonneroy

"New York, N. Y., February 15, 1938

Hudson Bay Mining & Smelting Co., Limited, a company organized under the laws of the Dominion of Canada (hereinafter sometimes referred to as the Company), hereby applies for the listing on the New York Stock Exchange of 2,757,973 shares of its Capital Stock, without nominal or par value, heretofore listed and registered on the New York Curb Exchange. All the shares, the listing of which is applied for in this application, are fully paid and non assessable with no personal liability attaching to the holders thereof. Under the 'Companies Act' and the Letters Patent of the Company, the duration of the Company is indefinite and unlimited."

In this prosaic manner did a mighty ore deposit make its humble debut in the vaunted halls of the New York Stock Exchange. Investors and speculators were furnished with a single paragraph of history containing exactly twenty-one lines of print. If metals could speak, there would be a roar of protest from the north, for the discovery and development of the Flin Flon is a treasured Canadian epic of mining and human endeavor, deserving of a more inspired chronicle than that stemming from the careful pen of a Wall Street lawyer. There is no mention of a swaggering ex-pugilist turned promoter; neither is there any reference to a silver-mining company no longer producing silver, nor a proud conservative financial house which ventured but guessed wrong. To the cautious author of the listing statement, the Pas is just a town, and not a revered, time-honored outpost, seething with tradition, from which bolder men dared to leave the last vestiges of civilization and face the unconquered bush.

Le Pas, the Step into the unknown, was eloquently named by the hardy French coureur de bois who penetrated this remote region far above Lake Winnipeg, years before the Hudson's Bay Company received its unique charter from indulgent King Charles II. Theirs was a herculean trip, an odyssey which took them from the familiar and comforting shores of the St. Lawrence to the Ottawa, across Lake Nipissing, and thence through the Great Lakes and the loosely connected waterways leading to the placid waters of the Saskatchewan River. If they were lucky the trip was accomplished in two years but this speedy record was not achieved often. The hazards of traveling in birch-bark canoes through unmapped regions alive with hostile Indians were tremendous; only men of iron will and inflexible resolution could accomplish this miracle. The French, effete as they were supposed to be in France, became human tigers in the Canadian bush. It is no wonder they sorely vexed the English, who, coming later, found experienced Frenchmen already rooted in the country, busily trading and periodically sending large peltry-laden flotillas back to Montreal.

The French established the Pas, and this spot became the focal point of a long seesaw struggle with the English to gain ascendancy. In 1773 Samuel Hearne was commissioned by the Hudson's Bay Company to end all rivalry and establish English hegemony in the disputed region. He surveyed the area and found the French firmly established and far better equipped to maintain their superiority than he was to undermine it. He chose pacific means to gain his ends, deciding that better goods and fairer treatment of the natives would, in the long run, achieve the object of his ambitious company. A post was established on Pine Island Lake, fifty miles north of the Pas, in the heart of French-dominated country. There were clashes inevitably, with the fortunes of war swaying first toward the French and then toward the English.

Later, when Mackenzie undertook his epochal voyages to the Arctic Ocean and the Pacific, he recruited men from the ranks of the French who, as voyageurs, were admittedly superior to the less-inured Englishmen. The Indians were far less reliable, and were used largely for packing. The Pas thus became a kind of recruiting point, and as the tide of empire swung in favor of the English the Hudson's Bay Company found in the town a valuable storehouse of hardy personnel. And so the Pas became an integral factor in English life long before the prairie provinces below were granaries and the city of Winnipeg was founded.

The Canadian National Railway, in building a spur northward to connect the great southern wheat belt with lower Hudson Bay, and so provide a shorter export route to hungry Europe, crawled into the Pas in 1905. The town grew into an important railway terminal and in the process its character underwent rapid changes. No longer a trapping and hunting center exclusively, it was now the jumping-off place for the great Pre-Cambrian complex, the periphery of which beckoned north of the settlement. Trappers and their dog teams still cluttered the main street, but the Pas was breeding a new kind of adventurer, the prospector, who pursued the even tenor of his ways, with indifferent results, for more than a decade. But then things began to happen. . . .

Into Jack Hammell's Toronto office walked Dan Mosher, a man of the Pas with tales of mines to be found in the blue of Manitoba. It was not an auspicious time, after the freezeup in 1914, with war raging in Europe and the Hudson Bay Railroad project threatened with discontinuance. But the bushwhacker had an intriguing story to tell, one which a man of Hammell's volatile temperament could hardly resist.

"We'll form a syndicate," said Hammell. . . .

Meanwhile, somewhere above the Pas, Mosher's bush partners were busy. Leader among them was tall, soft-spoken Tom Creighton, an old hand at prospecting and endowed with remarkable powers of observation and articulation. No mere prospector was Tom, but an intelligent and well-informed woodsman, a skilled trapper and a bush traveler with few equals. Tom had been directing his associates, Dan and John Mosher, Leon Dion, his brother Isadore, and Dan Milligan, across the line to Lac La Ronge in Saskatchewan where he had uncovered significant patches of gossan. The men panned assiduously, but not once did they see any welcome colors of gold. Tom was not unduly discouraged. Gold was hard to find, he knew, and the country looked promising. Financial assistance came from a few venturesome residents of Prince Albert, and once more the dogged squadron tried, this time on the shores of Beaver Lake where once the French plied their busy fur traffic. There some gold was evident, the first to be reported in the district, but the showing was not impressive for so distant a location. Creighton's backers lost heart and washed their hands of the project, but he decided to spend a winter trapping in the vicinity with his friends, meanwhile keeping a sharp lookout for signs of mineral. Dan Mosher went down to the Pas, and then east.

Alone, one day in the winter of 1914, temporarily camped at Phantom Lake, Creighton dragged himself wearily along his trap line. As he plowed through the tenacious snow deep moose tracks caused him to halt. Fresh meat! Dropping his pack, he took to the bush, gun in hand, but never reached his quarry. Bigger game claimed his attention. Cleared of snow by a whistling arctic wind, the top of a rusty outcrop made him forget hunting and trapping. Close inspection revealed that the rock was impregnated with copper sulphides. Breaking off a few small pieces, he hastily returned to the trap line and made his way to the main base at Beaver Lake where his partners awaited him.

The specimens were excitedly shown, and then the men sat down to formulate a course of action. The discovery would be staked and prospected in the spring, finances to be provided by the winter take of furs. A revision of plans became necessary, however. Dan Mosher, who had visited Hammell unknown to his partners, now appeared at Beaver Lake with complete supplies for a season of prospecting. He had an unexpected story to relate, of a syndicate agreement he had signed with Hammell sharing equally any claims to be staked in the vicinity of Beaver Lake. Questions popped. Was Hammell the only grubstaker? No, there was Alec Fasken, the wily lawyer in Toronto who was director of both the Nipissing and Dome Mines, Frank Currie, hotel owner, and a man named Hugh Ryan, all with plenty of money. Well, argued Dan, on the defensive, why not split his own half among them all, since they had first traveled together in the country? The suggestion was interesting. A long discussion ended with the partners shaking hands and agreeing to pool their efforts.

Breakup time found the men trekking north of Phantom Lake, bound for Creighton's discovery. Upon arrival, it was at once apparent that they had come upon a huge ore body, most of which extended under a small lake and showed brownly through the clear water. They broke off hand specimens with their picks, examined the massive brass-colored sulphides which looked like fine pyrite and yet had a distinct yellowish hue. There were purplish streaks too, such as they had never before seen.

"There's copper and stuff in it, all right," observed Creighton. "Let's stake 'er, boys."

And stake they did, little realizing that on this spot one day would rise the most northerly smelting plant in the British Empire. The claims required names, and so they drew from their knowledge and associations and produced the Surprise, Peerless, Unique, Killarney, Extension, Lakeview, Malla Malla, Liskeard, Climax, Crown, Victoria, Nancy, Pontiac, Bulldog, Munroe. By a strange coincidence, their staking lay athwart the provincial boundaries of Saskatchewan and Manitoba, but they provided for the requisite mining licenses and in due course completed their historic staking.

The property itself required a name, but the partners were happily prepared for this contingency. In the path of their meandering trap lines there was a deserted cabin, and among the debris which littered the floor they had rescued a cheap paper-backed novel entitled *The Sunless City*. The theme, curiously enough, concerned the discovery of an underground labyrinth wherein gold was heaped in endless piles, but for all this wealth the inhabitants had never seen the welcome light of the sun. Flinotin Flonneroy, the hero of this weird narrative, had accidentally wandered into the Sunless City and devoted his life to finding a passageway to the earth's surface. The six partners had taken turns reading *The Sunless City* and talked of "Flin Flon" as though he was living among them. Their disappointment was keen when they found the last few chapters of the volume had been ripped from the binding, probably to be put to a more important use, and so they were never to learn whether Flin Flon had indeed succeeded in climbing back to the surface with his golden hoard.

Now, when Tom Creighton panned some oxidized material near the lake and obtained a rich profusion of colors, he rose with a smile and addressed his partners.

"Well, boys," he said, "I guess old Flin Flon made it, after all. He must've shook himself right here when he crawled out of the Sunless City and scattered all this gold around."

So, by acclaim, the deposit was baptized "Flin Flon." When the enterprise appeared doomed after repeated failure and disappointment in later years, frequenters of board rooms in Winnipeg and Toronto modified the name to "Flim Flam." But we shall see how, in the end, Flin Flon came into its own again in a blaze of glory.

At Phantom Lake the partners were amazed to find Jack Hammell and his wife, freshly arrived from the Pas. It had been a grueling trip, but Hammell at once asked to be led to the gold showing about which Creighton had written him weeks before. Told that something new and far more impressive had been found, a large sulphide deposit, Hammell asked to see samples. Impressed, he suggested that more claims be staked, while he accompanied Mrs. Hammell on a long-promised fishing trip.

Meeting his faithful flock at camp headquarters once more, Hammell was conducted to the Flin Flon. He scrambled over the surface, peered into the lake, and then faced the expectant prospectors.

"Boys," he asked dramatically, "how much money do you want to put you on easy street?"

"Well," drawled Tom Creighton, "I think we'll settle for $100,-000 each and old Rockefeller can have the rest."

"I'll get it for you!" Hammell flashed back. "When I put this one over, there'll be nothing left to do in mining."

Back in Toronto, he exhibited specimens and maps to his syndicate partners with an enthusiasm unusual even for a man who was anything but a pessimist. Even Alec Fasken, flinty, shrewd, overcautious, was stirred, too faintly, however, to recommend the property to either Dome or Nipissing. Hammell was obliged to content himself with a few more thousand dollars from his associates to carry out the necessary assessment work. While Creighton and his followers began to dig trenches which revealed masses of finegrained sulphides, Hammell turned his thoughts in the direction of big money.

Feeling confident that no Canadian mining company had the courage, organization, and means to handle a venture of Flin Flon magnitude, Hammell fixed his mind on one of the major American financial houses. Logic pointed to the venerable Hayden, Stone & Company of Boston and New York, successful promoters of the porphyry coppers in the West which, despite general skepticism in American mining circles, were now providing the bulk of the world's copper production. A few long-distance calls were made, and Hammell left Toronto for New York. He registered at the Vanderbilt Hotel, engaged a large suite of rooms, and then sent word to the Hayden, Stone coterie that he was ready to receive them.

They came, they saw, they drank, they ate, and they were conquered. Never before had a mining deal of such magnitude been consummated in the record time of a few days. Hammell, bombastics and all, proved himself a master psychologist. As he explained later, "Never go to Wall Street with your can sticking through your pants. If you do, those boys will take off your hide." His show of opulence, his ready flow of eloquence, and the maps and samples, which indicated a mine of magnitude, convinced his listeners that here was an opportunity which could not be ignored. The Hayden, Stone men voiced a willingness to investigate the Flin Flon at once; and if their engineer's report was favorable, an agreement would be executed with the Hammell syndicate forthwith.

"No time for reports," snapped Hammell. In his rapid-fire way he explained that the breakup was not far off, and any delay in negotiations would result in the loss of a year's time, since drills and supplies could be taken into the property only while ice and snow covered the ground. Asked what terms he could offer, the ready Hammell replied that his syndicate would accept $1,000,000 for a 75 per cent interest, the purchasing group to guarantee a minimum expediture of $50,000.

Hayden, Stone communicated with Daniel Jackling, with whom they were associated in Utah Copper. Jackling is supposed to have protested undertaking work on a prospect without preliminary examination, but it was significant that he provided an engineer to conduct operations. Raymond Brooks was selected to direct drilling. With him went Orrin Peterson, then working in Utah, as assistant. To Hammell was assigned the more difficult task of assembling several tons of supplies and two diamond drills and transporting them through the bush from the Pas to Flin Flon before the spring thaws made such transportation impossible. It was the kind of work he relished. With an energy and ingenuity which amazed the natives, he mobilized every transportation facility in the vicinity and defeated the breakup by a narrow margin; the equipment was safely transported. Brooks and Peterson arrived in good time and the first serious development of the Flin Flon began. The drills were in operation by the end of March, 1916.

While only 6,000 feet of drilling was completed before the freezeup, Brooks and Peterson were convinced that the deposit was of major proportions. Cores had shown the presence of a barren "horse" of rock within the main ore mass, and this suggested some dilution of grade in mining operations. The large zinc content was regarded as unfortunate, since this metal, if recovered as a concentrate, would have to be shipped by rail to British Columbia for treatment or, as an alternative, to Belgium. No other existing facilities were available. Either way, Brooks and Peterson considered the zinc valueless. The course of the European War was such that a marginal property of the Flin Flon variety was not considered a good risk.

Hayden, Stone officials read the report with great care, conferred at some length, and then communicated with Toronto, respectfully requesting that the forthcoming payment to the owners of Flin Flon be deferred in favor of using such funds in further drilling. This was refused, and Hayden, Stone withdrew from the enterprise after having spent $50,000. Hammell, reviewing the situation twenty years later, had this to say: "Unfortunately, I was in the bush [at the date of the Hayden Stone incident]. Any time they spend more money on my property I will keep them going. One of my partners, a solicitor, threw the deal, and now I had to work it up all over again. I was in pretty good shape. I had kept the data of the engineers . . . the samples and all the maps . . . and could go out and work again."

His work at this point consisted of finding a new partner to foot the heavy bills of more exploration. By a process of elimination he found a man willing to assume the considerable risk, this time Dave Fasken, a wealthy Haileyburian. Dave, lumberman and water-power magnate, was bluff and generous as his brother Alec was curt and frugal. With a group of associates, he now formed the Great Sulphide Company, which purchased outright for $50,000 the 17 per cent interest in the claims held by prospectors Dan Milligan and Isadore Dion. At the same time, the Fasken Company agreed to perform a stipulated footage of diamond drilling, for which a further 18 per cent interest would be allocated.

Once more Hammell accepted the job of moving supplies into the Flin Flon, at which he was now fully expert, and with Ernie Neelands at the helm, the drills began biting into the puzzling sulphides. On this occasion work continued from March, 1917, to July, 1918, and forty-four holes were completed for an aggregate of 25,664 feet, truly a magnificent performance for steam-powered machines. But, as before, the intricate admixture of sulphides presented problems which, in that day of comparatively primitive flotation methods, appeared impossible of solution. The Great Sulphide Company, having performed as required by the agreement and increased its interest to 35 per cent, decided to step to the sidelines and await events. The tireless Hammell was thus confronted yet again with the apparently hopeless chore of finding new money.

But now, at least, he had in his possession two sets of reports, both of them confirming his contention that an ore body of unquestionably large tonnage, containing intriguing values in gold, copper, silver and zinc, existed. So fortified, Hammell turned to the Mining Corporation of Canada, which was then winding up its silver operations in Cobalt. The president, J. P. Watson, a lawyer by profession, listened to the story with manifest interest, and then called in his chief of mining operations, Scott Turner. This impulse was a happy one, for in Turner the Flin Flon found a new and worthy champion who proved to be fully as determined as Hammell, and, as will be presently revealed, well equipped technically to meet and conquer every challenge of the exacting Flin Flon.

A celebrated engineer who had operated in many countries and later became director of the United States Bureau of Mines under President Herbert Hoover, his old associate, Turner devoted several days to scrutinizing the voluminous data. To his trained mind, the Flin Flon seemed an exceptional ore deposit, and he recommended it strongly. Watson, mindful that the size of the project demanded prodigious capital advances before production could be attained, emphasized the necessity of enlisting a substantial partner. Turner agreed to this suggestion, and drawing from his long experience in the industry proposed William Boyce Thompson as one who had the vision and means to handle the larger part of so ambitious an undertaking. Hammell was called in and informed of Mining Corporation's decision.

"If you can get Thompson to come in, we'll take a slice," Watson told him.

Hammell needed no further suggestions. Armed with the precious reports, he left for New York.

Thompson, a rising figure in the mining world, was a modern Lochinvar come out of the West. Safely established in Wall Street, he had won sudden success in the rise, and fall, of Nipissing Mines, described by the *Wall Street Journal* in 1906 as "one of the most extraordinary events in mining finance." Born in Montana, son of Butte's first mayor, Thompson was educated at Exeter and the Columbia School of Mines. Combining a catholic knowledge of mining and a rare understanding of security markets, he listened to E. P. Earle and Captain J. R. Delamar and agreed to take an option to purchase several hundred thousand shares of Nipissing at $3.45 each, with the avowed purpose of making a market. His timing, save for an initial eagerness, which, we have seen, caused him to "lose" some cheap stock to the ubiquitous Delamar, was perfect. His hook, carefully baited, landed the biggest fish of all, the potent house of Guggenheim, for while he was engaged feeding stock to the public through the New York Curb, the "Guggies" sent their well-advertised $1,000,000-a-year engineer, cocky John Hays Hammond, to examine the Cobalt property. Hammond's report was favorable and the Guggenheims quickly signed an agreement with Thompson to purchase 400,000 shares at $25, of which 100,000 shares were taken immediately. The stock zoomed to dizzy heights and reached $40. Nip became the feature of the New York Curb.

It was a magnificent coup for the young promoter, but storm

signals began to flash. Rumors circulated; ore conditions in depth were less rosy as development progressed. Stout denials were sounded, but speculators noted with apprehension that one of Hammond's younger engineers had been sent north to re-examine the situation. Nip began to lose ground and soon approached the Guggenheim option price. Thompson nervously awaited word from 120 Broadway. Finally, he was asked to present himself at the Guggenheim office for an interview regarding the legality of the Nipissing claims. The time was set for 10:00 A.M. on a Saturday morning, the very date the option expired. Thompson arrived promptly, but was allowed to cool his heels in the waiting room. For almost an hour he anxiously watched the clock, and then his suspicion became a certainty. The Guggies, he decided, were bowing out of the Nip. Thompson was not given to inertia. Grabbing his hat, he raced for his office and by noon, closing time, he had sold 100,000 shares of stock. The price, of course, nose-dived, but this was as nothing to Monday when the Guggenheim office announced that the deal was off because of Nip's refusal to extend the option one month to permit examination of land titles. The Nipissing panic was now on with a ferocity which wiped out investors and speculators overnight, and evoked a hurricane of bitter criticism. Thompson and the Guggies were lashed by the press, and one unfortunate stockholder broke out in verse:

> Life is real,—but this vision
> Lasted only a short time;
> If you want my last decision—
> To hell with NIP and Guggenheim!

But Thompson was interested in neither doggerel nor newspaper editorials, for Nip had secured his long-sought fortune. He was now in the big leagues of finance, and could sit at conference tables with the mightiest. That Nipissing eventually paid over $30,000,000 in dividends was of small moment to the newly created mining tycoon. He was long out of Nip before this eventuated, and had moved on to greater things—Magma Copper, Inspiration Copper, Nevada Consolidated, Texas Gulf Sulphur, and his dearest baby, the fast-growing Newmont Mines. He was in fact the last of the Copper Kings.

In New York, Hammell's interview with this extraordinary man, then at the height of his power, must have been worth observing. Baldish, cold, inscrutable, speaking with an economy of words, Thompson sat in sharp contrast to the effervescent Hammell. But in the welter of words he perceived elements which were of interest.

"Let me see the maps," he commanded.

Hammell tossed a large portfolio on the desk, leaned over Thompson's shoulder, and declaimed at length on the shattering size of the ore body. Thompson's eyes darted over the plans and assays, and for the first time his features relaxed.

"Might be something in this," he admitted.

He then asked pointed questions. Satisfied by the answers and the terms of the proposed agreement, he then interrogated Hammell about the country. How could supplies and equipment be brought into such a remote area on a scale to permit full-scale mining operations?

"You leave that to me," stated Hammell—language Thompson understood. "I'll get the stuff in."

"All right." Thompson rose and extended his hand. "Get going. My lawyers will write the draft of contract immediately."

While Hammell was en route to the Pas via Chicago and Winnipeg, Toronto and New York worked out the details of what was hoped would be the last Flin Flon agreement. Thompson was given an option to purchase 75 per cent of the property and Mining Corporation 25 per cent, and in this proportion both groups would advance the funds to complete a program which embraced both drilling and underground work. Scott Turner, for the first time, was now responsible for technical direction of the enterprise.

At the Pas, Jack Hammell outdid himself. Rounding up the local storekeepers, he addressed them something in this fashion:

"We are going to buy everything from you men here, so don't push prices above ten per cent of cost."

The response was gratifying, and by the time Turner's engineers arrived from Toronto there was assembled on the property sufficient food to meet the needs of 118 men for eight months.

"It astonished those fellows to see ten tons of bacon and ten tons of ham," reported Hammell. "But they didn't have too much before they were through."

Plans called for the sinking of two shafts 500 feet apart at the south and north ends of the ore body. Turner's idea was to synchronize drilling to actual underground values and thereby obtain a "yardstick" of measure for all such future operations. Hammell, meanwhile, was able to obtain immediate delivery on only one complete mining plant. Since the breakup was imminent, he decided to purchase the second plant locally. Otherwise, he knew, Turner's ambitious two-shaft program would not be realized that year.

At Beaver Lake, the Prince Albert Company, which had suspended operations some time before, had exactly the equipment required. The directors were all elderly and experienced businessmen, and when Hammell approached them they were confident of securing an excellent price, cognizant, as they were, of the important time element. To their chagrin, Hammell offered only $10,000. They demanded $15,000, insisting that the equipment was in excellent working order. Hammell bluntly informed them it was valueless to the Prince Albert Company, and his offer was manna from heaven.

"Take it or leave it" were his parting words.

The directors were in no hurry, for time was working in their favor. But as the breakup neared and the remaining period for winter transport shortened correspondingly, they began to worry. Hammell, unconcerned, was putting the final touches to the winter road into the Flin Flon. He made no effort to communicate. Fearing they had overplayed their hand, Prince Albert officials hastened to summon Hammell.

"We accept $10,000," they informed him, and added the hope that he would be able to move in the equipment before the road became impassable.

Hammell produced a check and demanded a receipt. When this was handed him he confronted the pleased negotiators with a smile.

"Now, I want to tell you something. That plant has been on the Flin Flon and steamed up for two weeks."

There were angry words, threats of legal action, but Hammell stood his ground, then lashed back. He denounced tactics which he declared might have retarded the advancement of a country sorely in need of mining development, and in the end converted hostility and resentment into protestations of lasting friendship and messages of good luck.

The headframes on the Flin Flon marked the commencement of underground operations and a new turn in the mining fortunes of Manitoba. The first shaft, located well within the footwall of the ore, unexpectedly encountered disseminated sulphides from 135 to 200 feet. As the work progressed, the massive sulphide zone was reached at the point indicated by the extensive drilling. Ultimately, both shafts reached the objective of 300 feet with results fully confirming expectations. Turner was now able to represent the Flin Flon as a solid reality. His calculations envisaged an ore body of 15,900,000 tons minimum, averaging 1.8 per cent copper, 1.2 ounces silver, 3.8 per cent zinc, and $1.80 gold per ton. This was big game, indeed, even with recognized metallurgical problems facing the operators.

Hammell was not idle during this time. A railroad from the Pas to Flin Flon was imperative, but a 100-mile right-of-way through the bush, requiring several bridges to span the waterways, and the usual costly railroad construction in pioneer country, called for large capital. This was a matter of public concern, and Hammell, turning from bulldozing roads, supplies, and Prince Albert Company directors, now gave his full attention to a railway project. After a long session with the premier of Manitoba, he was informed that the Provincial House of Commons was badly divided on the issue of the separate school issue, and in any event the members were completely ignorant of mining in the north. With his usual promptitude, Hammell invited key members of the Manitoba legislature to visit the Flin Flon and learn of its magnitude at first hand. The junket was a memorable one. No effort or expense was spared to transport the curious southerners to the district that was merely a dot on the map to them, and by the time they returned to Winnipeg Flin Flon was the most publicized mining project in Canada. But political fences also needed repairing. More men to sponsor the railroad were necessary, and Hammell formed the North Line Association to plug the proper candidate in the forthcoming election.

It was a hot campaign. Hammell managed everything. The riding was a polyglot one, consisting of trappers, Indians, prospectors, small merchants, and a considerable number of priests and nuns. Never high-hat, Hammell mingled freely with the electorate and convinced the majority that his candidate would further the interests of the Pas. With the ecclesiastics, his persuasion was particularly effective. Of the thirty-four, only one, a priest, resisted his arguments, and he, as the indefatigable Hammell learned, was ineligible to vote, being an American citizen. The election, as was to be expected, was all Hammell, and the groundwork was successfully laid for railroad construction to the Flin Flon.

Meanwhile, the time approached for Thompson to declare himself regarding the considerable payment due the vendors. Turner impatiently awaited word from New York and at last it came, only a few days before the deadline. Thompson, enmeshed in a complexity of deals elsewhere and worried about the postwar deflation which threatened even lower metal prices, curtly informed Mining Corporation that he was unwilling to proceed further.

A crisis now confronted the directors, and opinion was sharply divided as to continuing alone. But Scott Turner, convinced as never before that the Flin Flon was a mine, persuaded his confreres that the claims should be purchased by the company.

"We would be derelict in our duty otherwise," he declared.

The die was cast. For $600,000 the 65 per cent interest owned by the Hammell Syndicate, Tom Creighton, Leon Dion, and the Mosher brothers was purchased. Hammell received $200,000, and each of the prospectors who had remained faithful, $100,000. Hammell made good his promise accordingly, and while this was far less than the kind of money old Flin Flon brought up from the Sunless City, a comparable treasure, as time was to prove, still remained in the ground. Hammell surrendered the reins to the capable hands of Scott Turner, who henceforth was to be the spark plug of the Flin Flon enterprise.

For four years little was heard of the Flin Flon, and many observers regarded Turner with compassion, a man who had overreached himself. But during this hiatus he was quietly effecting a long-planned program of claim acquisition. The original staking of Creighton's band consisted of twelve claims, and now, by further staking and judicious purchase, the Flin Flon grew to a prodigious size. More than one hundred claims were added at a time when most men thought the venture was dying on its feet. Nor was this all. Patiently, and with a thoroughness which often irritated his associates, Turner began the compilation of data which had never before been duplicated in Canadian mining. Among other helpful devices was an intricate glass model of the great ore body which became a "point of interest" in Cobalt. But this was not the first such model to be constructed. Years before, in 1916 to be exact, Hammell had hit upon the same idea.

Realizing his technical deficiencies for such a duty, he had turned to Bert Poirier, manager of the Vipond Mine in Porcupine, and commissioned this old friend to build a small model of the Flin Flon ore body and prepare cost estimates of operating by large-scale open-pit methods. Mindful that the neighboring Dome Mine was then conducting exactly such mining in the famed "Glory Hole" where the Golden Sidewalk was located, Poirier visited his colleague Charles Kaeding, manager of Dome. In the course of obtaining the required information, Poirier was casually informed by Kaeding that drilling below the open pit had recently encountered extraordinarily rich ore. Poirier was quick to inform his principals in New York. Considerable Dome stock was purchased, Poirier himself buying shares through arrangement with his bank. And then, only a few months later, rising costs induced by war conditions forced suspension of work at the mine, and the market on Dome dropped sharply. And so, long before the Flin Flon was generally known to exist, its repercussions were felt elsewhere.

In 1924 the Flin Flon was in a shape to satisfy the meticulous Turner. Accordingly, he addressed a letter to the Harry Payne Whitney office in New York, shrewdly anticipating an immediate response. Whitney, for whom mining was merely an avocation, a sort of corollary to his traction and banking interests, had, nevertheless, spent $15,000,000 in profitless exploration. "Kidded" by his friends, who lost no opportunity to remind him of his gullibility, he determined to revamp his organization and find a mine which would compensate for his considerable losses. Turner's letter, therefore, was beautifully timed. It was sent on to the West Coast where R. E. Phelan, chief of operations in that area, was then making his headquarters. Phelan was astonished to learn of the reputed size of Flin Flon and sent Turner a long communication questioning the accuracy of the ore estimates. Turner replied in one sentence.

"The ore reserves as represented are accurate to the best of my knowledge."

Phelan, at first annoyed by this economy of language, was impressed in spite of himself. He journeyed to New York, where it was decided that the younger Whitney, Cornelius, interview Turner in Toronto. Preliminary letters were exchanged, and Whitney departed on his important errand. Confusion in the Mining Corporation office resulted in neglect to inform Turner of the exact time of appointment, and in consequence Whitney was kept waiting almost two hours. This was an unfortunate faux pas, and might have had dire repercussions, but having come so far, Whitney swallowed his indignation and continued to wait. Turner finally appeared, most apologetic and full of explanations to account for the delay. Graciously, the Whitney scion accepted the apologies, and quickly turned to the pertinent subject of the Flin Flon.

In a matter of minutes, Turner skillfully outlined the situation, whereupon Whitney asked for terms. The reply was unexpected.

"Examine the property first," said Turner, "and then, if you are interested, we can discuss a contract."

Conditioned to the rigidity of New York agreements, Whitney was nonplused. In a quandary, he called for Parke Channing, the Whitney mining chief, and further discussion brought a promise from Turner that the terms would be in no whit different after the examination of the mine than they were at the moment, and these he outlined briefly. At the same time he gave his solemn promise that no other offers would be entertained while the Whitneys were engaged in their investigation of the ground. Channing pleaded lack of trained men available to examine the Flin Flon, but Turner met this objection by offering his own engineering staff. In the end, Whitney agreed to the proposal, and Phelan was sent to the Pas with a formidable corps of experts.

R. E. Phelan, who eventually became manager of the Flin Flon and guided it to ultimate success, later wrote in retrospect:

Among Mr. Whitney's varied mining interests was a company called Complex Ore Recoveries. As its name implies, this Company owned patents for the treatment of "complex" ores, so that, when the analysis of the Flin Flon ore-body was studied by Mr. Channing's organization, it seemed that the Complex Ores Recoveries Company's process might be applied to the treatment of the ore and thus make it the basis of a commercial operation.

As a result of this study, Mr. C. V. Whitney went to Toronto and discussed the property with The Mining Corporation of Canada. Later, Mr. Channing had his chief engineer, R. E. Phelan, arrange with The Mining Corporation of Canada and Mr. Alex Fasken, the then owners, for permission to unwater the workings and to sample the ore exposed, and otherwise to make such examination as was possible under the conditions. The examination was made in the summer of 1925. As the methods of treatment contemplated were electrolytic in character, and as small-scale operation was out of the question, it was realized that a very large amount of cheap power would be essential to the successful operation of any treatment method. Therefore, the examining engineers, after sampling the ore exposed underground and sacking and starting about 50 tons of the ore on its long trip to the testing laboratory in Denver, Colorado, directed their attention to looking over and checking all available power sites tributary to the mine.

The examination checked the character and grade of the ore and gave data on how it actually occurred in the ground. It also proved that ample reasonably cheap power could be secured by the erection of a hydro-electric power plant at Island Falls, on the Churchill River. It also disclosed many important facts that later were invaluable in operations on the property. This examination cost $11,000, which will give some idea as to its completeness.

Upon the result of the examination being reported to Mr. Channing, an option was secured upon the property.

Much lies behind this terse summary. Upon returning from Flin Flon, Phelan was received by Turner who requested that all other directors and officers of Mining Corporation, including legal counsel, refrain from disturbing negotiations. The session was drawn out, lasting several weeks. At one time Phelan, overwrought by protracted discussion, expressed blunt disapproval of Turner's demands and declared he was through. At this Turner soothingly suggested a recess of a few days, with perhaps a bit of entertainment at a local movie. And in the end these men, engineers both, composed a two-page memorandum embodying all the terms of the involved deal. Later this was expanded into eighty printed pages by the zealous and exacting lawyers of the various groups represented.

The agreement provided the Whitneys two years in which to explore the property. At the end of this period, if they elected to continue with the option, Mining Corporation was to be reimbursed $854,000 cash and also assigned a 15 per cent nonassessable interest in a company to be formed. The Fasken group, still in the running with its Great Sulphide Company, was to receive 35 per cent of the vendor stock. Signatures were fixed to the momentous document on September 30, 1925.

Subsequently, some question arose concerning the assessability of interests allocated to the claim owners. Phelan then joined Turner in insisting that the spirit of the original memorandum be kept, a circumstance which must have been surprising to the legal gentlemen of the Whitney organization.

Up to the entrance of the Whitneys into the Flin Flon situation, $1,500,000 had been expended on development by Hayden, Stone, the Great Sulphide Company, William Boyce Thompson, and Mining Corporation.

The Whitney board of strategy, satisfied that ore was plentiful, turned at once to the complicated metallurgy. Some answer here must be found, but it was realized the problem was not simple. Zinc and copper, composing three-quarters of the values in the deposit, had to be separated before the gold and silver, locked in massive pyrite, could be recovered. All the metals must be extracted if the ore body was to be mined profitably. The chief difficulty arose from the fact that the ore occurred in an already concentrated form, that is, massive sulphides containing less than 10 per cent gangue. Fortunately, the marvelous progress of the flotation process in the preceding decade had made a study of this type of material feasible.

Whitney's Denver Complex Ores Recoveries Company now conducted thousands of tests and experiments at the Colorado School of Mines. Large bulk samples in ton lots were sent down from the Flin Flon, and gradually a method to treat the ore was formulated. The process recommended was the concentration of the chalcopyrite (copper) and sphalerite (zinc) by differential flotation, each being stored as a separate concentrate. The tailings, composed of pyrite with which the gold and silver were intimately mixed, were then to be treated by cyanidation for recovery of the precious metals.

With a caution born of expert advice, the Whitneys decided to construct an experimental plant at the Flin Flon to test the process under actual property conditions. Plant construction was started in September, 1926, and continued throughout the winter. In March, 1927, the completed 30-ton pilot mill went into operation. "Bugs" were not long in manifesting themselves, largely due to organic matter in the water brought in the rising spring thaws. Turner's suggestions here removed the difficulties. Then equipment proved faulty, and many replacements were found necessary. At this point, the property was called the "Flim Flam," not many people, including residents of the Pas, being inclined to take the Whitney effort seriously. Dave Fasken *et al.*, losing heart, were willing to retrieve their investment at cost, so when William Boyce Thompson's Newmont Company made such an offer it was eagerly accepted. For the Fasken group, which parted with a long-held and dearly bought 35 per cent interest, it was a case of no hits, no runs, and one error. Thompson, with revised ideas of copper and the Flin Flon, was back on the score sheet, occupying a grandstand seat with several innings yet to be played.

The mill began to show improved results, but a wide gap between those demonstrated in the Colorado laboratory and those achieved at Flin Flon still remained to be closed before the huge capital outlays of final plant installation could be hazarded. And time was running short; the September 30 deadline was not far off. A two months' extension was requested and granted by Mining Corporation and the mill pounded on. Robert and I visited Flin Flon about this time, but little was said by mill technicians. A quiet serious mood, however, reflected deep anxiety. Would the Whitneys persist or would they, like others before them, throw up the sponge and count their loss? The shortening days brought the time of fateful decision closer.

The grade of ore was so closely approximated by this time that everything hinged on gold recovery. A gold content of .074 ounces per ton was equivalent, at $20.67 gold, to $1.50. Not all of this was recoverable, and the cost of treating the heavy pyrite tailings was calculated at $1 per ton. The hairsplitting phase of the quiet drama had now been reached, and metallurgists and chemists worked feverishly to increase recovery and lower costs. In gold rested the profit margin of Flin Flon ore, for all other metals had reached constant recoveries. Tests indicated that the gold in the tailings could be won, but, unfortunately, the amount of cyanide consumed in the process was excessive, making the cost prohibitive. Some means must be found to recover a large part of the cyanide for continual use; otherwise the entire project would have to be abandoned.

Channing turned to the San Francisco firm of Mills & Crowe, owners of the original Merrill cyanide patents. These estimable gentlemen sat in their shirt sleeves, listened to the tale of the Flin Flon, expectorated into the brass cuspidors strategically placed throughout their office, and declared themselves equal to the problem. Moving into their laboratory, they went to work and forthwith designed a satisfactory cyanide regeneration process, whereby the efficacious chemical could pick up the gold and then be used again *ad infinitum*. Whitney's prayers were answered and a Mills-Crowe regeneration plant was built as an annex to the Flin Flon pilot mill.

Did it work? The answer came on November 30, 1927, in the form of an announcement from the Whitney office in New York. The option, it was stated, would be exercised.

In the excitement of the moment, little attention was given to the statement that followed, but the sober words of R. E. Phelan denoted that much work and considerable uncertainty hung over the Flin Flon, even yet.

> At least 3,000 tons of ore [he wrote in summary] would have to be mined and milled per day. The mining system would have to be cheap and carried out that the ore would not remain in the mine long enough to become oxidized. There would have to be both an open pit and an underground mine for the first six or seven years of the life of the property. Very fine grinding was required and also a large capacity of flotation cells, both of which meant more equipment and higher costs in the concentrator. A cyanide annex was essential to the maximum recovery of gold and silver. An electrolytic zinc plant was necessary. A copper smelter was necessary. A hydro-electric power plant and 60 miles of transmission line from the power plant to the mine was vital. Ample shops with modern tools were required for repair and general work. Very large amounts of water would be used. A railway would have to be built into the mine before either construction of the plant or operations of any kind on any extended scale could be undertaken. The necessary camps, hospital, and housing facilities would have to be built.

Striking while the iron was hot, the Whitneys incorporated the 12,713 acres of the Flin Flon, swelled to giant size by the careful and astute work of Scott Turner, into the Hudson Bay Mining and Smelting Company (an outgrowth of the Flin Flon Company, which had been formed during the interim option period). The Whitneys received 500,000 shares of Hudson Bay, Newmont 350,000, and Mining Corporation, no longer producing silver at this stage, 150,000 shares in addition to the promised $865,000. Then, with a speed suggesting that full advantage would be taken of the favorable metal and financial situation, the company disposed of 1,000,000 shares of $10 each to favored Whitney associates, with the stipulation that such stock would not be salable for a given time. On the same date, January 20, 1938, 500,000 shares of stock were sold to others at $15.

Of this amount, Newmont passed on rights to its stockholders to purchase 237,804 shares at the same price, and Mining Corporation did likewise with 166,005 shares, after having itself bought 35,499. There were issued, accordingly, 2,500,000 shares in all, with a working capital of $17,500,000.

The public, largely ignored in the financing, rushed to buy stock and soon bid it above the $20 mark, and the Whitneys, who had spent approximately $1,000,000, were able to see an immediate $9,-000,000 paper profit. By comparison, mining stock merchants in Toronto were pikers, and for the first time Canadians realized why the Whitneys enjoyed their international financial reputation.

On the property, meanwhile, Phelan, the manager, was left to cope with the gigantic chore of bringing the now-famous Flin Flon into production. There were so many imponderables in the situation and so much time required before the pudding was ready for the eating that astute mining men began to express doubts about the enterprise, and once more Tom Creighton's creation became the Flim Flam. Phelan moved ahead with grim resolution, nevertheless. Fortunately, the powersite had been spoken for some time previously, and now all details were swiftly ironed out. In the larger question of a railroad, Hammell's groundwork also bore fruit. Negotiations with the Manitoba government culminated in a $3,500,000 guaranteed bond issue to meet the costs of construction, the Hudson Bay Mining Company being required simultaneously to deposit $3,-000,000 as a capital fund to be expended coincident with railroad work.

Phelan, dour and uncolorful, performed in a manner which tokened well for the stockholders. In addition to supervising the puzzling ramifications of plant construction, he devised a scheme of open-pit mining at once ingenious and daring. Flin Flon Lake was dammed and pumped out successfully, thus ensuring low mining costs for a goodly period. All went well in the erection of the 45,000-horsepower unit at Island Falls, the work proceeding with amazing rapidity, despite the rigors of climate and the complexities of the task.

The first annual report of Hudson Bay, covering operations for the year 1928, gave the dimensions and grade of the ore body as designated by diamond drilling and underground work to a depth of 900 feet. Phelan stated there were 18,000,000 tons averaging 1.71 per cent copper, 3.45 per cent zinc, 1.06 ounces silver and .074 ounces gold. In far-off London, a mining commentator noted the remarkable similarity between these figures and those quoted by Scott Turner in 1920, based upon drilling and limited underground work.

We suspect [wrote this Englishman] that the personal equation is involved in problems of this kind, and that an experienced engineer, carefully considering the preliminary data, can often make a pretty shrewd guess as to how an orebody will stand up under later and more intensive exploration.

By October, 1930, production had commenced. It was not an auspicious time. Unlike Noranda, Hudson Bay made its bow when metal prices had followed the disastrous decline of security prices everywhere. Phelan's remarkable performance, apparently, was to go for naught.

In June, 1930, foreseeing the need of more funds, the company increased its capitalization by another 500,000 shares and issued $5,-000,000 of convertible debentures against this stock, the exchange figure being $10 per share. Fortunately, the full severity of the great depression had not been reached and most of the debentures were purchased by stockholders. The august name of J. P. Morgan & Company as underwriters undoubtedly generated confidence. In the face of bleak times the mine continued to function.

Since Tom Creighton had discovered the Flin Flon, a matter of fifteen years had elapsed and approximately $22,000,000 had been spent, with little reward in sight. Reflecting dismal prospects, the stock made successive new lows on the New York Curb, dropping under the $1 mark in 1932. The first full year of production, 1931, told its own story. Metal production was anything but reassuring, calculated on a recovery basis. Only 68 per cent of the gold was retrieved, less than 55 per cent of the silver, 74.3 per cent of the copper, and only 43 per cent of the zinc. Worse still, the zinc could not be sold in any volume and so accumulated as a stockpile to await better days. While a small operating profit was reported for the year, the final net figures showed a substantial loss.

But a tiny ray of light on an otherwise clouded horizon gave promise of better times; for the first time since England adopted the gold standard in 1822 the price of gold was rising. Every effort was being made, also, to increase metal recoveries, and during 1932 some slight success in this direction was obtained. While breaking no records in achievement, Hudson Bay was holding its own. Busy metallurgists were conducting research to devise practical methods for the recovery of other metals, such as cadmium, tellurium and selenium, which were present in the ore, though in minor quantity.

Thanks to the Whitney resources and determination, the project forged ahead slowly. By the end of 1933 the company was at last earning a net profit and cash resources, after having reached dangerously low levels, began to increase. Significantly, almost 75 per cent of the copper was being recovered, more than 58 per cent of the silver, 68 per cent of the gold, and 46 per cent of the zinc. The tide had definitely turned, not only at the Flin Flon but on world markets where the demand for base metals was beginning to quicken after years of stagnation.

As the mine deepened, a perceptible improvement in the grade of all metals became manifest. In a marginal property of large tonnage, this was a change of prime importance. Coincident with this welcome event, metallurgy continued to improve. By the end of 1935 almost 3 per cent more of the gold content was being won from a higher grade ore. Silver recovery had jumped from 54.7 to 64.3 per cent, almost 3 per cent additional zinc was coming from the electrolytic plant, and copper recovery had reached the respectable figure of 80 per cent. By this time the company was handling 60 per cent more ore than in 1931, the tonnage treated in 1935 being 1,617,-000. And, a full twenty years after discovery, the Flin Flon paid its initial dividend of $1 per share. The stock, so long a "dog," had become a favorite trader and was approaching the 1928 issue price of $15. For the first time selenium and tellurium were produced in fair quantity and a sizable amount of cadmium was being derived at little cost. Confident now, the company constructed additional power units and special apparatus to improve rising metal recoveries.

Having safely navigated troubled waters, the Flin Flon was by this time cruising easily. Each successive year brought new records of production together with healthy additions to ore reserves. During World War II, Hudson Bay metals played a vital part in the battle against fascism. In 1943 alone, Flin Flon's "Sunless City" added 97,000,000 pounds of copper; 120,000,000 pounds of zinc; 3,150,000 ounces of silver; 193,000 ounces of gold, and 188,000 pounds of cadmium to the stockpiles of the United Nations. Open-pit operations had now been entirely supplanted by underground mining but, notwithstanding, costs remained low and profits large. Dividends to date total more than $52,000,000 and after large capital expenditures the company possesses almost $20,000,000 in net quick assets. Starting production with 18,000,000 tons, today's ore reserves stand at 27,000,000 tons of somewhat higher grade ore, this after mining 24,000,000 tons. A large part of the property still remains unexplored. At $40 a share, and paying $2, Hudson Bay is popular with investment trusts and speculators who pride themselves on their "progressive" conservatism.

As in so many mining sagas, there are the forgotten men of the Flin Flon. The prospectors have scattered or died, their names completely obscured by years crowded with other events. Scott Turner, in semiretirement, has nothing but fond memories and the pride of achievement to show for his indispensable role. At no time did he acquire any stock in Hudson Bay, for a rigorous sense of integrity prevented him from capitalizing on a situation in which he was a principal actor. R. E. Phelan, after yeoman service and devotion to the Flin Flon, no longer manages the mine he created from bush, but his work will never fail to inspire mining men everywhere.

Flin Flon remains a one-mine camp, but it is reasonable to expect that so intensively mineralized an area should contain other sizable ore deposits. Such, at any rate, is the contention of "Cranberry" Jack Callinan who long ago acquired dozens of claims crowding the Hudson Bay on all sides. His Callinan Flin Flon Mines has had rough sledding for almost two decades, but now, a sick man in Toronto, he has secured funds through promoter Bradley Streit for development of his ground. He is confident of success, and several capable engineers share his optimism. But only work and time will reveal whether or not the unpredictable Flin Flon scattered his gold for the Whitneys alone.

HUDSON BAY MINING & SMELTING
1930–1945

Gross production	$219,629,000
Copper produced, lbs.	865,785,309
Zinc produced, lbs.	1,098,890,048
Gold produced, oz.	1,959,388
Silver produced, oz.	27,483,650
Dividends paid	$52,401,486

CHAPTER XI

The Road to Rouyn

COPPER-GOLD ERA

First Edition

Vol. I   Rouyn, Wednesday, Sept. 15, 1926.   Price 25 cents

FIRST ROUYN NEWSPAPER

RAILROAD PROSPECTS   THE HORNE SMELTER   ELECTRIC POWER 6
ELECTION RESULTS___OUR TOWN___LE MAIRE___NORANDA
TOWNSITE___ROUYN___

What does the outside world think of Rouyn? What does the outside world know of Rouyn?

Much has been written of the wildness, the lawlessness, the wickedness of the camp by people who have spent two or three days here and who have, we venture to say, let their imaginative powers lead them rather beyond the absolute truth. One gentleman who favored us with his presence for a short space last fall, announced that Rouyn was the worst he had known, his experience covering apparently most of the camps in the North American Continent which have arisen since the boom days of '97. He spoke of naked women careering through the streets in broad daylight and solemnly asserted that two houses out of every three were occupied by bootleggers.

The Rouyn Mining District too has had its share of adverse criticism since it first came before the public in 1922. The Quebec mining laws, the railroad, the power question have all caused much dissatisfaction and uneasiness from time to time___Rumours and counter rumours have sped abroad and it was difficult to get at the truth.

The aim of the COPPER GOLD ERA is to set before those who are interested a true and unembellished account of conditions and progress in what is possibly destined to be one of the foremost copper gold mining camps of the age.

Before me is a letter dated February 26, 1924, postmarked Rouyn, Quebec. The blue lines of the co-ordinate paper are faded and indistinct. The writing is tidy and fine, as you would expect from the hand of an engineer trained in composing reports, and while the words are occasionally faint and blurred and the pages often smudged with the soot of campfires, the sentences are none the less legible. As I read, long-forgotten days crowd my memory, dead men come alive, and I realize how inexorable has been the passage of time.

"While I write in the snugness of our new cabin I can hear the puffing of the Noranda compressor across the lake. It is beautiful music to my ears, a song that every prospector longs to hear, for it marks a new phase in the history of northern Quebec. We are here to stay, my boy. The Noranda will make a mine, and a big one. I think I know something about replacement ore bodies, thanks to my work in Sudbury, and I'm betting my future against the recurrence of sulphide lenses on the other side of this lake. So I *must* be right.

"Fred and I arrived here a few days ago after a rough trip in Joannes. I am attaching a diary which you may find interesting. As you will note, we staked a large group of claims over the snow and after the breakup we'll return for some prospecting. Bert McDonald, who has a nice camp built on a small island near here, invited us to have dinner with him. It was quite a party. One of the boys had a beaver tail which was delicious, especially after a steady diet of beans and long clear for a couple of weeks. And there was plenty of fresh moose meat. Bill Gamble made a big pot full of cocoa and then served a mess of prunes for dessert. I ate so many Bill christened me 'Prunella.'

"You would enjoy meeting these men. There are only a dozen or so in camp but they're all tough babies who have been in the Yukon, Cobalt, Gowganda, Porcupine and Kirkland Lake. Gus O'Donnell is a great guy and so is Alphonse Paré who brought the Hollinger Mine to Noah Timmins. Then there was Jimmy Green who's building a hotel down the lake, Bob Gamble, Bobby Cockeram, George Ellis, Jim Murray, Eddie and Mike McDonough, Bud Mallory, Freddie Davies, the bad boy of Rouyn, Lloyd Rochester, Marty Wright and Johnny Dillon.

"It's a bit warmer, only fifteen below this morning. Even now everyone is anticipating a rush of new people next summer. When you come up I wish you would bring me a game getter, an Ingersoll watch, and a small flashlight with extra batteries. For yourself, take plenty of long woolen underwear and don't forget to buy a good pair of elk boots in Toronto. Eleven inch tops will be high enough.

"That's all for now, except that I cannot warn you too much about the hazards of prospecting. You've been here a couple of summers and so have had some experience, but remember that when you're here to stay it's another matter. You will be placing yourself in the same position with men who have had no college training. Up here we all start from scratch, and there's a lot of luck in the game. You must have guts; the weak sisters pass out of the picture quickly. I'm sure you can make the grade but if you fail, it's no disgrace. You are still young."

And then Bob's diary.

Feb. 9-11, 1924

Chopped wood so there'll be a fresh supply on hand when we return from our staking bee in Joannes Township. It was not easy work, due to the snow which made the logs slippery. One has to be careful in cold weather—cuts seem to infect easily. Fred is particularly good at this work. He handles an axe beautifully. I kidded him about this and to demonstrate his virtuosity he carved his initials on a big spruce. He did a neat job.

We pored over the government maps again and selected the spot where we would stake, in the northeast corner of the township. This area is in the greenstones just north of the Temiskaming sediments. Fred had spotted some northeast-southwest diabase dikes which he considered a favorable sign of rock movement. These dikes are young and may indicate post mineral adjustment. For a prospector, Fred is developing into an excellent geologist.

On the second day we had visitors, Tom Denton and Carl Erickson who snowshoed over from the Noranda. We discussed mining for a while and then became very philosophical. Covered about everything, the meaning of life, women, the importance of a family, what we'd do if we made a stake, etc. etc. A typical bull session but quite satisfying. There isn't much else one can do here for diversion!

Feb. 12

We pulled out early, while it was still dark. We traveled very light, no tent or stove, but at that our packs seemed heavy. There was a thin crust on the snow through which we crashed repeatedly. As usual, we took turns breaking trail and I must admit I didn't object whenever Fred swung in front of me. It was 35 below zero when we left the cabin and it seemed to grow colder as we approached the Kinojevis River. Wind, I guess. Not many bird or animal tracks showing. Probably due to the thin crust or maybe the weather was too cold. Only damned fools like us go out in such weather!

It began to snow as we reached the river, fine stinging flakes which cut into our faces. Our snowshoes were not helping much now, for we were sinking knee deep. Neither of us could break trail for more than five minutes at a time. At noon we spotted the cabin Austin Dumond and Ed Miller built last fall. [Miller was one of the co-stakers of Noranda and made several of the early discoveries.] It was almost buried in snow, but we got busy and dug a path from the river bank to the door, using our snowshoes as shovels. The door was open, fortunately, and it wasn't long before we had things warm and comfortable. Hot tea and a feed of bacon and beans restored our morale completely. Meanwhile, the weather turned worse, a regular blizzard now, and so we decided to remain here until morning.

Fred wears well. The bush is a severe test of companionship, especially this time of year when the going is tough. Cool, courageous, excellent company, my partner is everything one can ask. In a time like this, his sense of humor is uppermost and his profanity a joy to hear. When things are dull, he regales me with his experiences as an admiral in Central America and a machine gunner in the last war. He has been around the world several times, in sailing vessels, too, of all things.

Feb. 13

Another day of bad weather. We started east late, hoping the snow would diminish, but no such luck. We waited until 10:00 A.M. and then decided to bull our way through. Did not reach the Bend of the Kinojevis until 1:00 P.M., a distance of just over two miles. Wind particularly bad. I felt it in the crotch particularly—at one time I thought my privates were frozen. I must remember to get a weasel skin!

Wanting to get into green bush, we headed northeast along Davidson Creek, a crooked little devil, and at about two o'clock reached the trapper's cabin. Imagine our surprise when we met Tom Middleton and Dave Rainey comfortably camped inside. They had just completed staking a group of claims near the Bend and were now waiting for weather before returning to Rouyn. They had been out almost two weeks and were damned happy to see us. Tom is quite a character, tall, aristocratic looking, something like Buffalo Bill without the goatee. In spite of staking an important part of the

Hollinger Mine, he is flat broke today, but he doesn't seem a bit concerned.

"I had a good time," he says.

Feb. 14

Said good-bye to Tom and Dave and followed a straight compass line dead east. No wind today but we had trouble with fine snow. However, there were large areas of muskeg which made comparatively easy going.

Pitched camp at 7:30 P.M. long after dark, having been on snowshoes for eleven hours. Figured we had covered about nine miles. Fred supervised building camp. First we made a roaring fire. Then we tramped down an area about 10' x 15' and then shoveled this clean with snowshoes. Cut brush, mostly spruce with some balsam, a dirty job, for the snow kept falling over us, down our necks, etc. Shook boughs and laid them down as a mattress, then constructed a lean-to with spruce poles and more brush. Next we had our dinner. Tea had a rotten taste, too much smoke in it. The idea of melting snow for water may sound romantic in books, but actually it's hard to take. Aftermath is a burning sensation when you urinate.

Constructed an incline runway and filled it with logs so there'd be fuel for the fire all night, a sort of automatic feed idea. Rolled into our eiderdowns at 9:30 P.M.

Stars out tonight, also vivid display of northern lights.

Feb. 15-16

Staked four 200-acre claims. Very cold, down to 39 below. First day spent largely in locating old lines of staking done in 1911 during the Bousquet rush. Once we got going made excellent progress. Same work in summer would require at least five or six days.

Back to camp 6:30 P.M. the second day. Glass down to 48 below. Water pail only six feet from fire showed almost an inch of ice. Trees cracking like pistol shots and frost on the outside of sleeping bags. Our shirts were covered with snow which shook loose when we blazed trees and cut posts. Stuck close to fire, but my back half frozen. Cuffs of underwear solid, outside moccasins like iron. The dinner dishes were glazed with ice as we put them down after washing.

Many tracks in the bush, deer, moose, caribou and a few marten and fox. Big timber here, mostly pine and spruce.

Feb. 17

Completed staking two claims and returned to base early, for this is Sunday, after all. Fixed camp, banking sides and back of lean-to with several feet of snow. This warmed things a bit but it is still uncomfortable sleeping out.

Feb. 18

Staked group east tying on to Bousquet Township line. Fred and I worked alone, meeting at claim posts by arrangement. Of course, it's impossible to arrive on schedule—a patch of dirty country or a bad fall may delay you, and then your partner does a bit of worrying. Cutting half-mile lines on these 200-acre claims is no hell, especially on snowshoes. One has to pace distance, blaze trees, and keep direction straight, all at one and the same time. We must carry packs with extra clothing, food, etc., in case we are caught out. The slightest false motion, therefore, throws you off balance, and down you plunge into several feet of damned cold snow. With a load on your back, falling is easy, but regaining your feet is another story. Snowshoes are four feet long and they seem closer to ten. You can't use your hands unless you've planned your fall so that a young tree is within reach. Otherwise, the pack must come off, the snowshoes adjusted to a standing position, then a twist, a turn and lo! you are once more on *terra firma* if you can call the top of snow *firma*. During this process, Fred's profanity is useful.

Negotiating a steep hill requires another kind of technique. Sometimes you have to crawl on your hands and knees, and acting like a plough in five feet of snow is a job I'd like to wish on the Kaiser. Impossible to climb straight up—one must zigzag. And that's where falling is more the rule than the exception.

Feb. 19

Snowed in all day. Fred grins when I talk about his forthcoming marriage. Seems funny that a soldier of fortune will soon be domesticated.

Feb. 20

Up long before dark and completed staking entire group, 18 claims in less than five days, or about 3,600 acres, an area twice that of Central Park in New York. Fred tells me I'm a hard-looking specimen, with ice and snow covering two weeks' growth of whiskers, my clothes torn and patched and my skin the color of fresh strawberries. Says that if I appeared on the streets of Boston now I'd be locked up as a dangerous character.

Feb. 21

Broke camp early. In a way I regretted leaving, we were so well dug in and comfortable by this time. Snowing hard when we started and as usual we alternated breaking trail. My feet began to play hell with me, very sore and chafed by the rubbing of the strings. The bottoms, also, had become unbearingly painful and I was forced to stop frequently. Fred was very patient. When we arrived at the trapper's cabin shortly after twelve he announced we would wait over until the following day.

I cleared a small square on the creek after a half hour of steady shoveling and then chopped a water hole with my ax. This meant another half hour of unpleasant work, for the ice was almost three feet thick. I had to watch my footing closely in order to avoid cutting myself. However, the sight of clear water rising in the hole when I finally broke through the last inch barrier of ice was reward enough. After more than a week of drinking melted snow, *aqua pura* was truly a nectar of the gods! And the tea we had with lunch!

Fred spent a large part of the afternoon composing a record of the trip for his fiancée. He worked hard and faithfully, from time to time stopping to ask how to spell such words as "ecstasy," "panoramic," "metamorphosis." Or he would say, "What is a good word to use instead of wonderful? I've used it too much, already." Love conquers all, even a bushwhacker!

Feb. 22

Washington's Birthday. But Valley Forge was never like this. Today was the worst yet for snow, it simply didn't have a bottom anywhere. Strong wind from the northwest, too. Partridge having a fine time, though, diving under the snow and coming up with frozen berries. Perfect day for that kind of hunting.

Just after lunch the gut on one of my snowshoes broke. Fred and I patched it up with laces and string but I dared not place too much weight on it for fear it would break through completely, leaving me to wade through deep snow for almost four miles.

Met a couple of French prospectors camped in a tent on Lake Routhier. They were real old timers, both well over sixty, throwbacks of the hardy coureurs de bois who roamed over northern Canada in colonial days. They had very little food—just a spot of tea, some sugar, and a partridge they had just killed. We gave them a half slab of bacon, several pounds of flour, baking powder and a bag of rice. Noblesse oblige! They were sorry to see us go.

Arrived at Bert McDonald's cabin on Osisko Lake in late afternoon. Couldn't have gone much further—my feet in bad shape. Bert had a gang with him; they were throwing a big dinner and we were just in time for the feast. And a feast it was!

Among others present was Alphonse Paré, a mining engineer and nephew of Noah Timmins. He it was who examined the Hollinger shortly after it was staked and urged old Noah to buy the claims. He has been all over the world, participated in the Yukon rush and has the rare ability of painting his experiences in a few expressive words. He is in Rouyn to negotiate a deal on the Gamble claims next to Noranda. If he gets this ground and finds ore on it, the camp should take a marked step forward.

Late to bed.

Comfortably seated in a Manhattan apartment, it is not easy for me to accept the fact that I, too, in a modest way, was part of those brave, hopeful days. Forgotten are the black flies, brûlée, spongy muskeg, and howling blizzards raging down from Hudson Bay. I can only think of the miracle of a new community hacked out of the wilderness at a time when most men have lost the art of creating primitive wonders.

Now, if Ed Horne had never been born . . .

Horne was a Nova Scotian who had worked in the gold mines of his native land and then prospected with little success. Attracted by the news of gold discoveries in Ontario, he left Nova Scotia and journeyed to Kirkland Lake. Few of the old-timers there remember him, for he appeared only briefly and was naturally taciturn and uncommunicative.

Ed Horne

In the summer of 1911 we find him in the bush of north-western Quebec, accompanied by Bob Bryden of Cobalt. There had been talk of gold and Clem Foster of Haileybury had sent in a party to investigate. Horne had been settled in New Liskeard for some time, not far from the Quebec border, and this proximity must have had some bearing on his decision to visit the new area. But there had been others long before him.

Two French Canadians, Alphonse Olier and Auguste Renault, had discovered a rich, though small, gold vein on the shores of Lake Fortune in 1907. The news created scarcely a ripple; Cobalt was then just gaining momentum and Porcupine and Kirkland Lake were as yet unknown. In Montreal the Pontiac Company was formed to undertake development work, but little was accomplished until the Union Abitibi Company assumed ownership later. A 40-mile road was cut from Larder Lake to the property and a twenty-stamp mill put in operation. While the enterprise ended in failure by the time war broke out in 1914, a few prospectors became interested in the district. Gold was reported in the environs of Kienawisik (Montigny) Lake to the east and then in Bousquet Township, approximately thirty miles east of Lake Fortune. Horne, therefore, was making no blind quest; he was heading into a country where gold was known to be present.

On the lower Kinojevis River, Horne and Bryden met Foster's men, who were on their way back to civilization. They spoke only in terms of disappointment, even derision. The "find" was a wash-out, the country a pesthole of black flies and loon dung, the rock a hungry, tight graywacke. But having ventured this far, Horne decided to continue north.

In his own words, "We followed up the Kinojevis River, look-ing over the formation as we went along. Near Turnback Lake, a Mr. Richmond was working on a molybdenite property; we did not spend much time there, as being more accustomed to gold forma-tions, did not find it interesting, so we turned back and branched off at Routhier Lake, then to Osisko by way of Rouyn Lake. The only formation that attracted my attention was on this rather hasty trip on the west side of Osisko Lake. I noticed that a sudden change had taken place in the rocks and though I found nothing that indi-cated values, it left me with a desire to see more of it."

The memory of the "sudden change in the rocks" apparently haunted him, for he returned to Osisko Lake in the summer of 1914. Carefully prospecting, he noted further marked alteration in the rocks and discovered an outcrop of gossan along a creek later named for him. His assays, however, returned negligible values.

Was it a hunch, as he describes it, or an instinct born of acute observation and experience that impelled him to visit Osisko Lake again in 1917? It is difficult to say, for Horne was anything but a talker. In any event, he was once more irresistibly drawn to this spot which seemed to have fascinated him. In simple, direct language he declared, years later: "At this time the large body of mineralized rhyolite on the northwest side of the hill was located . . . and a small part of it uncovered, which gave me disappointingly low values. . . . While not exactly discouraged, I found the undertaking too great for one man with a shoestring capital, as I realized that a large amount of stripping would have to be done . . . and a lot of blasting, so tried to form a syndicate. I found this rather difficult, as times were so bad and was advised that even if I found a mine, would not be able to sell it . . ."

But necessity taught Horne to wait. Another three years passed, during which time he had married the niece of John Buchner, proprietor of the Grand Union Hotel in New Liskeard. Buchner lent a sympathetic ear to Horne's story of gold at Osisko Lake and as a result the Tremoy Lake Syndicate, destined to be one of the most famous in the annals of mining, was formed in the spring of 1920. Twelve Liskeard residents purchased units while Horne and Ed Miller, his new partner, were allocated 40 per cent interest, for which they were to stake claims, prospect, and otherwise conduct the business of the syndicate.

Horne and Miller lost no time moving into Quebec and this time one 200-acre claim was staked and recorded in Ville Marie, where the recorder's office was then located. The syndicate was now a going concern.

The breakup in 1921 found Horne and Miller once more on the shores of Osisko Lake. This time, however, they worked with pick and shovel, stripping, digging trenches, and sampling the tantalizing rhyolite. The best assay returned .25 ounces of gold, far from commercial value at that time, but in the fall sampling results, though erratic, improved. Another claim was staked, south and east of the original claim, and the partners departed for Liskeard.

Near Opasatika Lake they met three men in a canoe, Mel Robb, youthful Bill Beaton of Haileybury, and Pete Graham, a fellow townsman of Horne and Miller's brother-in-law. The trio represented a syndicate for which they were trying to locate the scene of Horne's discovery, but after a vain search they, too, were en route home. Horne advised them about Lake Osisko, suggesting they stake a group of claims and "carry" the Tremoy Syndicate for an interest.

"Can't do it, Ed," said Pete Graham. "We're just about out of chuck, unless you have some to spare."

But Horne also was practically without food, and so the two canoes together returned to Lac Quinze. A truly golden opportunity had been missed, but Pete Graham, as events developed, was able to participate in the later affairs of the Tremoy Syndicate.

In Liskeard, Horne, worried most of the winter lest Graham's syndicate might stake ground, after all, at length persuaded Ed Miller in March, 1922, to trek with him one hundred miles through the snow and stake two more claims. The syndicate was now in possession of eight hundred acres.

A small crew was engaged to work during the summer and a trench eighty feet long blasted in the hard rhyolite. Sampling yielded fair but inconclusive values. At this point, a smudge which had been kindled to drive off the flies was fanned by a sudden wind, causing a bush fire. The men, who were eating lunch, moved to the lake shore until the fire died out. As Horne related it: "Thought it a good time to see if I could find any float or outcrop, but failed. It so happened that I came around to what later proved to be the 'A' ore body; it was covered with overburden . . . I stuck the pick in . . . and found only about six inches of surface at that particular point. I cleared it off some; it was very smooth and hard; could not break anything off, but found, by picking it, that it was full of sulphides . . . cleaned it off for about two feet, chipped the rest off the top and sampled it. This assayed one half ounce gold."

During this time, while Horne imagined his group was alone in the area, Marty Wright, staker of the Kerr Lake Mine in Cobalt, had been camped on Pelletier Lake, a few miles southwest. With his partner, Ed Billings, he had been prospecting since the spring, oblivious to the fact that others were actively working near at hand. Less secretive than Horne, Wright and Billings, who had found considerable evidence of commercial gold deposits, informed friends. In consequence several prospectors, notably Bob Gamble, Fred Davies, and the McDonough brothers, made the hard trip into Rouyn and staked a number of claims. Davies and Gamble, more adventurous than the others, portaged to Osisko Lake, found the Horne discovery, and pegged claims adjoining it. Horne and his men had returned to Liskeard.

Horne was vastly encouraged with the new assays. He communicated with John W. Morrison, a mining engineer representing Henry A. Wentworth of Boston. Impressed with what Horne showed him, Morrison promptly visited the scene of discovery. With him, engaged as a sampler, was Jack Costello, the veteran prospector

from Larder Lake. Satisfied with his examination, Morrison wired
Wentworth, urging that an option be taken at once. Wentworth,
however, sent a negative reply; he had already closed a deal on the
Central Manitoba Mines, a property which had been carried to an
advance stage of development, and all his funds were tied up. Ironically, the Central Manitoba venture met with only indifferent success.

The dogged Horne now approached the M. J. O'Brien Company.
The local manager in Cobalt, J. G. Dickenson, sent one of his
junior engineers into Quebec and he returned with a favorable
report. Unfortunately, the chief engineer of the company was
engaged in the west, and Horne was informed that final word could
not be given until the "chief" could return a verdict later in the
season. Horne, however, refused to wait. He had already been
discussing matters with Pete Graham.

Graham promised quick action if Horne gave him a free hand.
Horne consented. Graham traveled only five miles south to Haileybury, and there went into conference with L. K. Fletcher. Responsive
at once, Fletcher wired Messrs. Thomson and Chadbourne whom he
represented. And an option agreement between the Tremoy Lake
Syndicate and the Thomson-Chadbourne Syndicate was speedily
executed. This provided for the purchase of 90 per cent interest in
Horne's ground for the sum of $320,000, of which $7,000 was to be
paid on or before January 15, 1923, $5,000 by July 15, 1923, $5,000
on every 15th day of January and July during the years 1924 to
1927 inclusive, and the balance of $268,000 by January 15, 1928.
Graham received a small commission for his services but this was
enough for a competence eventually.

Sam Thomson and Humphrey Chadbourne were American
engineers who had joined forces to acquire mining properties in
northern Canada. Thomson was a technical man of skill and long
experience. His associate, also well trained, had important financial
connections through his brother, Thomas L. Chadbourne, one of
Wall Street's legal giants, and largely through this connection a
matter of $50,000 was raised from such men as Percy Rockefeller,
Ward Paine, Irving Bonbright, Charles Hayden, William Boyce
Thompson, and Robert Stanley. Units were at first issued in the
Thomson-Chadbourne Syndicate, but later these were exchanged
for 5,000 shares of Noranda Mines, Ltd., which was capitalized at
20,000 shares. The name was derived from a contraction of "Northern Canada."

Fletcher retained J. H. C. "Ike" Waite to make an examination of the Horne claims. Accompanying him into Quebec were

Arthur Cockeram, a prospector in the employ of Noranda, Bud Mallory, who was to handle supplies and transportation, and six others. By the time the party arrived at Lake Osisko a gold find on the claims of T. A. Powell, a few miles northwest of the Horne, had been reported. Waite hurried to inspect the discovery and so taken with it was he that he negotiated an option agreement immediately on behalf of Noranda Mines. Cockeram staked a considerable block of ground for Noranda between the Powell and the Horne, in the name of Chadbourne. Bud Mallory managed to stake the greater part of Heré Lake.

After sampling the Horne showings, Waite returned to Haileybury. He submitted his report and then conferred with Fletcher, Thomson, and Chadbourne. Waite, apparently, was more interested in the Powell than the Noranda and strongly recommended that work be concentrated on the former. The Noranda brain trust decided to retain the Horne option while devoting the main effort to the Powell.

News of the Powell had now percolated throughout the north and a rush into the area followed. Between December 1, 1922, and April 1, 1923, about fifty men negotiated the hazardous trip from the railroad to Osisko Lake, and the history of the new district had fairly begun. In a matter of five months more than 100,000 acres of ground were staked and recorded.

Noranda proceeded to trench, sample, and drill the Powell during the winter of 1923. Said Thomson of this period: "The low average surface values obtained in the Horne sulphides were not particularly encouraging, and little work was done on this group until August, 1923, the work being confined to exploring the Powell group held on option and the Chadbourne group staked by Noranda Mines."

On January 15, 1923, Noranda completed a payment of $7,000 to the Tremoy Lake Syndicate. The Powell then proving a disappointment, orders were given to transfer the drill to the Chadbourne. At the same time, Noranda sought an extension of the $5,000 payment due the Tremoy group on July 15, giving as a reason the inconclusive results obtained on the Horne to date. More time was required to complete the investigation, and it was stressed that any further advances must be allocated to development work if the option was to be retained. At a hurriedly called meeting, the Tremoy Syndicate voted to send Graham and Miller into Rouyn for the purpose of reporting the situation. Accordingly, they left New Liskeard in late June.

At Sturgeon Rapids, the party, which included my brother Bob, transferred from the steamer to a river launch. At midstream the engine stalled, and while the operator strove desperately to repair the damage, the boat swept toward the rapids. Fortunately, there were several canoes in tow. Into one of these jumped Bob, Pete Graham, and Ed Miller, at the same time shouting instructions for the remaining passengers to seek safety in the other canoes. An attempt was then made to pull the launch ashore, but no headway was possible. The rapids were now dangerously close.

"Cut the line!" Graham called to Bob from the stern of the canoe. It was the only alternative; otherwise the entire party would be flung into the rapids. Bob raised his ax, but the sight of almost a half dozen men on their knees in prayer unnerved him.

"Cut the line, or we'll all go!" cried Graham.

Down came the ax. The canoe, caught in a swirl of current, seemed hopelessly trapped, but the three occupants, all expert paddlers, dug their blades into the foaming water. Four canoes followed them closely while the launch, swinging about helplessly, was borne into the rapids with several passengers who refused to trust the canoes. All of them perished. The canoes made little progress, and for several moments it appeared that they, too, would be destroyed. But the leaders of this grim flotilla turned with the current and steered diagonally into a lifesaving back eddy, and soon a dozen badly shaken men were being helped ashore by cheering spectators.

It was a harrowing experience and not without vital bearing on the Noranda story. For had Miller and Graham been victims of the accident, there would now be a different tale to relate. Their subsequent inspection of the Horne and discussions with Noranda officials enabled them to persuade the Tremoy Syndicate to grant the payment extension. It is highly improbable that Noranda would have made a $5,000 out-of-pocket disbursement at the time, and had they dropped their option the district would have suffered an irreparable blow.

While surface pits on the Chadbourne gave hope, drilling proved to be negative. Having signed a contract for a definite footage to be drilled, Noranda was compelled to do work elsewhere or forfeit a considerable sum. On this fortuitous circumstance hinged the fate of Noranda, for it was decided to complete the contract footage on the Horne. This decision was made possible by the indefatigable Arthur Cockeram, who had discovered a new and attractive outcrop of mineralized rhyolite. The gods were bent upon favoring Noranda, and the first of a series of prodigies was about to startle the mining world.

The drill was moved and installed on the Horne claims in August. Again quoting Thomson: "A diamond drill hole was put down at an angle of 35° to explore a sulphide body exposed by a surface trench. This trench, 37½ feet long, showed an average gold content of $6 and less than 1½ per cent copper, the solid sulphide being mainly pyrrhotite. This bore hole was the beginning of the company's success. The core, starting 11 feet from the surface, remained in solid sulphides for 131 feet, the average value being $4.36 gold and 8.23 per cent copper."

This was the first indication of a commercial copper deposit in northern Canada. Had Horne been cognizant of copper possibilities all along? Certainly, his main interest seems to have been gold, which was to be expected in a gold country. It has been suggested that he was aware of the presence of copper, but considered it an unfavorable sign, inasmuch as its presence in a gold ore introduced serious metallurgical difficulties. This seems possible, since he had gained a rudimentary knowledge of milling in Nova Scotia. In any event, the Noranda drill hole had repercussions which are still being felt.

The drama was only beginning; the curtain had just been raised on the second act. Further drilling disclosed the presence of several rich but small ore bodies, and as preparations for shaft sinking went forward, the camp sprang into a fever of activity. It will be recalled that Fred Davies and Bob Gamble, who had first located in neighboring Pelletier Lake, later staked claims next to Horne's in the fall of 1922. Gamble, a man of dexterous mind and enterprise, now persuaded Davies, a mining engineer, that the Adsit-Davies claims next to the Horne should be swapped for various Gamble claims in Pelletier Lake adjoining several belonging to Davies, thus making a compact group. So convinced was Davies that this exchange would benefit him that he agreed to pay Gamble a sum of cash in addition. Gamble at once interested Fred Connell, a well-known promoter-engineer. Connell obtained an option to purchase the ground for $50,000 cash and then communicated with Noah Timmins. Timmins thereupon visited Rouyn, where he met Bob Gamble. The two, after some discussion, agreed to somewhat different terms than those outlined in the Connell option. Gamble, for a consideration of $50,000, assigned to Timmins the Adsit claim and a one-third interest in the Edith Gamble claims to the south.

Not long thereafter, Timmins turned in the Adsit to Noranda, for which he received 500 shares. In December, 1925, when the capital of the company was increased to 1,500,000 shares, stockholders of record received 100 shares of new stock for one of old.

Timmins, therefore, became the owner of 50,000 Noranda which in time reached a value of $80 per share, or $4,000,000, certainly a high ticket for one claim, but as far as Noranda was concerned, Timmins' position might have justifiably been presented gratis, for without him the later fortunes of the company would have been sorry, indeed.

As for Fred Connell, the commission he received for his services started him anew on a brilliant career which was climaxed by the Central Patricia Mines. To Bob Gamble, the Adsit episode was the beginning of a series of transactions which have placed him high on the list of successful prospectors. Fred Davies, however, was not so fortunate.

The question of financing the Noranda enterprise became a trying one. Underground work in 1924 and 1925 disclosed several hundred thousand tons of high-grade ore, direct smelting stuff, but smelters are expensive installations and require considerable feed to justify construction. Significantly, the original members of the Thomson-Chadbourne Syndicate, who were now owners of approximately 500,000 shares of Noranda, were strangely quiet and inactive when matters had reached an impasse, though they represented enormous capital and unquestioned mining talent.

At this critical moment, Robert once more made his contribution to Noranda. Luckless throughout, he nevertheless played no inconsiderable part in the finely spun skein of events which led to the final masterpiece. He had formed a connection with the American Metals Company of New York, an ill-fated one as he was to learn in the course of time. Specializing in the smelting and refining of ores produced by others, this organization, an outgrowth of a German company of unpronounceable name, was anxious to obtain direct ownership of a producing mine, or a portion thereof. In 1925 the company was still smarting under the shadows of an Alien Custodian scandal involving the suspiciously cheap sale of stock to various interested associates of the old enemy-controlled cartel. Noranda, therefore, had a special appeal to this hyphenated corporation.

When Bob walked into the downtown New York office of the Metals Company with a plan to purchase the interest of the Tremoy Syndicate, the response was electric. He was commissioned to confer with Horne and his associates and make an outright bid for their 10 per cent interest in the Horne Mine, the offer being limited to $250,000 maximum. Confident of success, he caught the first train north.

In New Liskeard, a meeting of the Tremoy Syndicate was

called to deliberate the proposal. Changes had taken place, however; the original membership had increased to fourteen through sale of units to others, and trading with so many different personalities proved cumbersome. Most unit holders reacted favorably to Bob's offer, but a few, notably a local banker who had bought a unit for $150, felt that the ante should be raised. Asked to what extent, the reply was: "Make it a half a million and the 10 per cent is yours."

Bob telephoned New York and explained the situation. Later, he was authorized to bid $350,000, but no higher. This he did, but by now the syndicate was obdurate. An attempt to persuade the estimable gentlemen of New York that $500,000 was not an unreasonable price was useless. Thus far and no further, were the instructions. Under these circumstances, negotiations were irrevocably broken off. Later, as we shall see, Tremoy accepted 125,000 shares of Noranda Mines for its equity in addition to the full payment of the purchase price, and to date this stock has received over $6,000,-000 in dividends while having a present capital value of $7,500,000.

Now, with a smelter under consideration by Noranda and no definite prospects of finding underwriters, Bob perceived another opportunity to participate in a situation which hitherto had eluded him. He conferred with Noranda officials and was encouraged to present the matter of smelter construction before the Metals Company. This he did, at the same time submitting his own report of the property, dated May, 1925. He estimated 250,000 tons of ore blocked out to a depth of 200 feet, but strongly emphasized the probability of considerably more smelter feed below this horizon, declaring, "While one lens might bottom, there is no reason geologically why others should not be found in depth."

The careful Metals Company officials agreed that here was business they fully understood. A smelter? Why not? This was their metier, and the answers they could themselves supply. In the late fall of 1925, accordingly, their engineer, who shall be among the few nameless individuals in this book, met Bob and me in Haileybury. He was a personable, direct man who had traveled extensively and worked in many of the important mining camps of the world. Not having been in Rouyn, however, he expressed some concern about the wildness, and danger, of the place.

"Perfectly harmless," Bob assured him. "Just a lot of noise, that's all."

I left the two en route to Lac Quinze and Rouyn, meeting Fred Thompson later for a little staking project of our own, but I have a reasonably accurate report of what happened in Rouyn. The trip in was dreary and uneventful, but once arrived, things happened fast. As Bob and his friend were registering at Jimmy Green's hotel, one of the town bullies who had been loudly swearing to punish the Hoffmans for an adverse report on a property he was supposedly managing, stalked Bob as his back was turned and dealt him a sneak blow behind the ear. The man was once a professional fighter and inspired fear throughout the area. Now, as Bob turned, partially staggered, his antagonist danced about nimbly with his arms outstretched. The Metals Company engineer was about to be shown how really innocuous life was in Rouyn.

Bob managed to remove his mackinaw. Outweighing his opponent and in superb condition, he soon managed to land a few telling blows of his own. Down went the attacker, only to be revived and sent back to the log-floored arena. A feint, a hard right hook, and Rouyn's bully fell back against the wall, slumped weakly, and sat with a vacant and bloody stare.

"Put the boots to 'im!" cried the men watching, for it was an old lumberjack's custom to kick away with corked (spiked) boots on such occasions.

Bob, rigidly adhering to the Marquis of Queensberry code, allowed himself to be led outside.

"Harmless? Did you say harmless?" The celebrated engineer smiled wryly. "Let's get over to Noranda before we're sent out of here in pine boxes."

On October 16, 1925, he wrote his report, which began with this sentence: "Apparently Noranda has not yet developed sufficient ore to justify the erection of any smelter." He quoted the published ore reserve figure of 611,500 tons of $20 per ton material, but added: "Only a small tonnage of this ore will be susceptible to direct smelting as a marginal flux." A careful summary of known ore was submitted, together with a comment stressing the indications of impoverishent on the 200-foot level. As to development work, he stated: "The disappointing results of the 200-foot level to date, together with the meager showings from drilling, do not give one an enthusiastic view of deep possibilities. On the other hand, there is a large area of surface from which, geologically, as good results might be encountered as in the area under development." Regarding the large tonnage of massive pyrrhotite tributary to No. 2 shaft: "This ore is fairly massive . . . allegedly running $4 gold and .8 per cent copper. This ore cannot be smelted direct and its inclusions as ore depends on a successful concentration operation and their ability to get a spread between costs and recoverable values."

And in conclusion: "It is apparent that the Noranda is not yet prepared to seriously contemplate a smelting plant because of an insufficient total tonnage, because from their known ore it would be impossible to intelligently determine whether a blast furnace or reverberatory plant is best suited to their needs, because the present net value of their known ore is so little that any mistake in smelting program might easily destroy any hope of profit."

Privately, this careful technician was less equivocal. "I wouldn't piss on it," he declared. In later years, when confronted with the knowledge that Noranda eventually developed 50,000,000 tons of ore, he grinned and said, "I was wrong," an admission which most engineers would have qualified with justifiable explanations.

But he performed a service, even though his report cooled the ambitious spirit of his worthy principals in New York. Graciously assenting to an interview with Noah Timmins in Montreal, he freely answered pertinent questions regarding the type of smelter that was suitable for Noranda ore, and its cost. His astonishment must have been great when shortly afterward he read in the press that the Hollinger Gold Mines, Ltd., would advance $3,000,000 to Noranda, in the form of purchasing 7 per cent debentures, the funds so obtained to be used in the construction of a 1,000-ton smelter.

Noah Timmins to the rescue! Never a respecter of experts, he was now courageously staking his future on the eventual success of Noranda. Of this there is little doubt—without a man of his vision and intestinal fortitude the enterprise could have easily melted away at this crucial point. Certainly, no aid was offered from any other quarter, particularly from the moneyed associates of Chadbourne and Thomson. On the contrary, when the company's capitalization was increased and shareholders were given rights to purchase one share of stock at $10 for each share of record, and the market price rose sharply, a large part of these early stockholders sold out completely. For, despite Noah Timmins, Noranda had entered the twilight zone of mines. Would it emerge into the sun of another day or disappear into the darkness of night? Many stockholders, including insiders, as noted, decided to take the cash and let the credit go.

Some additional ore was disclosed in 1926. In June, 1927, the capitalization was again increased, this time to 2,250,000 shares. Rights were again given to purchase stock at $15 on a share-for-share basis. Meanwhile, a model townsite was being constructed while the towering smelter stacks rose higher. Finally, the great event took place. On December 17, 1927, with appropriate ceremonies, the smelter was "blown in." Underground, by that time, were 1,000,000 tons of ore blocked out, all of which was direct smelting material.

Rumors in a new mining camp are always in circulation. According to the grapevine telegraph, the following dialogue is supposed to have occurred between two Noranda officials:

"If we don't get more ore, my boy, you will find me somewhere in Mexico."

"I won't have to find you," was the reply. "I'll be with you."

If this conversation did take place, the gentlemen concerned would have been under necessity of making their escape to Mexico quickly, for in a matter of months high-grade ore was encountered while the No. 2 shaft was being deepened in the footwall area of the large pyrrhotite mass described so lugubriously by the American Metals engineer. It was bonanza stuff, and Noranda stock soared until it eventually reached $80 per share.

By the end of 1931, despite the extraction of 2,000,000 tons, the company reported reserves of 11,000,000 tons. When it appeared that the ore had bottomed, work on lower horizons revealed the astonishing fact that the deposit, named "H," had again "come in" much in the shape of an hourglass. In 1932 alone, 11,000,000 more tons were added to the reserve. A curious fact was now revealed. The small scattered ore bodies first discovered were found to be as fingers of a hand leading to a wrist and forearm, the mighty H, which on surface appeared to be worthless pyrrhotite. And this changed to chalcopyrite in a few hundred feet of depth. Had the glaciers eroded the old surface slightly more, the rich and extensive ore of H would have been exposed to view. Fortunately, the tributary ore bodies had been formed in loftier horizons, and thanks to Horne they served as a key to open the doors of the big bonanza.

And what of the Tremoy Syndicate? By terms of the agreement with Noranda, they were to receive 10 per cent of "a company to be formed." For this purpose the Horne Copper Corporation was organized. When this company issued $3,000,000 in bonds to the Hollinger Company in 1925, however, negotiations with Tremoy Syndicate were undertaken to resolve what had become a complicated situation. The result was satisfactory to all concerned: the Tremoy Syndicate accepted 125,000 shares of Noranda Mines, the holding company having many equities other than the Horne Mine. In addition, the balance due on the original purchase price of $320,000 was paid in full. Thus a syndicate of 200 units of $25 each, $5,000, received stock currently valued at $7,500,000 and paying yearly dividends of $500,000. Of the original unit holders, few retained their holdings. Horne sold part of his shares, purchased a farm in Nova Scotia, and retired from mining. Ed Miller is reputed to have kept a large part of his Noranda, and still lives in Liskeard.

In due course, a concentrator of 5,000-ton daily capacity was constructed adjacent to the smelter, itself enlarged to treat 2,000 tons of ore and concentrates. Yearly production increased steadily, reaching a peak of $20,000,000. From commencement of operations in 1927 to the end of 1945, Noranda produced approximately $258,-000,000 of which amount $107,691,912 has been paid in dividends. Not satisfied with this, the company has had outstanding success in outside exploration, due to a combination of Oliver Hall as engineer and J. Y. Murdoch as guiding genius.

Approximately $12,000,000 was required to bring Noranda into production. The first railroad from the north was completed into Rouyn late in 1926, and only fourteen months thereafter production began. Remarkable is the fact that at no stage in its colorful history did Noranda have recourse to public money. Stockholders themselves, aided by the Hollinger purchase of debentures, provided the necessary funds.

Before leaving Noranda, one last incident must be recorded. Shortly before the company discharged its obligations to the Tremoy Syndicate, several of the Horne claims, including the vital one containing the bulk of ore, had, unknown to officials, come open for restaking. Through a clerical oversight, assessment work had not been recorded on the date due; therefore, the Noranda ground automatically reverted to the crown. Inasmuch as this kind of information was not published by the Department of Mines, it remained for the interested individual to ascertain the status of any particular claims. About this time, Alphonse Paré purchased several claims from Q. A. Shaw, Jr., of Boston and staked several more adjoining. There was some question he wished to resolve regarding the validity of his own claims. He went to the recorder's office, therefore, and asked for the latest blueprint of the Rouyn District. This was given him and in the course of consulting it he found, to his horror, that various Horne claims were marked "open." Reacting quickly, he telephoned his uncle Noah Timmins in Montreal, who requested him to restake the ground immediately. Paré, accordingly, rushed to Rouyn and restaked the claims on behalf of Noranda. Noranda was saved, thanks to Paré's fortuitous visit to a recorder's office and the swift—and unselfish—action of the incomparable Noah Timmins. Aside from the loss of indispensable claims, Noranda was spared the embarrassing necessity of making explanations and possible reparations to the Tremoy Syndicate. . . .

For some time northwestern Quebec was regarded with skepticism. Ore of the Noranda type was novel and the region itself was a geological question mark. Nevertheless, prospecting went ahead and discoveries were not long in being reported.

Soon after the McDonough brothers found zinc and copper north of Noranda, Tom Montgomery and his young son, in the course of treeing a bear cub, discovered a rich outcrop of copper sulphides in Duprat Township. In time the two occurrences were merged into a single company, the Waite-Amulet, and came under control of Noranda. Ike Waite, who grubstaked the Montgomerys, went on to become one of the leading mining men in the industry.

In the immediate environs of Noranda, Bob Gamble led a parade of new properties, all of them "straight" gold. Then came the awakening to the east, Cadillac, Melartic and Bourlamaque, all of them great gold camps in their own right.

Fortune smiled in unexpected ways, but the luck of Prospectors' Airways was an incredible freak, outstanding in a camp of constant surprises.

Bobby Cockeram and Pete Graham, piloted by aviator Glyn Burge, scoured the bush from Manitoba to Quebec without result. One summer day in 1932 their small aircraft came to roost on the smooth waters of Osisko Lake, whence they had started. While their aircraft was being overhauled, Graham and Cockeram were accosted by Dave McWatters, an old friend, who insisted that his claims near the bend of the Kinojevis, only a few miles from town, merited examination. This section of Rouyn had long been passed over by prospectors and engineers but the day was fine and the trip was short, so the party, accompanied by Mrs. McWatters, proceeded to the property. In a holiday mood, they enjoyed a picnic lunch washed down with beer, preparatory to examining Dave's "favorable formation." But Bobby Cockeram had a duty to perform first, a call of nature. Retiring from the campfire to a thicker part of the bush, he found it necessary to peel a handful of moss from a small outcrop. To his surprise, he detected the familiar texture of quartz. Looking again, he found it well fractured and of a bluish color. More important were lumpish specks of native gold.

He returned to his companions with the news. In a twinkling, the entire party was busily stripping the outcrop and a sizable dome of quartz was revealed, all of it high grade. Cockeram and Graham acted fast. An option agreement was executed on the spot, and in short order the Noranda area was enriched with another mine. While the McWatters proved to be a comparatively minor producer in "big elephant" country, it kindled interest in a neglected section of the camp. The Rouyn Merger, Heva Cadillac, and Hosco

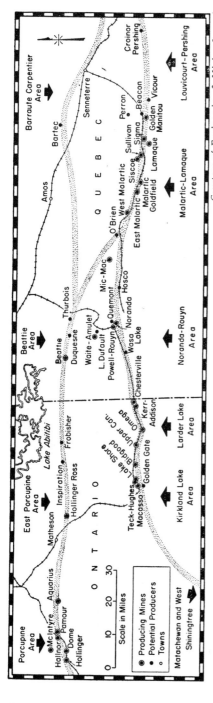

CANADA'S MOST PRODUCTIVE GOLD AREA

Courtesy of Engineering & Mining Journal

The various camps here denoted were developed independently, beginning with Porcupine in 1909 and followed by Kirkland Lake, Larder Lake and the Noranda-Northwestern Quebec districts. Only recently have geologists and engineers correlated the structural relationships between these different areas, and the importance of this region is being recognized in mining circles for the first time. The combined output of the mines has already reached close to the 2 billion dollar mark, with many new properties being readied for production. It is along the two roughly parallel "belts" of favorable rocks, extending from Ontario into Quebec and comprising 400 lineal miles, that the large part of Canadian mining exploration is now being directed.

Mines were later drilled, all of them successfully, and a new string of mines beneath the muskeg of Joannes Township seemed assured.

And so, in fits and starts of alternating hope and despair, a magnificent new mining area began to emerge. The anchor of hopes rested in Noranda Mines whose smelter, once started, has continued to belch forth the smoke clouds that demonstrate the comforting presence of major ore tonnages. The Lake Dufault and Quemont incidents demonstrated that more large mines were awaiting discovery, and today the camp, revitalized by scores of new and promising developments, looks forward to even greater days.

Two Quebec belts have been traced westward for more than 150 miles. By a curious coincidence, the south break leads to the gold of Kirkland Lake, where a disappointed Ed Horne turned eastward thirty-five years ago.

QUEBEC GOLD PRODUCTION
1926–1945

1926	$76,072
1930	2,930,170
1935	16,558,725
1940	39,238,238
1942	42,056,938 (record high)
1945	25,596,109

NORANDA MINES, LTD.

1927–1945

Ore treated	27,384,292 tons
Copper	1,609,367,996 lbs.
Gold	4,208,608 oz.
Value production	$258,000,000 *
Dividends	$107,691,912

NORTHWESTERN QUEBEC

1927–1945

Production—Gold and base metals $528,000,000 *

* Estimated

CHAPTER XII

Where Is Dan Willans?

" 'Mush on,' goes out the cry as yet another impatient prospecting party hits the trail for Red Lake, Canada's newest gold field, which is now the center of the greatest gold rush since Porcupine."

Boston Post—Feb. 28, 1926

He had been away since the breakup. The all too short summer had come and gone and now the first snows of the season were sweeping in from Lake Temiskaming. Motherly Mrs. Winters was becoming increasingly anxious about her tenant. True, he had paid his rent months in advance, but then she had grown attached to the elderly bachelor who had lived so long without the comfort and indulgence of a woman's softness. Courtly but reticent, affable and yet recluse, he had defeated her repeated attempts to win him with extra attentions. Despite his long residence in her establishment, she knew little of him, but with housewifely blandness had assumed a kind of proprietorship, coyly deposited home-cooked delicacies on his table when he was absent, mended his clothes, surreptitiously decorated his room with calendar pictures, and performed other services which, in her mind, transformed his quarters into a home. He regarded her efforts with polite and amused detachment, removing the pictures and replacing them with strange, colored geological maps before which he often stood in rapt meditation. Silently, she disapproved of the stock of liquor he always maintained, but then he was a quiet well-behaved man, unlike most prospectors. When he drank, it was in the grand manner. He was never boisterous or uncertain in his gait; always, as she explained to her neighbors, a "perfeck giantleman."

And now he was long overdue from one of those periodical trips about which he never gave her the slightest information. He might have sent her a penny card in all these months, a mere word to relieve her anxiety!

Then, without warning, he appeared one day, his large frame bent under a sizable packsack. Hearing the slow familiar footstep from the recesses of her kitchen, Mrs. Winters hurried to the front door, all the while gushing maternal greetings.

"Surely, Mr. Willans," she declared, upon recovering her breath, "surely you 'ave found somethink—bein' away so long as you 'ave!"

"Not necessarily," he replied gravely, shifting the load on his shoulders and walking toward the stairs to his room, "not necessarily, madam."

In later years, when he had made a fair stake in the Lightning River boom, he purchased a shack on the lake shore and there he lived undisturbed. His departures to the bush were unannounced, as were his returns. In most cases he traveled without a partner. To the parties he met in the woods he was always a valuable addition, for he was an accomplished cook and seemed to find nothing distasteful in performing a chore so generally despised. And his smiling willingness to assume heavier tasks of camp life made him doubly welcome in a country where rutting the dog was common.

"Have a spot?" was his usual greeting in Haileybury, and thereupon he would concoct exquisitely mixed drinks. He was a thoughtful and pointed conversationalist, with an unaffected Oxonian accent, but any attempt to elicit a clue of his earlier life was skillfully parried and friends soon learned to avoid a subject obviously distasteful to him. Some said he was a duke or lord who had quit England for unknown reasons and then erased his past in the polyglot humanity of the north. That he was not a remittance man was definitely known—no envelope with the revealing English stamp had ever appeared for him at the post office. Titled or not, his charm and easy polish stamped him as a man of breeding and background, though nothing he said, even in moments of inebriety, furnished the slightest hint of his true identity.

His one vice was an occasional visit to Toronto, usually when he had sold mining claims. Then, immaculately dressed, his long mustachios carefully groomed and his bald head shining and fragrant, he became a conspicuous figure at the King Edward Hotel. Hampers of champagne were taken to his suite, and gay visitors, mostly feminine, imparted a sophisticated air of Old World gaiety to a hostelry conditioned to middle-class solidity and frontiersman ribaldry. After several weeks of high living, never to be seen in public without his impeccable dress clothes, Dan would pay his considerable bill and return to his Haileybury shack. For the next year or two he would pursue his even ways until circumstances again permitted another trip outside.

Apart from a journey to Quebec at the time of the Rouyn rush, he confined his prospecting to Ontario. Willans claims were as distinguished as their staker, neatly cut posts with firm clear lettering and blazed lines which even a tenderfoot could follow in the most impenetrable bush. Never in his long career was he involved in a dispute of any kind; his integrity was a part of the country. A firm sense of right was perhaps his most affirmative quality and he was often called upon by others to settle differences out of court.

His cabin was frequently the scene of poker games marked by their high stakes. Whenever tempers flared to dangerous heights there was always Dan to smooth the waters and keep play congenial. Occasionally, however, even his efforts were ineffective and then his action was quick and decisive.

"That's all for tonight, gentlemen," he would say, gathering up the cards, "play is over. Kindly cash your chips."

And the game was finished.

There came a day, in 1936, when Dan slipped from Haileybury as he had done so many times over a period of three decades. No longer sprightly, his once vigorous frame bowed and uncertain, his departure went unnoticed. To his friends he gave only a general hint as to his destination. Later, it was recalled that his speech was more than ordinarily repetitious and several times he had stopped to inquire whether or not he was becoming a bore. At the moment no significance was attached to these lapses.

The summer passed and Dan failed to appear. This caused little worry at first, for he was known for his protracted absences. But when the freezeup had come and the familiar cabin continued unoccupied and cheerless, devoted Haileyburians met and decided on a course of action. Communications were sent to all who had known Dan and inquiries made at the various mining camps in Ontario. Replies were either negative or vague. Months went by, and then searching parties, financed locally, were organized. But to no avail. The missing man had disappeared without leaving a trace. Cables to England, dispatched in the vague hope that he might have returned to his native land, brought no response. Thereupon, in the spring, government authorities took possession of the Willans cabin and advertised extensively for the benefit of heirs or kin. None came forward. Dan was never seen again.

This was the melancholy end of a man who came from nowhere and just as unobtrusively disappeared into the blue, a not uncommon episode of the north. But this time there was a sequel to the story, by no means common. . . .

The scene shifts back to early 1925. The place, Haileybury. In Dan Willans' shack Lorne and Ray Howey, one of the many brother prospector teams to whom Canada owes so much, were busily discussing a new area which, as yet, had received only minor consideration. Before them were spread sundry maps and reports which a diligent government survey had published, outlining all known data on the Red Lake district of Patricia. In terse language, dull, perhaps, to the layman but of decided interest to the intelligent prospector, the history of the area was given.

As early as 1786 the Northwest Company, later absorbed by the Hudson's Bay Company, had established a trading post at the northeast end of the lake. Not until 1872, however, is Red Lake again mentioned in the records, probably due to the difficulties of travel in this height-of-land country where portages are many and long. A. R. C. Selwyn, in 1872, reported that a group of Indians in the English River basin remarked the occurrence of "slaty rocks" at Red Lake, but he did not himself investigate. Not until 1883 was Red Lake examined, at which time Robert Bell reported the presence of a wide belt of Keewatin rocks, and ten years later D. B. Dowling mapped the area. Up to 1924, this was the only accurate source of information on the country. The first discovery of gold in Red Lake was made in 1897 by R. J. Gilbert, who headed a party for the Northwestern Ontario Exploration Company. Three claims were staked, but Gilbert was accidentally killed by his own revolver. Eventually, the company sank a small shaft on the occurrence near Slate Bay, but results were disappointing. The company pulled up stakes and the entire episode was soon forgotten. In 1912, Dr. W. G. Miller, Provincial geologist, issued a report which emphasized the gold possibilities of the area, but the prospecting that came later failed to disclose anything of promise.

Another blank decade passed, and then prospectors began to trickle into Red Lake again, due to the circulation of a report that quartz veins containing gold- and silver-bearing galena had been found. Gus McManus staked claims at the head of the Chukuni River after having discovered several narrow but rich quartz stringers. E. L. Bruce, an energetic Provincial geologist, hurried to the scene and made a preliminary examination, as a result of which he was sent back to make a complete report. Published in late 1924, his data evoked a stir of interest and now the Howeys were preparing to beat the gun into what they considered the most promising new gold area of Canada.

"It's a long slug in there," sighed Ray.

"Sure," agreed Lorne, "but we'll use twenty-foot canoes with keels and squared sterns for kickers. Them outboard motors'll do the trick."

"And what do we use for money?" inquired the ever-practical Ray.

"Louis Cohen," replied Lorne. "I'll go get 'im right now."

He did not have to travel far. The Cohen shack was located next door and so Lorne was absent for only a few moments, returning with a small man of hesitant gait and a complexion unhealthily rosy. Cohen was famous in his own way. Years earlier he had landed in Gowganda where he became a poolroom proprietor, at the same time conducting various outside activities. His interest in mining was keen and he was soon backing prospectors in a small way. On one of his few ventures into the bush, his legs, never strong, failed him completely and he was carried from West Shiningtree to Gowganda by Fred Thompson, who was prospecting the area. Cohen therefore remained close to his poolroom until he sold out to Jack Dick, an ex-jockey from the States, and then moved to Haileybury. There, in the course of time, he acquired a companion, Dr. Crane, a lank and garrulous Southerner who breezily sponged upon his undersized host. The two made a strange incongruous pair, yet they were bound by deep ties of affection which mystified Haileybury. Many townsfolk suspected that Crane was addicted to drugs, and it was freely said that he had wandered north from his native Alabama where he had been barred from practicing medicine. Apparently grateful for the companioship, however, Cohen was deaf to gossip. He remained stanchly faithful to Crane and shared his substance with him.

So went matters until the end of 1924 when the uncomplaining breadwinner was stricken with a brain tumor. In Toronto, Cohen was given up as a hopeless case by physicians. Crane mourned; his future was truly dark.

Hearing the sad story, Robert visited the dying man. Overcome with sympathy, my good brother insisted that Dr. Harvey Cushing, internationally famous brain surgeon, was the one man who could successfully remove the tumor. When the question of money came up for discussion, Bob enlisted the aid of J. T. Tower and L. B. Norrie, Harvard friends who had gone north to prospect at his advice. The three young men advanced $500 each, and these contributions, together with Cohen's savings, aggregated a sum judged to be sufficient for the Boston expedition.

I was a senior in college at the time, and to me Bob now wired long instructions. Assuming that he was known to Dr. Cushing, I instantly telephoned the eminent surgeon. I had some difficulty reaching him, since he was then at the height of his distinguished career. A reluctant secretary finally gave me a line to the inner sanctum. The great man was at first annoyed and incredulous, for, it appeared, he had never before heard of the Hoffmans, but as I continued to talk out of sheer misery and confusion, his irritation changed to amusement and then definite interest. Apparently, this was something new, even for him.

"Have Cohen come down here," he said kindly. "I'll take care of him the best I know how."

I wired Haileybury, and within a week the dying man, accompanied by jaunty Dr. Crane, arrived in Boston. Cohen was half blind and barely able to walk. I met the unique visitors at a room in the Parker House which I had reserved for them, and found Cohen sprawled out on the bed. He was fully clothed, even to the detail of his cap. The lantern-jawed Crane sat idly by, resting his chin on a gold-handled cane which undoubtedly came from the "treasury" of the syndicate. At my entrance, he was holding forth in great style, nor did my presence deter him in any way. As he continued to mouth long medical terms and describe the intricate incisions required in the forthcoming operation, the man on the bed stirred uneasily.

"Lay off, you lanky pig rutter," he muttered.

Crane tapped his head and winked at me. Pausing to light a cigarette, he resumed his unsolicited diagnosis. His detachment and objectivity were sublime. Cohen, however, was not appreciative. He rested his head on the pillow and rolled his eyes toward Crane.

"Who's doing the operation?" he asked weakly. "You or Dr. Cushing?"

The following day Cohen was in the care of Dr. Cushing, a slight brisk man. After a thorough examination, the patient was assigned a room at the Peter Bent Brigham Hospital and an operation performed at once. Crane, who acted as banker as well as companion-nurse, promptly departed for New York, there to attend to details of a mythical business affair. Cohen, meanwhile, recovered with such rapidity that patients in adjoining beds complained of his language.

"A bunch of Christy old women," he explained when I visited him. "Nothing but common pig rutters."

But his esprit took a decided drop when Crane wired from New York, frantically demanding money. The message came to the attention of hospital officials, who showed immediate concern regarding Cohen's ability to pay the considerable fees that had accumulated. Provoked, they asked for a consultation at which I was a somewhat reluctant participant. Cohen, ready to leave the hospital by this time, offered syndicate units as part payment. This was declined with polite amusement. (Not many years later, the units were exchangeable for stock in a company now valued at $12,000,000.) By dint of a small payment and solemn promises, however, Cohen was allowed to depart on the recommendation of Dr. Cushing. The debt, incidentally, was fully discharged in time and Cohen and Dr. Cushing became fast friends. Bob, Norrie, and Tower also were repaid, for not many years later Cohen was in the big money, thanks to his Chalcocite Syndicate which staked the Central Patricia Mines.

As for penniless Dr. Crane, who was stranded in New York, he found in Norrie and Tower, who had returned from the north, a ready source of cash. And so he was able to rejoin Cohen in Toronto, whence, after recriminations, accusations, and then reconciliation, the two journeyed to Haileybury, inseparable as ever. And Louis Cohen became known in the north as the man who had cheated death.

Now he was engrossed with Lorne Howey, outlining a syndicate plan, his specialty. Interests were worked out and a unit-selling campaign planned. To Dan Willans, who listened patiently and made occasional suggestions of value, an undertaking was made to keep him fully informed so that he would be the first to know of any discovery the Howeys might make. A budget was drawn up and, with a final word of encouragement, Cohen, whose powers had been remarkably revived by his operation, departed.

Money was slow in arriving and, anyway, Ray Howey was not overly enthusiastic about venturing north all summer without pay. Accordingly, he entered into an agreement with the McIntyre Mines, which provided that he and W. F. Morgan would be retained on a salary and interest basis to prospect Red Lake for the company's account. Lorne Howey, however, remained with the syndicate and chose as partner his brother-in-law, George McNeely. Residents of Haileybury, recruited by Cohen, finally supplied sufficient funds for the venture and the expedition of four men and two canoes set forth on what became a historic journey.

The jumping-off place was Hudson, Ontario, along the dreary stretches of the Transcontinental Railroad. A small powerboat, owned by the Hudson's Bay Company and used to transport supplies to the post at Red Lake, accepted the quartet as passengers, towing the two canoes over the great reaches of Lac Seul. Disembarking at Goldpines, the men struck off into the bush. Portaging the heavy canoes, together with outboard motors, gas, oil, and supplies, was heavy work, but rest came on Pakwash Lake which was crossed without incident. Then came a succession of portages on the Chukuni River, along the Hudson Bay route, before the broad waters of Gullrock Lake were navigated and the placid Chukuni was reached once more. Red Lake finally stood before them, quiet, pristine, its heavily timbered shore line reflected in the greenish-blue water. A beautiful spot, surely, but was there gold to be found? The Howeys and their partners lost no time in idle speculation. Splitting forces, they began the weary routine of prospecting.

June and July brought no tangible results, though favorable geological structures, as the reports promised, were everywhere to be seen. They worked along the extensive eastern lake shore which afforded a cross section of the entire country. Then one day late in August Lorne Howey visited his brother's camp on what is now properly called Howey Bay. The brothers followed a small quartz vein which led to a wide shear zone only a few hundred feet from the lake. Lorne, it was, who first detected the presence of native gold in a series of veinlets forming a kind of mosaic pattern in the rock. After the first ecstasy of discovery had passed, the men went to work with a will. Lorne Howey and McNeeley staked nine claims embracing the find while Ray Howey and Morgan staked nine adjoining claims to the west for the McIntyre Mines. Delaying their return to civilization only long enough to strip the occurrence and take a number of samples, the men turned southward and made for the nearest recording office.

Arriving in Haileybury before the freezup, the Howeys soon apprised Dan Willans of the new find. Dan enlisted his old friend Bill Cochenour as a partner. But many others had by this time learned of the discovery and the quiet waters of Lac Seul were already resounding to the shouts of prospectors, professional and amateur, racing toward distant Red Lake. The rush was on and before it ended hundreds had swarmed into the area by canoe and later by dog team. Overhead an occasional airplane roared, the first time this method of transportation was used in Ontario.

Old hands at the game, Willans and Cochenour were soon on their way. With them were Ed Cochenour, Bill's brother, "Hard Rock" Bill Smith, who was destined to come into his own years later in the Little Long Lac field, Bobby Cockeram, and Ross Ferguson, the last three constituting an independent group. Arriving at Red Lake, Willans and the Cochenours struck off in a northerly direction while the Cockeram party traveled west to stake a group of claims as near to the Howey as possible. But Dan Willans and the Cochenours had different ideas. Bill, with long experience in Cobalt, Porcupine, Larder Lake, Kirkland Lake, and Lightning River, was, like Dan, anything but a wildcatter. For him and Dan there were no quickie sales of claims; they had learned that the only satisfactory method of beating the game was to secure a property of merit and stick with it. Dan, speaking little, was in full accord with the plan to "find something first," but then a horde of "Sunday" prospectors snapped at their heels. East of McKenzie Island they pitched camp, reconnoitered the countryside and found a carbonate zone within which tiny quartz stringers crisscrossed.

"Hm," mused Bill, "looks like the old Kerr-Addison in Larder Lake."

Dan and Ed reached for their axes. There was no time to waste. For experienced bushwhackers the work of staking was routine, but there was the ever-present danger of interlopers. Luck smiled on them, however, for they completed their line and post cutting without hindrance. Unmindful of the rush which had by this time risen to unprecedented proportions, they headed south. Recording their claims, they returned to Haileybury to await the coming of spring.

In Haileybury, events moved rapidly. Cohen and Bobby Cockeram suggested to the Howeys that Jack Hammell, of Flin Flon fame, be consulted at once; he was just the man to finance and develop any discovery in a remote district. Lorne Howey made a long-distance call to Toronto, and his conversation with Hammell was short and pointed. When Howey described the discovery, Hammell expressed excited interest and quickly asked for terms.

"We'll discuss that after you've seen the show," Howey replied.

With his usual energy, Hammell departed for Red Lake immediately, anxious to examine the Howey find before the freezeup. With him went Alec Gillies and Cooney Wood.

Arriving in good time to inspect the claims, Hammell was enthusiastic. Beating the freezeup by a margin of days, he sped to Haileybury, and there came to a rapid agreement. The Howey Gold Mine Syndicate was formed, and the units divided between the Howey group and Hammell, the latter putting $50,000 into the treasury as consideration for the units he received. By this time the freezeup had come and the problem of transporting supplies into the property, 200 miles from the railroad, was one which no ordinary man would care to solve. But Hammell relished the impossible. In an unprecedented move, he applied to the Ontario Forestry Department for the use of seven aircraft. This was a novel suggestion, and at first met with a cold reception. But Hammell wore down opposition to the idea. The idle machines were chartered to the Howey Syndicate and supplies began to move northward from Sioux Lookout. This ushered in a new era of Canadian mining; from that day on, air transport became standard practice as the frontier retreated before the wing-equipped prospector.

Dome Mines, with a party already in Red Lake, was easily persuaded to deal with Hammell, due largely to the insistence of the chief geologist, Doug Wright. Terms were liberal—$500,000 to the Howey Syndicate plus 25 per cent interest in a company to be formed. A capital expenditure of $1,000,000 was guaranteed if preliminary development was favorable. Thanks to Hammell's foresight in providing supplies, Dome was able to commence work in the early winter of 1926. Results of trenching and diamond drilling were considered favorable by Wright, but H. P. de Pencier, Dome's general manager, was in violent disagreement with his own engineer. At length the option was dropped. Wright angrily resigned and joined forces with Hammell, who purchased the Howey stock which Dome had been assigned for expenditures. These shares Hammell transferred to the Howey at cost.

In January, 1927, the public was invited to participate in Howey Gold Mines, notwithstanding the Dome incident. One-half of the authorized capital was allocated to the Howey Syndicate for the property, and 1,000,000 of the remaining 2,500,000 shares were sold at 50 cents each, thus providing a working capital of $400,000.

The redoubtable Hammell himself purchased 200,000 shares. As the enterprise continued, more stock was sold, largely to individual mining men, including Albert Wende of the Wright-Hargreaves Mine, and Harry Oakes, both of whom served as directors in the company. Others were Ray T. Birks, a Toronto barrister, whose client, W. S. Sherry, had invested heavily. The situation appeared impressive and the stock for a time enjoyed high public favor.

Having scaled the first hurdle, Howey started shaft sinking before the freezeup, and by the end of 1937 the shaft had reached a depth of 500 feet with four levels of work disclosing what was considered to be medium-grade ore over excellent widths. When raises to connect the levels were driven, however, the grade of ore showed unexpected variations. These were far from realizing expectations. Special test raises yielded much lower grade than the average sampling of the horizontal levels. Plans were necessarily changed. Originally, the management expected to construct a mill on the basis of development down to the 500-foot level, but now, in a more cautious mood, the shaft was deepened to 1,000 feet. Howey stock became less popular, but Hammell stuck grimly to his task. Realizing that the operation was destined to be that of a low-grade mine, he set about immediately to reduce costs. The summer route from Goldpines to Red Lake was rendered economically feasible by construction of rail lines over which the ponderous barges from Lac Seul were hauled. The Ontario government met half the cost of this expenditure and the Howey, somewhat aided by other operators in the district, advanced the other half. But this was not sufficient. Cheap power was necessary if the new gold camp was to survive. Negotiations with the Ontario Hydro Electric Power Commission were speedily undertaken. Hammell had lost none of his persuasiveness, for the government agreed to develop the powersite at Ear Falls with the excellent rate of $25 per horsepower-year. The only fly in the ointment was that Howey obligated itself to pay almost $200,000 for the cost of transmission-line construction, this to be rebated at a 10 per cent monthly rate on the current power bills. On February 15, 1930, the first power was delivered.

In the interim rapid progress had been made at the mine and in April, 1930, the 500-ton mill was put in operation. Design of the plant was such that capacity could be doubled at relatively small expense. A weakness soon became apparent as the first ore was passed through the plant—the scheduled tonnage could not be handled because of faulty ball mills. This difficulty was remedied in time, but then a more serious one arose. Grade of ore which had been estimated at $6.67 per ton above the 500-foot level was found to average something less than $4.50, due to heavy dilution resulting from mining wide stopes. Financially, the Howey Mine was not prospering and remedial action was imperative.

Long before the production stage was reached, the company had sold all its treasury stock. With the pressing need for funds, reorganization seemed inevitable. A sum of $1,500,000 had already been expended and yet the ambitious program of the management had not been fulfilled. Even reorganization and issuance of more stock for sale seemed hopeless, for the shares, already selling at a reduced figure, could hardly be sold to a disillusioned public. Another $500,000 must be obtained immediately if the enterprise was to continue. At this moment, when all seemed lost, W. S. Sherry, a Canadian-born American merchant who had prospered in Rhode Island as head of a store chain, rose to the occasion. With his associate, Frederick Webb, he came forward dramatically and made the required loan. Changes in the management followed, Hammell, Oakes, and Wende resigning. Every effort was bent toward working out profitable mining and milling techniques and a special report for this purpose was prepared by J. L. Mennell. Among his recommendations was that of sorting ore at the surface in a specially designed plant.

In 1931 Fraser D. Reid became general manager. Aided by the gradually increasing price of gold and a carefully devised mining system, he was able to eke out a small operating profit. By the end of 1932, Sherry's loans, which had been increased from $500,000 to $750,000, were at last discharged. By this time Hammell was once again on the Board of Directors, finally triumphant. Fortune, which had frowned on the enterprise from the start, now smiled benignly, for the price of gold advanced to $35 per ounce, and later, with the exchange premium, to $38.50. In February, 1934, Howey reached a new high when the first dividend was distributed to the patient and long-suffering stockholders. Dividends have been maintained since that date although the mine itself suspended operations in 1941 when ore was finally exhausted. But in the period from April 1, 1930, when milling operations started, to November, 1941, the mine produced $13,167,134 from the treatment of 5,158,376 tons of ore, or an average grade of $2.55 per ton, a new low-grade record for Canada. In the same period $1,950,000 was paid in dividends. With assets of nearly $2,000,000, the Howey continues to function as an exploration and investment company, its dividend record now past the $2,000,000 mark. But its chief place in history is the achievement of the lowest mining costs in Canada and, even more important, its persistence at a time when failure would have plunged the entire district into oblivion. For, while the Howey struggled to emerge from darkness, hope kept other operators alive and the camp, after several false starts, began to assert itself strongly, until the gold of Patricia is today a great and growing segment of Canada's mining industry.

While the Howey affairs dominated interest, side shows were taking place elsewhere in the area. During the winter of 1925–1926, when snow blanketed the ground, a group of sixteen claims was staked west of the Howey townsite by C. E. St. Paul and Colin and J. W. Campbell. In the spring it was learned that most of the rock exposed was granite, not generally considered a favorable host rock to gold ores, but, defying tradition, the men proceeded to investigate. A large irregular lens of quartz, rich in spots, was discovered, and not long thereafter the Red Lake Gold Shore Mines, Ltd., was incorporated to develop the find. The market crash of 1929 delayed operations, however, and it was not until midsummer of 1934, when the Howey was a demonstrated success, that the Gold Shore was able to obtain the funds necessary to venture underground. Like the Howey, the shaft was taken to 500 feet. Never large, the ore body appeared to be fairly consistent and of medium, if erratic, grade. Mill construction was announced in 1935 and the stock advanced briskly on the Toronto Stock Exchange.

Shortly after production had commenced in 1936, Gold Shore officials issued a public statement. The mill was "now running at a rate of 115 tons daily. . . . It is proposed to gradually increase the daily tonnage . . . to around 150 tons. . . . Underground developments have produced some very nice widths. . . . Officials estimate three years' ore supply at the 150-ton rate developed. The break in which the ore occurs has only been partially opened up so far."

The shaft, meanwhile, was continued. At a depth of 700 feet the ore body began to shrink alarmingly. Worried, the company sank a winze and followed the remnant of ore downward, and this work was still in progress when the mill began to operate in mid-1936. At the outset, it was apparent that first estimates of values had been much too optimistic. The gold was found in quartz blebs and stringers contained in an area of crushed granite, and while assays were occasionally high, millfeed, diluted by masses of granite which could not be avoided, lowered grade sharply. This was disheartening, but the continuing winze disclosed even more serious news—the ore had completely disappeared. At the 1,000-foot horizon, there was not, as one Red Lake resident informed me, "enough ore to fill your pipe." Frantic efforts were made to find ore elsewhere, but all these failed. After two years of production, the mine was shut down, and Red Lake had thrust upon it the ignominy of a major fiasco, threatening dire implications.

And what of Dan Willans and his partner and the claims they had staked in the almost-forgotten days of the Red Lake rush, which was compared to Porcupine? Had they, like so many firstcomers, abandoned their ground and gone on to other camps? Decidedly not. While others quit, they remained, living on their claims and scouting about patiently. The myriad quartz veinlets in the carbonates, which reminded Bill Cochenour of Larder Lake, were obviously too small to be mined, even though a few of them were impregnated with coarse gold. The entire occurrence was bewildering in its irregularity and absence of pattern; there were no familiar large veins or dikes which could be followed along a normal dip and strike. And to render this condition even more puzzling, the mineralized zones were torn into ribbons by a complex network of faults.

"This'll take money," opined Bill. "We'll form a syndicate, Dan, just like Jack Hammell did with the Howey."

Again Haileybury. The time—April, 1928. Once more the familiar huddle in the Willans shack with Dan looking calm and detached as ever and bluff Bill Cochenour doing most of the talking. It was an ambitious plan he outlined—a syndicate of 10,000 units, half of which would be divided among the three who staked the claims. Then units would be sold at $50 each, providing plenty of working capital. But who would buy units? Were they to be sold direct or through a broker? Cochenour scratched his head.

"The boys'll buy 'em," he finally decided. "Fred MacLeod, Lorne and Ray Howey and the rest. You'll see."

The "boys" did buy, not much, to be sure, but enough to keep men employed on the property. It is noteworthy that mining men are the quickest to respond when units or shares are offered. Few of them can resist the lure of a new venture, for they are at heart men of hope and instinctive optimism. But money was becoming scarce. As an inducement Willans and Cochenour granted a bonus to new purchasers of units at $16.50—for every fifty purchased two would be given free. In this way a total of 2,000 units was disposed of and the enterprise kept alive. Realizing that more decisive action was necessary, Bill enlisted the interest of Ventures, Ltd., the Lindsley-inspired exploration company which had been only lately formed and now was aggressively on the hunt for new properties. The Cochenour-Willans Syndicate came to an agreement with Ventures in November, 1932, and drilling was recommended coincident with intensive surface mapping and sampling.

"If Lindsley doesn't take hold, no one will" was Cocheneur's observation to the syndicate. Dan Willans remained unscrutable as ever.

But the impossible happened. Ventures, unable to solve the riddle of fickle gold values and unworkable structure, dropped the option and withdrew from Red Lake.

A new and vital personality fortuitously appeared at this juncture. Bill Mackle had lately made his appearance in Red Lake and, while his visit went unnoticed, his presence was to be eventually felt in no uncertain way. Mackle, an engineer, had worked for McIntyre Gold Mines, and had been transferred from Porcupine to the west, where the company made an abortive attempt to enter the coal industry. Out of a job, Mackle eventually found employment in the coal fields of Pennsylvania. As the depression became more aggravated in 1932, he drifted back to Canada. In Toronto he conferred with George Quinn and Jack Oliver, mining promoters who had already been working on a plan to acquire the McKenzie claims in Red Lake. These were located on a large island of that name immediately west of the Cochenour-Willans. This prospect had been examined *ad nauseum,* and all reports had been monotonously negative. Mackle and his principals, however, were encouraged by the increasing gold price and felt that the McKenzie offered reasonable possibilities of developing into a producer. Accordingly, Mackle left for Red Lake, where he made careful examination of the ground. His conclusions were unequivocally favorable, with the result that the ground was acquired from the McNeely Red Lake Holdings. This syndicate, which was controlled by residents of North Bay, had in 1931 granted an option to Hammell's old sidekick, Jack Munroe. Later the project was taken over by the Coniagas Company, but their tenure was short-lived when drilling gave inconclusive results. Mackle's group now organized the McKenzie Red Lake Gold Mines, the consideration being 600,000 shares and $55,000 to the McNeely syndicate, $5,000 of which was immediately paid. Mackle then left for New York, where he tried in vain to interest capital. Back in Toronto, it was decided that the necessary funds be raised locally. Conversations were held with Charlie Gentles and his young associate, Sammy Zachs, who had just organized a brokerage firm. Mackle was most persuasive, and Gentles decided to finance the venture. He and Zachs immediately purchased stock and were granted options on the remaining treasury shares. Mackle hurried to Red Lake and began shaft sinking.

It was soon apparent that the geology was a complicated affair and gold values were extremely erratic. Notwithstanding, mill construction was ordered and on March 1, 1935, the McKenzie became the second producer in Red Lake. Gold yield, confounding critics, was surprisingly good and at the time of the unfortunate Gold Shore incident, McKenzie was forging close to Howey's production. Skeptics, however, with various and good reasons to support their conclusions, expected the ax to fall momentarily. Others, noting the prevalence of new finds in an increasingly wider radius of activity, were not so sure.

Cochenour and Willans, meanwhile, refused to submit to the unfavorable dictum of Ventures, Ltd. Lindsley's company was well known for its daring and perseverance, and when its negative pronouncement of Cochenour-Willans came, the syndicate felt the impact of the blow. It was hopeless to interest new money now, but the partners hung on grimly. Dan, detached and unruffled as ever, steadied his more temperamental associate, who was given to alternate enthusiasm and despair.

And so they continued to prospect and meet the drudgery of trenching and test pitting. Gradually, the bitterness of the Ventures incident passed. Encouraged by faithful Dan, and also heartened by the discovery of more high-grade veinlets and the consistent optimism of Bill Mackle, Cochenour began conversations with Noah Timmins, Ltd., and in August, 1935, a new option was successfully negotiated. This was transferred to the Hollinger Gold Mines, Ltd., which announced immediate shaft sinking. Work went ahead rapidly, with levels established at the 150- and 275-foot horizons. Drifting was accompanied by frequent channel samples, and while numbers of good values were obtained, the average was below ore grade. Hollinger decided the property was a teaser, and once more the Cochenour-Willans Syndicate was plunged into despondency when the option was allowed to lapse after an expenditure of $100,000.

Two of Canada's greatest mining organizations had now tried and failed, and even confirmed optimists conceded that Cochenour-Willans was beyond hope. But Cochenour, always seconded by Dan Willans, insisted that a mine could yet be developed. Nor was this insistence entirely emotional. Bill Mackle offered unfailing encouragement, particularly as the adjoining McKenzie was in production by this time and steadily opening up new ore horizons. Why not Cochenour-Willans? Long discussions took place and it was finally decided to form the Cochenour-Willans Gold Mines, Ltd. This was done in April, 1936, the syndicate receiving 1,250,000 vendor shares of a 3,000,000-share company. A distribution of 175 shares per unit was made to syndicate members, this after a wait of more than a decade, and Dan Willans and Bill Cochenour each received several hundred thousand shares as their well-deserved portion.

Red Lake was still unpopular, but Cochenour managed to enlist the aid of Alec McKenzie and Sam Gibson, Toronto businessmen, who purchased $75,000 of Cochenour-Willans treasury stock. Bill Mackle was appointed resident engineer and directed resumption of operations at the point where Hollinger had quit. But with this vital difference: convinced that the ore was lensy in character and flat in dip, Mackle cut a raise above the almost barren 150-foot level. And in the amazingly short distance of 25 feet excellent ore was encountered! Had Hollinger established the level at 125 instead of 150 feet, there would have been a different story to tell. For one thing, the fortunate Charlie Gentles and Sammy Zachs would have had one less mine to display on their promotional circulars.

To Dan Willans the unexpected luck of the Cochenour-Willans meant nothing; he had already taken the long journey from which no man has yet returned. To Bill Cochenour, the sweetness of victory turned to gall, and for once his cherished mine was forgotten as he headed efforts to find his missing partner. And as the fall of 1936 deepened into winter, he returned to Haileybury a defeated man, with the whisper "Poor Dan" on his lips.

On the property, work proceeded briskly. Additional raises passed through the mineralized zone into barren rock, and it was realized that the ore body, while rich, was comparatively small. The general reaction was that the situation appeared to be a minor one, satisfactory for individual lessors, no doubt, but unsuitable for company operation. The struggling Cochenour, however, managed to interest the firm of Stratton-Hopkins of Toronto in a plan to purchase treasury stock. Old John ("Turn 'em Down") Reid, known for his hard-boiled but accurate mine appraisals, was sent north to report on the Cochenour-Willans. His findings, surprisingly, were favorable. Stratton-Hopkins purchased $90,000 of treasury stock, in consideration of which they were granted options on all the remaining treasury shares.

Operations were then resumed by Mackle. Apparently unsatisfied with results, Stratton-Hopkins demanded that an independent report be made to obtain an unbiased opinion of the enterprise. With misgivings, Cochenour and Mackle agreed, and forthwith a well-known firm of Toronto consultants flew into the property to make an exhaustive report. The conclusions were dismal. Little chance was given to the development of ore and recommendations were made to sell the equipment and wind up the enterprise. Stratton-Hopkins, of course, refused to purchase any more stock, and by the end of 1937 the situation of Cochenour-Willans once again seemed irredeemable. To many of his intimates, Bill Cochenour became a pathetic figure, weighed down with the loss of Dan Willans and plagued with a property which came close to being a mine, but not close enough.

Remembering John Reid's earlier optimism, the Cochenour-Willans Company asked him to report on the property once more. The examination took place in late 1937. Unsatisfied with later results, the veteran engineer lived up to his reputation of "Turn 'em Down Cold." The report was completely unfavorable, and the property was shut down and largely forgotten.

But the final bell had not yet rung. Bill Cochenour, groggy with disappointments, for the first time showed signs of wavering. Long conversations with Mackle restored confidence. Mackle, sanguine of success, insisted that work should certainly go forward. Accordingly, in the summer of 1938, valiant attempts were made to sell stock, and a matter of $25,000 was finally raised through various individuals. The property was reopened in January, 1939, Mackle agreeing to accept stock for his engineering services. Working under the pressure of necessity, the dogged manager feverishly assembled 5,000 tons of material from the first level and made shipments by truck over frozen Red Lake to the Gold Eagle, the property next to the McKenzie, which had constructed a mill a year previously and was now at a loss for ore. To everyone's astonishment, the grade averaged $23 per ton. The handsome revenue obtained by Cochenour not only enabled work to proceed, but also provided grounds for optimism, for here was conclusive proof that a much higher grade of ore existed than had been anticipated. It was now somewhat easier to secure funds. Charlie Gentles and Sammy Zachs, more confident now, purchased a sizable block of stock. This they distributed to willing clients who had profited by the McKenzie. Among those attracted was John Baker, a mining engineer with offices in New York. After examining the mine personally, he bought a goodly amount of stock from Gentles and Zachs. Baker was among the first technical men to agree with Mackle that a definite pattern of structure was beginning to unfold. The property was cut by a regional break from which a series of subsidiary fractures radiated. Flat, podlike ore bodies "made" in these zones with some semblance of regularity. While it was agreed that considerably more development was necessary to find more pods and build up ore reserves, the grade was high, compensating for limited tonnage.

Below the Cochenour-Willans and south again of the Howey, a newcomer was beginning to stir. Incorporated in 1935 and promoted by Joe McDonough, the Madsen Mine was developing important ore, following discoveries made by prospector Austin McVeigh. By 1937 sufficient ore had been blocked out underground to warrant mill construction, and in the next year, almost on the same day the Gold Shore ended its overambitious career, the Madsen became a producer. Deepening of the shaft revealed richer and unexpectedly wider ore shoots, and erstwhile prospector McDonough found himself with Red Lake's most consistent mine.

Jack Hammell came to life explosively. Even while the Howey approached exhaustion, he. eyed the adjoining McIntyre ground, which was lying inactive. McIntyre, breathing caution, had authorized some diamond drilling in 1927 but considered the results unpromising. When Hammell came forward now and offered $110,000 for the claims, McIntyre immediately accepted. They were soon to realize their mistake. Sinking not one, but two, shafts, Hammell, with speed and precision, began to outline large ore areas. It was an astonishing performance, even for a man who thrived on doing the unexpected. But he had more surprises in store for a camp where anything could, and did, happen. Seizing upon a situation seldom offered in Canadian mining, he purchased the idle Gold Shore mill, together with the defunct company's claims. In October, 1938, both the McIntyre and Gold Shore properties were assigned to the Hasaga Gold Mines, Hammell being the sole recipient of vendor stock. To obtain working capital by the sale of treasury stock was a simple matter at this stage, and a month after its incorporation Hasaga was in profitable production. Jack Hammell had done it again, a knockout in the first round! Confidence, long a stranger to Red Lake, was not slow in returning now.

On the Cochenour-Willans, where Mackle succeeded in finding the requisite ore, a 150-ton mill was built. Production began shortly before the outbreak of war in September, 1939. It was not an auspicious time, but the mine responded gratifyingly. In the face of labor and supply shortages, production was maintained at a profitable rate until February, 1944, at which date general conditions, brought on by four years of warfare, forced suspension of operations. Before the shutdown, however, the mine had reached a flourishing position. Despite the extraction of 250,000 tons of ore for a yield of $4,500,-000, the Cochenour-Willans was in better shape than at any stage in its checkered history. A small smelter and sintering plant had been erected to treat high arsenic-content ore. With this expenditure, the company had paid $920,000 in dividends, leaving a comfortable working capital of almost $800,000. Bill Cochenour's triumph was tempered by the absence of Dan Willans, for only Dan, the companion of his staking and subsequent trials, could have made the joy of success complete.

The accomplishments of the Cochenour and a better understanding of regional Red Lake geology pointed to ground even farther east, an area which had been overlooked by most mining men. By most, but not all, for the late C.J.A. Cunningham-Dunlop had prophesied long before that the Cochenour-Willans section would eventually become the mainstay and salvation of Red Lake. The "Major," as he was usually called, had been in the employ of the Coniagas Mines for years, his first job being that of assistant to the smelter superintendent at Thorald, Ontario, where the mine's arsenic-rich ores were treated. Thrifty farmers brought suit against Coniagas, claiming that smoke fumes from the smelter had killed off their honeybees and so destroyed the chief industry of the neighborhood. Major Dunlop conducted a revealing experiment; he placed several beehives under the very shadow of the smelter stack and proved that not only were the bees unharmed by the fumes but the honey produced was of superior quality. Coniagas won the lawsuit, and the ingenious Major himself began to produce honey in Haileybury when Coniagas suspended Cobalt operations in 1934. This, however, was an avocation; Coniagas retained him as a fieldman scouting new mining properties.

By 1926 Dunlop was on his own. A visit to Red Lake had convinced him that the area contiguous to the Cochenour-Willans claims was a promising one. His employers, however, thought otherwise. The Major severed his connection with Coniagas and staked thirty claims east of the Cochenour-Willans for the Dunlop Red Lake Syndicate which later transferred its assets to Dunlop Consolidated Mines. For more than five years, until his tragic death, the gallant Dunlop tried to raise enough money to develop his ground adequately, but few were moved by his pleas. Piddling sums restricted work, and in 1932 the claims were allowed to lapse. Ironically, it is this very ground that now constitutes the holdings of Campbell and Dickenson Red Lake, currently valued on the market at more than $10,000,000.

Dunlop's claims were staked and restaked over a period of ten years. Then I. K. Isbell, though in his seventies and one of the few surviving brokers of the early epoch of Canadian mining, surveyed the Red Lake scene and decided that here were possibilities to recoup for long lean years. The old Dunlop holdings looked particularly good to him, and so, for a few thousand dollars, he acquired several blocks of claims, part interests in which he sold to the budding young brokerage firm of Brewis & White. Companies were formed with a rapidity that set a precedent even for a country where mining incorporations were commonplace. Resumption of operations on the Cochenour further heightened public fervor as did also the phenomenal success of Hasaga and Madsen in opening new and extensive ore bodies. Red Lake was now one of the "hottest" camps in Canada.

One of the Isbell groups, in which Brewis & White had acquired a one-third interest, was taken into the Dickenson Red Lake Mines, considered a good geological bet. Dickenson had been manager of the M. J. O'Brien Company in Cobalt for many years, but had now, with Mike Kennedy, another O'Brien man, decided to take a plunge into the broad sea of mining exploration. Drilling was quickly started and unexpectedly good results obtained at the outset. The stock skyrocketed from pennies to $1.50 a share and fickle speculators turned from Quebec and Yellowknife in favor of a host of Red Lake issues. Campbell Red Lake, another child of the Brewis & White "venture capital" menage, also clicked in its first drilling and at once Dome Mines, which many had considered surfeited with Red Lake, now negotiated with Brewis & White for a "position." The result was that Dome became a majority stockholder in the company and even the most stolid elements of the industry were impressed. Red Lake appeared in the headlines of the financial press with monotonous regularity, and full-page ads by busy promoters crowded others out. Established mining companies, now fearful of missing an opportunity in a camp they had long ignored, sought participations miles from the Cochenour on the premise that the break was continuous regionally. Noranda, McIntyre, Mining Corporation, American Smelting & Refining Company led the parade. This was a boom to delight the prospector's heart and replenish his lean purse.

With Cochenour-Willans stock soaring to more than $5 a share, Bill Cochenour is today regarded as something of a prophet, though he would be quick to point out that considerable pick and shovel work and years of time have had much to do with his success. And Dan Willans. For without Dan, the "anchor man" of the syndicate who bowed out of the world of mining and all else, the current Red Lake boom would not have been possible.

"What became of Dan's stock?" I asked one of his oldest friends in Haileybury.

"The government took it," he replied. "Spent a year or more tryin' to pick up traces of Dan all over the damned British Empire but it wasn't no use. Dan Willans wasn't his real name, you know, but then the boys has to do the thing legal."

"And what was done with the old shack?"

"Sold, it was, to that Norrie fellow in New York. He's bought some lots along the lake to make a memorial park in memory of Joe Tower, his old partner, you know, who was drownded in Texas. Norrie had the Willans cabin pulled down; it was just about to fall apart, anyway."

Sad, I thought.

"Yes, it ain't good. Dan would have enjoyed all this here Red Lake excitement and the feelin' of havin' staked a bloody producer."

"And the money? By today's market Dan would have been a millionaire."

"Money?" Dan's friend shrugged. "I don't think it'd've made a hell of a lot of difference to Dan. He would have spent it. To him that was what money was for. He either enjoyed it or give it away. He was one grand guy."

"He was," I agreed.

"Suppose you'd like to know how he died. Well—" and he blinked rapidly—"I'll tell you what I think. Dan did himself in. Sure of it 'cause he told me not long before he disappeared that he was reachin' the end of the tether, 'at's jest what he says. Gettin' too old fer the bush, y' see. He was a proud man, Dan, independent as all hell, and he didn't want to be no burden on his friends. So he took what he thought was the decent way to go out. For Dan was a gentleman."

And once again I agreed.

RED LAKE, ONTARIO

Production and Dividends
1935–1945

	Production Date	Production	Dividends
Howey	1935–1941	$13,246,506	$2,150,000
Red Lake Gold Shore	1936–1938	747,577	—
Gold Eagle	1937–1941	1,496,844	—
Madsen	1938–	9,016,714 *	1,239,625
Hasaga	1938–	4,811,000	—
Cochenour-Willans	1939–	5,478,003	798,147
McMarmac	1940–1944	1,472,485	—
McKenzie	1935–	9,372,038	2,801,850
		$45,641,167	$6,989,622

* To Feb. 28, 1946

CHAPTER XIII

Yellowknife, the Last Frontier

"August 18, 1938

The plane is ready to take off and so I can only send you a short note. But boy, oh, boy, have we hit it this time! I wish you could see the gold on Treasure Island, big coarse stuff you can see without a glass—all over the place. Colin Johnson has flown in and after seeing the show said this was a great day for Canada. Charlie Camsell has been in, too, and he was a happy man—he's been plugging the Northwest Territories all his life, you know. Funny thing is that the veins occur in the hot sediments which the geologists say are not favorable to gold deposition and now all the boys are staking like mad where they're not supposed to be. Well, old timer, if this discovery doesn't make a mine I'd better sell insurance for a living. It's the real McCoy and I wish you'd hop a plane and come out here to see it. More later. . . ."

Thus, in Fred Thompson's own words, was the Thompson-Lundmark Gold Mines, Ltd., introduced to the outside. Within a week, newspapers were to herald his sensational find and condition the world to a new name in mining, Yellowknife, which today spells a kind of magic. For a number of reasons this arctic outpost has captured the imagination of even sluggish New Yorkers, and the dreams of men like Mackenzie, Hearne, Franklin, and Camsell are finally coming true.

The Northwest Territories—bounded on the west by the Yukon, by the 60th parallel on the south, the straits leading into Hudson Bay on the east, and the dim regions of the North Pole to the north —comprise an area of 1,309,682 square miles. This region, comprising two-fifths of Canada, is inhabited by only 12,028 human beings, of which 9,400 are Indian and Eskimo. It has a rich history and tradition. When Canada successfully pressed Britain in 1867 to release an immense northern tract from the possession and rule of the Hudson's Bay Company, the Dominion, for the first time, became a single geographical entity. The area freed, of which Northwest Territories was only a part, was obtained for the general citizenry after a payment of £300,000. The "Fertile Belt," where Canada's granary now flourishes, was included as part of the "deal." When examined by members of the British Parliament in 1857 and asked whether there were possibilities of settling the lands, the oldest governor of the Hudson's Bay Company replied, "None, in the lifetime of the youngest man now alive." Of different clay was Malcolm Mac-Leod, once an employee of the company but in later years a northern enthusiast, who wrote prophetically in 1872: "There is, in our northwest an area containing over 300,000,000 acres of wheat and pasture lands, with forests of finest timber, and the largest known coal and bitumen, and also the richest gold areas in the world. . . ." The first Yellowknife booster!

An early explorer of the Territories, after Frobisher, was Henry Hudson, whose ill-fated search for the elusive Northwest Passage is too well known to be repeated here. Two years later, in 1612, Thomas Button, the third entry in the derby, discovered land he designated as New Wales in honor of his native country. Others followed, climaxed in 1668 by the grand entry of the Hudson's Bay Company cohorts whose object was to "draw down the Indians by fair and gentle means to trade with us." The company was able to operate until 1748 without challenge to its safe monopoly. Then the House of Commons, goaded by public pressure, called for an inquiry "into the state and condition of the countries adjoining Hudson Bay and the trade carried on there." Hearings brought out the surprising fact that the area was "no mere waste and howling wilderness" but, instead, one possessing great attractions and possibilities for settlement. While the unpopular Hudson's Bay charter was not canceled, interest in the northern regions was kindled.

Among other edifying facts brought out by witnesses was the presence of rich copper deposits reported by Indians along a river they called Neetha-San-Dazey—"the far-off metal river." Twenty years later, the factor at Churchill induced the company to organize an expedition to locate this copper. The man selected as leader was Samuel Hearne, mate on one of the company's vessels. Instructions were explicit: he was to take off from Great Slave Lake and there be guided by Indians to a river represented to "abound with copper ore, animals of the fur kind, etc., and which is said to be so far to the northward that in the middle of the summer the sun does not set, and is supposed by the Indians to empty itself in some ocean. . . . And if the said river be likely to be of any utility, take possession of it on behalf of the Hudson's Bay Company, by cutting your name on some of the rocks, etc." Hearne made three attempts, the last of which succeeded after he had learned to skirt the barren lands and keep within the wooded sections along the fringe. He found native copper but in small amounts. The river, which flowed into the Arctic Ocean, he named the Coppermine. Sporadic attempts to develop the deposits, all of them unsuccessful, have been made since, the last one being conducted by the American Metals Company of New York in 1945.

In 1789 Alexander Mackenzie, a curious Scot, made his famous trip from Athabaska to Great Slave Lake and thence "down" the mighty river that bears his name today, the first white man to gaze upon the western waters of the Northwest Passage. Two years later, taking off from the same base, he established an even more difficult trail, a straight route to the Pacific.

The voyages of John Franklin, which extended over a period of thirty years following his first in 1820, mark the beginning of the modern history of the Northwest Territories. His first trips were inland from the northern stretches of Hudson Bay to Slave Lake and up the Yellowknife and Coppermine rivers, into the Arctic Ocean and on to Bathurst Inlet and Coronation Gulf. Franklin's expeditions were made on behalf of the British government and it is notable that he accomplished his task with almost religious zeal. It was Franklin who first reported oil seepages along the Mackenzie, later to become the important Fort Norman field. For a quarter of a century he toiled in the far north. He surveyed the Arctic coast west of the Mackenzie delta and then in 1845 organized what was to be his last effort. With two ships and crews numbering 129 men, he left England in the spring to complete the survey of America's northeast coast and thus finally establish the Northwest Passage. But nothing more was heard of Franklin despite a series of searching parties sent along his projected course over a long period of years and his disappearance became one of the classic mysteries of the north.

Following the acquisition of the Territories by the Dominion of

Canada, far more systematic and reliable information was obtained by a number of government parties. From 1872 onward such men as John Macoun, Dr. D. M. Dawson, Charles Horetzky, and Dr. Selwyn, director of the Geological Survey, compiled voluminous reports of the once designated "Terra Incognita." Dr. Robert Bell, also of the survey, spent forty years of his life extending the knowledge of the north, his reports furnishing the impetus for many mineral discoveries in later years along the waterways of what is now northern Manitoba. Others following him were William Ogilvie, who completed the first micrometer survey of the Mackenzie, R. G. McConnel, first to report on the famous tar sands of the Athabaska, and J. B. Tyrell, still alive and vigorous, whose investigations of the rugged northland closed important gaps in Canadian geological knowledge. Vilhjalmur Stefansson was among the first of modern explorers to emphasize the importance of the Canadian northwest which he called the "Friendly Arctic."

Dr. Charles Camsell, C. M. G.

Dr. J. Mackintosh Bell

In 1900, J. Mackintosh Bell of the Geological Survey, though only twenty-three years old, made what proved to be the most provocative survey of all, for while his report remained obscure for thirty years, a fortuitous study of it by Gilbert Labine resulted in the earth-shattering discovery of uranium at Great Bear Lake, which in turn led to the gold discoveries at Yellowknife farther south on Great Bear Lake. Bell, a famous nephew of a famous uncle, had taken his doctorate at Harvard, but returned to work in his native Canada. Tall, thinly built, and of a refined nature, he seemed a far cry from the hardier explorers who had preceded him. But he has left a record of which his descendants may well be proud. At Fort Norman, on the Mackenzie, he was joined by Charles Camsell. (A "native son" of the region and a graduate of the University of Manitoba, Camsell has since devoted his life to the furtherance of the Territories). With three bushmen, the party started north on

June 18, 1900, equipped with two canoes and the simplest of larders. Reaching Great Bear Lake on June 23, they were surprised to find a solid sheet of ice. Not until July 3 was there sufficient water to permit canoe travel. By August 1 they reached the deep, rocky northeast arm of the lake now known as Echo Bay. It was here that Bell made the following note, two weeks later:

> In the greenstones east of McTavish Bay occur numerous interrupted stringers of calcite containing chalcopyrite, and the steep rocky shores which here present themselves to the lake are often stained with cobalt bloom and copper.

Bell's report gathered dust until 1930 when Gilbert Labine's sharp eye was arrested by what to him were compelling words. Labine, with his brother Charley, had first come to Haileybury from southern Ontario, both of them engaged as itinerant stock salesmen.

Gilbert Labine

Infected by the stories of mining told by their uncle, Jim Labine, who had fortuitously shared in Benny Hollinger's gold discoveries, and falling into the spirit of a mining community, the brothers were soon actively engaged in prospecting, gaining valuable experience in Cobalt and Porcupine. Gilbert, aware of his technical deficiencies, enrolled at Haileybury Mining School where he underwent a comprehensive training in mineralogy. Armed with this fresh knowledge, he was at once struck by Bell's observations of green stains and cobalt bloom. His knowledge of cobalt suggested that wherever cobalt occurred silver should be found also. Having learned that a trapper named Charles Sloan and his partner Harrison had staked "copper" claims at Hunter Bay a few years previously, Labine decided to proceed north and investigate without loss of time. Flying from Edmonton, he satisfied himself that this region offered little in the way of copper. But the environs of Echo Bay, the scene of Bell's significant observations, made a lasting impression when he surveyed it from the air. That winter he made careful plans which he proceeded to put into execution at the end of March, 1928.

Taking off from Waterways with Charles St. Paul and piloted by Leigh Brintnell, he landed at the headwaters of the Camsell River. Improvising a crude sled, the two men hauled almost a ton of supplies to Echo Bay, a journey which required six full weeks and was accomplished despite terrifying hardships. St. Paul became a victim of snow blindness and Labine had to act as his nurse, but he managed to sneak off on short prospecting trips. It was not long before he found what he sought—heavy native silver accompanied by cobalt bloom and a black massive mineral which, in his new academic role, he recognized as pitchblende. And so the Eldorado Gold Mines, Ltd., which had failed to develop a gold mine in Manitoba, now began to produce the uranium which eventually found its way to the unfortunate shores of Japan. Labine, truly a man of destiny, served early notice on an incredulous world that the atomic age was about to become a reality.

The Bear Exploration Company, most of whose early funds came from the ample pockets of Bill Wright, began its corporate existence in the Echo Lake district and then turned southward to the less-heralded shores of Yellowknife Bay, a long north arm of Great Slave Lake. (The name "Yellowknife" was coined by Hearne in 1781, when he observed the Indians at the mouth of the river using native copper—"yellow"—implements and ornaments.) Prospectors Jack Baker and Herb Dickson, forming one party, worked out from Great Bear Lake in 1933 to the headwaters of Yellowknife River. Following this precipitous waterway south, they came across gold-bearing quartz veins near Quyta Lake, thirty miles from the mouth of the river, called Yellowknife Bay. They also made another discovery at Prosperous Lake, and staked claims in both localities. As in the case of so many camps, this was by no means the first evidence of mineral in the Slave Lake region. In 1898 prospectors bound for the Klondike via the inland Mackenzie River route, were caught near Fort Resolution by an unexpectedly early freezeup. Nothing daunted, they built winter camps and prospected the area. On the south shore of Slave Lake, in the rocks of Paleozoic age, they discovered rich outcrops of lead-zinc ore. But the lure of Yukon gold was too strong, and in the spring the men continued northward. Years later, Dr. Mackintosh Bell, with John Erickson, acquired the base metal deposits and transferred them into the Northern Lead-Zinc Company, ownership of which was divided between Consolidated Mining & Smelting, Ventures, Ltd., Bell's own Atlas Exploration, and a few individuals in Boston and New York. Comparatively undeveloped, the occurrence still awaits large-scale investigation.

Other Klondikers reported finding gold in the environs of

Yellowknife Bay, but there was no immediate follow-up, save for one expedition organized by a fraudulent promoter. The first authenticated gold discovery in Yellowknife was made in 1900 by the much-traveled Dr. Mackintosh Bell. Windbound on the north shore, he reconnoitered the immediate terrain and collected a suite of specimens. One of these later yielded a high assay in gold. Almost thirty years later, Bell interested "Smelters" and Ventures, Ltd., in joining him in a search for the source of gold. Work was conducted north of the present locus of operations, and nothing of interest was found. About this same time, Thayer Lindsley and Colonel C. D. H. MacAlpine formed the Dominion Explorers Company and Jack Hammell the Northern Mineral Aerial Exploration, both of which were to "crack open the north." While results were largely negative as far as mineral discovery went, valuable experience in northern flying was obtained. This paved the way for future operations on a scale which enabled the sourdough to fly through the clouds instead of paddling a canoe or mushing by dog team.

The work of Bear Exploration was the first serious effort made in Yellowknife Bay. Under the direction of Major L. T. Burwash, the Quyta and Prosperous Lake gold discoveries were prospected in 1933 and 1934. Using these localities as bases, a party was sent farther south, and to Jack Baker and H. M. Muir must go the honors for the first modern gold discovery in the Yellowknife Bay area. Their find was made on the east shore, and though small in dimensions was exceedingly high in grade. Word of this slowly percolated to the outside, and a few hardy prospectors arrived from the south, but not before the Bear Company had staked liberally and honeycombed the district with its holdings.

Anxious to increase knowledge and interest in the last frontier, Ottawa commissioned the Geological Department to conduct a survey of Yellowknife in 1935. In the course of this work, one of the observant geologists reported the presence of gold on the west side of the bay. This information was immediately released and caused a flurry of new staking.

Among those who came too early was Murdock Mosher, of Cobalt. "Murdie," who with his brother Alec had staked the Central Patricia Mine in Ontario, had learned through the grapevine that things were happening in Yellowknife. Though still young, he was a veteran prospector. Venturing north just before Christmas in 1935 was no hardship for him. Picking up a hired man at Fort Smith, he continued on to Yellowknife, where, after appraising the situation, he staked a group of claims on the west side of the bay. Subsequently, when Bear work failed to live up to early promise, interest in the camp began to languish. Under the circumstances, Mosher decided to forgo the expense of assessment work and allowed his claims to lapse. The ground was greedily snapped up by the Ryan-Freeman-Payne syndicate of Edmonton which had long been awaiting this opportunity.

For on the west side of Yellowknife Bay the tireless Consolidated Mining & Smelting Company had finally come to rest. After searching for years throughout the Dominion and meeting with a series of disappointments, W. M. Archibald, the chief engineer, decided that here at last was the long-sought El Dorado.

"Yellowknife," he declared at this time, "will be one of the truly great gold camps of not only Canada but the world, provided there is plenty of hard work done."

He did more than enthuse: he caused his men to stake all the open ground on the west side of Yellowknife Bay which he considered favorable geology. Work commenced on a small high-grade quartz vein, and when values provided encouragement the first important shaft work in Yellowknife was begun. The ore was rich but the occurrence small. Logic demanded additional development before mill construction could be even considered. But Archibald, with a courage not often found among employees of such large organizations as Smelters, insisted that large rewards necessitated large risks, and that all orthodox procedures would have to be thrown overboard in Yellowknife. Transportation was involved and cumbersome; supplies must be taken in one year ahead of requirements. Since time was money, he faced the directors and urged that the plunge be taken at once. And to the amazement of all, Archibald's resolute ideas prevailed.

Mill construction was quickly started. Then, like a veritable thunderbolt, came the startling news that the Ryan Syndicate, stakers of Mosher's old ground, had sold 60 per cent of their claims to the "Con" for $500,000 cash on the line. Prospectors sprang to action; this Yellowknife camp must be more than a trick name if hard-boiled Smelters parted with that kind of money.

Persistent Glyn Burge furnished most of the initial enthusiasm which resulted in the discovery of the Thompson-Lundmark Gold Mines. An English aviator who emigrated to New York and thence to Canada, Burge became a bush pilot in the early days of northern flying. In time he accepted employment with the Prospectors Airways Company, flying Bobby Cockeram and Pete Graham throughout northern Canada. Under the tutelage of these two astute prospectors, he was soon familiar with the broad aspects of the game. No bushman or geologist himself, he unfailingly cultivated a wide acquaintance of mining men, religiously pumping them for information. In 1936 he formed G. B. Explorers, Ltd., and tried to find his own properties. Two field seasons yielding no results, he decided to move into the Northwest Territories. Handicapped by shoestring resources, he persuaded New York friends to form the Thompson Prospecting Syndicate to investigate the Yellowknife district, G. B. Explorers agreeing to purchase 10 per cent of the units at $50 each. In all, 84 units were sold to net the Syndicate $4,200.

Fred Thompson was appointed manager and was assigned a 10 per cent interest and a modest salary. Before the breakup of 1938 he was winging his way to Yellowknife, accompanied by his younger brother, Bob. The two stopped in town only long enough to pick up supplies and a sectional canoe, then requested the pilot to drop them off at Sunset Lake on the Beaulieu River, ninety miles northeast of the Yellowknife settlement. There they pitched camp and awaited the breakup, ready to prospect the granite-greenstone contact which Fred decided was a structure identical with that of Yellowknife Bay.

The thaw came, and the Thompsons began the familiar routine of cross-sectioning the country. The bush was thin and the terrain rocky, and their progress was rapid. Within two weeks they had found a regional shearing within which occurred welcome veins and lenses of quartz, all of it mineralized. Then followed the monotonous toil of crushing samples with mortar and pestle and panning the fines for evidence of gold.

"Here she is!" cried Fred one day in July, and showed his eager brother a tailing which stretched halfway round the pan.

Calmly, with the knowledge and temperance of a true miner, he now mapped the discovery zone and marked locations for trenching and sampling. (The property is now Sunset Yellowknife Mines.)

"I am in Yellowknife again," he wrote some time later, "picking up a few men to fly back to Sunset. We have found what looks like a major shearing with excellent values here and there. But we must do more work before we know what we have. Coming in yesterday, the plane was very low and I spotted an area near Hidden Lake which was lousy with pegmatite dikes and quartz veins. I said nothing to the pilot but I want to see Burge and tell him about it. Maybe his plane can drop me down there one of these days. It's in the hot sediments which aren't supposed to have a chance, but I've heard that story before. I want to have a look-see."

And a look-see he did have. Meeting Burge in Yellowknife several weeks later, arrangements were made to have Norbert Miller, a pilot servicing the Waco plane which Burge's company had char-

tered for the summer, deposit Fred Thompson and the late Roy
Lundmark on a small lake close to the spot "lousy with pegmatite
dikes and quartz veins." Miller landed swiftly and just as swiftly
took off for Yellowknife. A fine rain began to fall. Thompson and
Lundmark quietly agreed to separate and make their own investigations. They struck off north in the meager bush, alert, watching
the rock intently. The rain began to increase, and the two men, of
one accord, trudged back to the shore where they had pitched a silk
tent. They arrived almost at the same moment.

"Well, I found it," said Fred Thompson, with his warm quiet
smile which later reminded newsmen of Ronald Coleman, and he
held out a fragment of quartz well covered with gold.

"So have I," replied the equally contained Roy Lundmark, ex-
hibiting similar specimens.

The men shook hands gravely and then ducked into the tent.
The familiar whine of an airplane motor roused them. They peeked
out and saw Miller's Waco gracefully landing on what was soon to
be named Thompson Lake. Murdock Mosher climbed out of the
cockpit.

"Got anything, fellows?" he shouted.

"Come and see!" was the answer.

Mosher, whose untimely relinquishment of claims had resulted
in a fortune for others, was determined to recoup in the Yellowknife
area. He was now about to realize his desire. After a discussion with
Thompson and Lundmark, it was decided to stake a large claim
group embracing the discoveries as well as ground to the north and
south along the general strike of the ore zone. Lundmark and
Mosher, representing the Lahti-Lundmark and Burmos syndicates,
were to share equal thirds in all the ground with the Thompson
Syndicate. Burge was heavily interested in all three syndicates, and
in this way his G. B. Explorers commanded the largest, and con-
trolling, position in the enterprise.

During the staking, spectacular gold was found on a small island south of the campsite, and this was promptly named Treasure
Island. The quartz exposure was sixty feet long and thirty feet wide,
and all through the mass splotches of coarse gold were alluringly
visible. High grade could also be seen through the water along the
shore. It was a true "prospector's delight." Pausing only to gather a
few hand specimens, the men continued their work at top speed.
Lahti and Bob Thompson joined the crew, and in little more than a
week's time ninety-seven claims were staked. Then the news was
allowed to spread into Yellowknife.

Staking reached the proportions of a rush. Visitors, including

Dr. Charles Camsell, thronged to Treasure Island. Newspapers carried headlines about a new and sensational find and mining scouts wired excited messages to headquarters. In the midst of the furor Burge gathered a bagful of specimens, obtained a sketch of the staking from Thompson, and headed for Toronto. There he interviewed Thayer Lindsley, and shortly thereafter the two were Yellowknife bound.

Bob and I, meanwhile, presented the Thompson-Lundmark to the ill-fated American Metals Company. We urged haste: the story of discovery had traveled swiftly and far, was even lyrically described by silken-tongued radio announcers, and bidding for the property was getting out of hand. With unaccustomed energy, the Metals Company sent two of its engineers to Yellowknife. They were to submit a report with all possible speed, and then, if warranted, a purchase offer would be made the Thompson Syndicate and associates. But even when the wheels of a large organization are accelerated, the pace falls short of Canadian mining tempo. The fast-acting Lindsley walked over the Thompson-Lundmark and immediately advanced $50,000 for drilling operations. This was accepted with alacrity, long before the Metals Company formulated its own involved financing plan. Stung by this failure, the New Yorkers resolved to find their own mine. Accordingly, a Stimson aircraft was purchased and several prospectors retained, among them Roy Lundmark. A Metals Company engineer was sent north to supervise fieldwork and operations commenced in 1939.

Lundmark, reared in the bush of western Ontario, was among the brightest of the younger prospectors in Canada. By midsummer he had found gold near Slemon Lake, not far west of Yellowknife Bay. His plane sped to town with the good news and carried back the supervising engineer.

"Too small," he gave his judgment after inspection of the vein, "we only want something big up here."

Told that most Canadian mines began life modestly, he shook his head. His instructions were unequivocal: he was not to waste time on anything less than a mine of healthy proportions. Yellowknife was mystified by this attitude, but Lundmark accepted the verdict calmly. Later, when his term of employment ended, he was allowed to retain the claims for himself. His tragic death overseas deprived Canadian mining of a man who would have gone far in exploration, but the Slemon Lake claims remained as some small consolation to his young widow. In 1945, Fred Thompson, in his capacity as field manager for Frederick Yellowknife, made a gold find next to his old colleague's ground. Joe Hirshhorn, sponsor of

Frederick, listened to Thompson's suggestion that the Lundmark property be bought.

"Okay," said Joe briskly, "go ahead and buy it. Write your own ticket on the price."

The Slemon Yellowknife Mines resulted, Mrs. Lundmark and associates receiving $10,000 cash and 300,000 shares of stock. As I write, George Radisics, manager of Slemon, reports promising development results. . . . But I am getting ahead of the Yellowknife story.

We left the Thompson-Lundmark about to undertake drilling in the late summer of 1938. At the same time, important events were transpiring in the Yellowknife Bay section. At the Con Mine, where Yellowknife's first gold mill was under construction, a new vein had been found quite by chance. In the course of driving his tractor from the shore to the shaft site, the operator struck a boulder in the muskeg. In extracting the "cat" from an awkward position, he noted that the boulder was rather a quartz outcrop which barely protruded above the scrubby growth of Labrador tea. Bending closer, he observed welcome specks of yellow. Henry Geigerich, manager of the Con, was excitedly informed of the strange discovery. Trenching and stripping soon disclosed a sizable quartz outcrop of unexpected richness. Dimensions were considerably larger than those of the No. 1 vein on which all mining operations had been predicated.

From the 400-foot level, a crosscut was directed to probe the new vein, No. 4, underground, and the intersection was duly made in a blaze of golden glory. The Con now seemed assured of a goodly supply of excellent ore. Actually, Archibald had made the earlier hard choice of purchasing the Ryan claims at a fantastically high price, so worried was he at the dismal prospect of lacking sufficient millfeed. This act of desperation, thanks to an accident and an unusually wide-awake cat operator, was entirely unwarranted. Ironically, the Ryan claims have responded indifferently to development, though the possibilities of the property are by no means completely exhausted.

South of the Con, Joe Errington and the Honorable Charles McCrea, one-time Ontario minister of mines, were wrestling mightily with the Negus Mines. Several years previously, McCrea had sent prospectors into the area, and in a happy moment the men staked a group of claims overlooked by others for no understandable reason. Errington was invited to supply funds shortly after Smelters' decision to sink a shaft at the Con. Joe needed no second bidding.

"The richest God-damned gold camp in Canada" was his Yellowknife opinion, expressed to me in typical Erringtonese.

When drilling disclosed a number of narrow but high-grade ore sections, Errington and McCrea decided to take the bull by the horns and follow the Con's bold example of dispensing with the usual drawn-out program of development work.

"We'll sink a shaft," declared Joe, "and mine the ore as fast as we open it up."

Fortunately for Joe and his friends, the relatively small veins were extremely rich, the average value being well over an ounce of gold to the ton of quartz. Though tonnage was limited, there was no hesitation in ordering mill construction.

Smelters had a "new one," the Ptarmigan, ten miles northeast of town, and there, too, underground results were pleasing. Unlike the north-south Con and Negus, which were located in the lavas, this "show" was a wide east-west striking across sedimentary strata. Surface and diamond drilling assays had been erratic, but Archibald, convinced that Yellowknife made its own laws, ignored old rules and moved full steam ahead. Ptarmigan became a producing mine. To Archibald, no longer with Smelters, must go major thanks for Canada's youngest gold camp. In faltering hands, the Con would undoubtedly have degenerated into a lost enterprise and the Ptarmigan would not have been attempted. During the critical years, Yellowknife's staying power rested entirely in this one man's determined spirit. If the Con had been abandoned, the camp might have slipped into the shadows, probably not to have been revived again in our time.

The fateful year 1939 was important to Yellowknife, for then the Con and Negus mines produced the first gold bricks in the long history of the Territories. There were disappointments too. The Camlaren, financed by Mining Corporation, threw up the sponge after sinking a shaft. It was judged that not enough ore was indicated for such high-cost country. But south of Gordon Lake the Thompson-Lundmark was moving ahead, overcoming the large expense and vexing problems of transporting supplies and equipment entirely by aircraft, and unwaveringly opening the Kim vein by means of an incline shaft. In midsummer, Hugh Fraser, a brilliant geologist employed by the company to map and prospect the claims, had found a high-grade vein adjacent to the Kim and this was quickly named the Fraser. Not content with thus adding to possibilities of the mine, he then investigated a small island nearby, and there, too, was rewarded for his perspicacity. The management, somewhat bewildered by these events, was confronted with the dilemma of where to concentrate work. From the south end of the Kim to the Discovery Vein north of Treasure Island, there stretched a zone more than a mile in extent along which rich exposures of gold had been found at intervals. It was too much for Ken Muir, the manager, and his urgent letters brought the directors of the company, together with the venerable consulting engineer, Ernie Neelands, to the far-northern outpost.

The young Thompson-Lundmark Company was a kind of hybrid organization. While Thayer Lindsley's Ventures, Ltd., had taken a good slice of the 1,000,000 shares sold privately at 25 cents per share, and further participated through its stockholding in G. B. Explorers, a large part of the vendor stock was held by twenty-eight individuals and companies which had purchased units in the three syndicates dividing the claims. Hence the directors were "independent," and yet one company, Ventures, was the heaviest single shareholder. While Muir and Neelands wrestled with mining problems, we directors, all familiar with mining, worked to resolve the ever-vital question of money. War clouds were gathering, and the stock, which had in the beginning spurted to 45 cents, was now apathetically hovering around the 20-cent mark. Neelands, efficient and conservative, decided that more development work was necessary before mill and expenditure would be justified. A new shaft on the Fraser was recommended.

"Fine," said Murdock Mosher, "but what do we use for money in a time like this?"

"I'll wire Lindsley," suggested Burge, the president. "The plane's right here and I'll be in Yellowknife in half an hour."

Forthwith he departed, leaving an anxious group of directors behind him. Some dissatisfaction was expressed at the state of affairs. The prevailing opinion was that we could afford to take risks similar to the Con and Negus, but Neelands stressed the difference between the situations. The Thompson-Lundmark was not in Yellowknife Bay and transportation was infinitely more complicated than that of the mines there, so located that they could unload supplies, equipment, and particularly oil direct from barges. The unhappy directors listened to the voice of experience and bowed to the wisdom of an older head.

Next morning, the Waco landed at Thompson Lake, and an excited Burge burst into our tent, waving a telegram.

"It's all right, boys!" he cried. "Thayer Lindsley will put up the money!"

The telegram was quickly read. True enough, Lindsley was willing to purchase 250,000 shares at 35 cents but there was one condition—the directors would have to match this. We exchanged looks of dismay.

At that moment the first results of drilling on the Fraser vein had come to camp, and these were edifying. Only a few nights previously, Burge, who had waited at the drill until an expected intersection was obtained at 2:00 A.M., had awakened us from a troubled sleep to exhibit a quartz core literally plastered with gold. He now reminded us of this. The first to speak up was Bob. While not a director, he had been invited to participate in the discussion, due to his association with Thompson.

"I'll underwrite 100,000 shares," he declared. "It would be a crime to let the development go at this stage."

"Can you handle that much?" he was asked.

"Not myself," he admitted, "but I'm sure my friends and associates in New York will take a large part."

"How about the Mosher Company?" asked Kelso Roberts, solicitor for the Mosher Long Lac Mines as well as Thompson-Lundmark.

"Well." Murdie Mosher scratched his thinning pate and smiled boyishly. "It's all right with me and I guess the other directors will come along for, say, 150,000 shares."

In Yellowknife town, the word was soon passed that the Thompson was to dig in for more work. The richness of the Fraser was discussed in terms of superlatives. Just then closing of the property would have been a hard blow, for the camp was beginning to suffer from a wave of unfavorable publicity. In Toronto wiseacres declared that the veins were too small and the structure too shallow to make for permanent operations. Geologists who had never visited the camp unhesitatingly declared that the glacier, in that northern area just below the Arctic Circle, had planed down the bulk of deposits, leaving Yellowknife with the remnants and stumps of what originally might have been sizable ore bodies. And there were brokers too, either uninterested in a region where little promotional money had any play or jealous that funds might be diverted from their own favorite localities, who lost no opportunity to knock the struggling camp. Yellowknife still had a long hard road to travel.

North of the Con, engineer Charlie Hershman was quietly bagging high-grade ore on the Giant Yellowknife Mine. Owned by the Bear Exploration Company, the Giant was one of several Bear subsidiaries ailing with financial anemia. Hershman, an engineer with a long record in the western States and Canada, had found a number of promising shear zones and veins, but handicapped by lack of funds, he had sunk a small shaft on the high-grade Brock Vein where he hoped to derive enough revenue to finance larger scale work, despite arrears in his own salary. No great tonnage came from the Brock, but values were enticing. A shipment of twenty tons, made by barge and rail to the Trail Smelter 1,200 miles distant, grossed $20,000, but the transportation costs absorbed most of this amount. Hershman, who was living on the property with his wife, his constant companion even when he operated in such a place as Contact Bay at Great Bear Lake a few years previously, decided that he was working uselessly. Unable to obtain enough money for the program of wide development he had recommended, he now resigned his position and returned to Toronto. To many, this signalized the end of a misnamed mining company, but events were to demonstrate that Bear officials had been happily inspired when they hit upon "Giant" as a name. Had they supported Hershman, this fact would have long been evident.

Fortunately for Yellowknife, Smelters had begun construction of a 4,500-horsepower hydroelectric site at the head of Prosperous Lake, twelve miles from the town. Few others, at this stage, would have risked such large expenditures, but the sure hand of Archibald was at the throttle and his direction was full speed ahead. The Con was finding excellent ore and, to confound criticism, had disclosed the fact that the No. 4 vein had widened greatly on the 500-foot level. The Negus, however, was barely able to supply its 50-ton mill. I recall visiting the mine in the late summer of 1939, when a stoppage threatened, but fortunately a new vein was discovered underground and the entire working force, including the staff and bluff J. G. McNiven, the manager, scrambled down the shaft and helped muck ore to keep the mill operating. "The show must go on," an old theatrical tradition, thus had its application in Yellowknife.

The year 1940 found interest in Yellowknife, as in other gold areas, completely subordinated by the unhappy progress of Hitler's war in Europe. Airplane travel was restricted, miners began to drift southward to the colors, and, in consequence, little hope was felt that operations could continue. But the Con, Negus, and Ptarmigan hung on grimly. At the Thompson-Lundmark Mine, the Fraser shaft had revealed a sizable high-grade ore shoot, but the company, laboring under conditions which made further financing impossible, was forced to consider shutting down. But this sad event did not materialize. Burge communicated with Archibald. Smelters agreed to take over the enterprise and bring it to the production stage, notwithstanding the war. The contract authorized loans up to $700,000 for the construction of a 125-ton mill and the purchase of supplies, this sum to be repaid from first profit. Following this,

the Thompson stockholders would be reimbursed the $467,000 they
had provided through purchase of treasury stock. The respective
group interests in the enterprise would then be determined on a pro
rata basis, which meant that Smelters would receive 58 per cent and
the Thompson company 42 per cent. Ventures, Ltd., teamed with
Smelters and advanced $150,000. Work went forward rapidly.

The next few years in Yellowknife were interesting. Despite
the war, daily tonnage at the Con was increased to 350 while the
Ptarmigan began to produce from a 100-ton mill. The Negus, gradually enlarging its scant ore reserves, made a surprise payment of
5 cents a share on April 10, 1941, the first gold mine dividend in the
Territories. At the Thompson-Lundmark, milling commenced on
August 19, 1941, and continued until September 30, 1943, by which
time labor and supply conditions made further work impractical.
However, $1,765,000 in gold was obtained from 73,215 tons treated,
enabling the company to repay all loans, while leaving the sum of
$90,000 cash plus something more than $200,000 in supplies at the
mine.

The Ptarmigan, less fortunate, was able to produce only from
November, 1941, to September, 1942. The Con continued to produce
until late 1943, when the reduced crew of miners was transferred
to work on development. The Negus, except for a short period of
suspension, was able to maintain production for almost the entire
war period. It might be supposed under the circumstances that
interest in Yellowknife, never high, would now disappear altogether.
But the grand climax was yet to come.

We return to the Giant, abandoned for several years. Glyn
Burge, now elevated to the presidency of Frobisher Exploration,
the Ventures, Ltd., subsidiary which had been devoting its large
efforts toward mining strategic war metals, leveled his sights at the
Giant. Armed with Charlie Hershman's excellent maps and satisfied
by technicians that the ground held out alluring gold possibilities,
he set himself to deal with lawyer J. J. Gray, chief factotum of the
company. Burge worked at this intermittently for two years, finding
in Gray a worthy antagonist. Others had tried, for the merits of
Giant were generally recognized, but all had failed. In each case
Gray had been asked to reorganize his company, since so much stock
was outstanding that a new financing group, under the circumstances, could not obtain majority control. Burge, however, nimbly
accepted a deal under the prevailing framework of the company,
with the important condition that Gray vote his stock with Frobisher, so assuring working control to the Ventures group. Negotiations were expedited by Ralph Pielsticker, a New York broker

who had long been recommending the purchase of Bear stock to his clients.

The final agreement is worthy of mention. With an authorized capital of 3,000,000 shares, Giant had already distributed 1,785,000 (1,200,000 to the vendor companies—Burwash, Bear, and Yellowknife Gold; and 585,000 sold to the public, leaving 1,215,000 shares unissued, or 40 per cent of the company), which explains the refusal of various earlier negotiators to accept a minority position. Frobisher now immediately purchased 100,000 shares at 10 cents, in consideration of which an additional 1,115,000 shares were optioned at prices from 10 to 30 cents, the last installment falling due March 15, 1945. If the options were to be exercised in their entirety, Frobisher would then have purchased 1,215,000 shares for a total consideration of $240,125, or an average of approximately 20 cents per share. The Pielsticker group, apprised of the deal, purchased Giant stock on the Toronto unlisted market at prices of 15 to 25 cents per share.

Burge, agreement in hand, conferred with Thayer Lindsley and was bluntly told that funds were not available for any large-scale work. Undismayed, he elicited the promise that the first money received by Ventures in repayment of the Thompson-Lundmark loan would be allocated to the Giant. Thereupon Lindsley asked for maps. These were placed before him. A short study of the various surface plans brought a significant gleam to his eye. Like a hunter on the scent of big game, he turned to Burge decisively.

"Why," he said with a smile, "it seems very simple. The West Bay fault has moved the country north four or five miles, and the Giant is really part of the original country east of the Con Mine. Whoever located those claims, by accident or design, has picked the right spot. You've done well, Glyn. And now call in Dadson."

A. S. Dadson, one of the several Ventures geologists, spent an hour or two with the "chief." A program of careful geological mapping, following ore disclosures by prospector Don Cameron, was outlined and Dadson departed for the north where Ken Muir was in charge of Frobisher. Later, geologist Hugh Fraser was engaged to assist Dadson and Muir. Burge was assigned a task to his liking, the acquisition of various Yellowknife properties which straddled the north-south West Bay Fault, and the name "Frobisher" was soon to become a familiar one on claim maps. Conveniently, Thompson-Lundmark discharged its loans to Smelters and Ventures. Nothing hindered Giant plans now.

On March 9, 1944, the *Northern Miner,* in a banner headline story, dramatically announced that the Giant had intersected an unbelievably large ore body, in the so-called Discovery Zone. Located at the south end of the two-mile-long property, widths of up to fifty feet were encountered with values of close to half an ounce. The stock spurted from a few cents to $2 a share, but this was only a beginning. More drills were brought in and within a short time the mining world began to realize that Lindsley had indeed unearthed a Giant. And as new zones, all of them of major proportions and grade, were opened by the industrious drilling crews, the stock shot up rapidly, not halting until it had reached the astounding figure of $11.50 a share. The public became "Yellowknife drunk." Once derisive, Toronto now jumped on the bandwagon like a stampeded rabble. Long-ignored issues climbed from too hastily dug graves; wildcats began to howl again. In the van was New York, hitherto coy in matters Canadian. Wall Street, thanks to Pielsticker, had timed its buying perfectly. Giant was large enough to be generous to newcomers.

Lindsley, of course, had handed over the $150,000 received from Thompson-Lundmark. And now, when success came, his head was not turned. On the contrary, as on similar occasions, his mind worked with dispatch and clarity. At his behest a Giant meeting was called and the capitalization of the company increased to 4,000,000 shares. Stockholders were then given rights to purchase 250,000 shares at $5 each and these were snapped up hungrily. The company now had almost $1,500,000. But that was not enough, Lindsley decided, as the ore potential increased. More rights were announced and as quickly gobbled by the insatiable stockholders, and the once-humble Giant was now financed for the most ambitious of development programs, calling for two shafts and a 500-ton mill. And Charlie Hershman, who had laid the groundwork for all this, became the forgotten man of Yellowknife.

During this time, brokers rushed to capitalize the situation. Yellowknife companies were born at a pace to provoke a Mrs. Dionne to envy. There began a period of boiler-room promotion with liberal use of long-distance telephones and 100-word telegrams. Newspapers carried weird stories of the Yellowknife community, as though it had been freshly discovered. Here was a boom such as the north had never seen.

The fever has abated somewhat, but interest continues high, for the camp is large, containing almost 100,000 square miles of favorable geology. New finds can be confidently expected with swarms of companies, well financed, in the field. Geologists, some of whom formerly sounded warnings, are now of one mind: Yellowknife has enormous possibilities. In the din of praise and hope, however, a few notes of caution have been sounded. The camp is remote, transportation and labor are problems, and costs are high and likely to remain so for some time.

Sober mining men have been deeply impressed with Giant performance and the recent drilling of the Con and Negus, which has yielded good values and structure at a vertical depth of 2,500 feet from the surface. The Con has also been meeting with encouragement underground on the 1,400-foot level. In the Beaulieu River area, where Smelters has constructed a 25-ton mill on the high-grade Ruth Mine, many discoveries point to a crop of new mines. The Thompson-Lundmark unscrambled its ramified deal with Smelters and Ventures and so is now in a position to resume work with a large property as yet only partially tested, the stockholders receiving full benefit of any additional ore which may be found. At Indin Lake, 150 miles north of Yellowknife town, several interesting developments have been reported; also at Slemon and Russell Lakes. While, of course, only an occasional producing mine will result from all this activity, one fact is inescapable: the innumerable companies, for the most part, have considerable working capital in spite of the liberal cuts taken by promoters, an important difference between this and other booms. And costs, while still remaining comparatively high, should, with the return of normalcy and the establishment of a year-round highway from Grimshaw to Hay River, tend to decrease. But the field is one which can be attacked effectively only by experienced operators. Amateurs, bitten by the Yellowknife gold bug and intrigued by newspaper and magazine yarns, will be badly burned.

It is a large country in every sense of the word, containing in the Mackenzie a waterway as large as the Mississippi. Great Slave and Great Bear Lakes are greater in extent than either Lake Ontario or Erie. Yellowknife, a rocky outpost of only a few hundred people in 1936, is today bursting at the seams with a population crowding 5,000. It is, perhaps, the most air-minded community on earth. Dogrib Indians, who have never seen a railroad train, are indifferent to the hum of aircraft—this is old stuff to them. Even the automobile is not a matter of wonder to the native, for as early as 1941 two passenger cars were transported by barge into Yellowknife from Waterways and Fort Smith. The only road at that time circled the island and this was used until the cars, traveling in opposite directions, collided one day. The local press, at the time a mimeographed sheet, noted the accident philosophically. Two cars, one road, one accident, no cars.

The Mounted Police maintain headquarters at Yellowknife and

so the town is comparatively well behaved, particularly now that a jail has been built. Before the war, however, offenders were sent to Fort Smith, save in cases when transportation happened to be unavailable. This, in 1939, seemed to be more the exception than the rule. On the Thompson-Lundmark, a sampler was caught high-grading. The offense, ordinarily, is a serious one, but in this case it was almost fatal, for he was stealing gold at a time when the value of the property was being appraised. The Mounted Police received a radio signal to come in and arrest the culprit, who had readily confessed his crime. The plane arrived speedily and with it a Mountie who lost no time getting his man.

Weeks later, when we flew to town after our memorable directors' meeting, we were surprised to find the prisoner, in company with a Mountie, eating at the best restaurant in town.

"Why didn't you send him down to Fort Smith?" inquired Murdock Mosher.

"Couldn't," shrugged the Mountie. "Planes all booked up solid. So we had him pitch a tent near the barracks and he's doing the chores for us until we can send him out."

And so, in more ways than one, the arctic is truly friendly!

CHAPTER XIV

Senator M. J. O'Brien

Styles in Financing

"Para desarrollar una mina de oro se necesita una mina de plata."
Old Mexican proverb

"It takes a silver mine to make a gold mine." The Mexican
miner speaks from an experience which reaches back to the hazy
period before Cortez. Through the ages he learned that silver was
usually found at grass roots and so could bring the locator quick and
easy profits. But gold mines, he came to realize, were of a different
category, requiring prolonged surface and underground development.
In consequence, capital was as important as discovery. Ergo, find
a silver mine before trying to satisfy your lust for a gold mine.

Canada has proved the wisdom of Mexico. Were it not for the
silver of Cobalt it is doubtful whether the gold of Porcupine would
have eventuated. Noah Timmins and Captain Delamar were successful silver operators who financed the Hollinger and Dome enterprises when others were shrinking and timid. But as the years passed
and more discoveries were made, it became apparent that larger
sources of money were essential. More Cobalts were not forthcoming
and a couple of men were incapable of providing the sinews which
an expanding mining industry demanded. Canada required fresh
facets of capital.

The primary matter of discovery merely involved grubstaking
a prospector, and this want, in the early years, was supplied by
venturesome storekeepers, bartenders, and sundry small folk. A
find having been made, however, the vital problem of finance had
to be faced. And lest anyone be deceived, Canadian mining is costly
business. It is not a poor man's country where a burro, pick, and

gold pan, so dear to the romancer's heart, suffice. Bush transportation alone is difficult, not to mention housing, equipment, supplies, and power before the protracted development can be entertained. Cabins are built in the early stages, but once the mine is a going concern, refinements—permanent insulated houses, running water, recreation facilities—must be installed in bushland far from civilization. The heavy plant is hauled in over winter snows, and the small gold bricks are carried or flown to the mint without much trouble. Power, however, is an item which cannot always be provided cheaply. Steam may be generated in locomotive-type boilers, wood being plentiful. But this is cumbersome, for it requires a sizable timbering operations. For this reason diesel is chosen wherever practical. In the final phase, hydroelectric power is necessary, and this entails expensive construction and long transmission lines.

Kirkland Lake is young, as camps go, and so complete cost statistics are available. These are revealing. For the seven producing mines $4,118,426 was expended in preparatory work before a single ounce of gold was shipped. Add to this $2,286,760 for plant construction and several million dollars more for the purchase of claims and we arrive at a total of $10,000,000, or more than $1,000,-000 for each mine. Nor does this computation account for $6,000,000 spent by a score of nonproducers in the vicinity. And Kirkland, be it remembered, was only six miles from the railroad when discovered, so that transportation was not the major problem and expense it is in remoter camps. That close to $500,000,000 has been produced so far, of which almost half has gone into dividends, is an extraordinary record, but at the outset Kirkland presented the usual risks and uncertainties of mining. Large profits mean large risks— and outlays. Canadian mining is played with big stakes; it is no penny-ante game.

Are there men wealthy and courageous enough to assume the heavy burdens of a new mining venture? Once in a generation, perhaps. Such an individual was the late Senator M. J. O'Brien of Ottawa who began mining when he was past middle age, a time of life when most men of wealth begin to think of retirement. Certainly, the rough-and-tumble northern world was anything but a quiet retreat for this towering bearded patriach who said little and did much. O'Brien, who had made a fortune in railroading and lumbering, was constantly on the alert for fresh business opportunities. Fortuitously, his Toronto solicitor, J. B. O'Brian, learned from a neighbor, Thomas Southworth, that there was ground to be acquired in the recently discovered Cobalt field. Southworth's young son had just returned from the north where he had met Neal King, a fire ranger, who had staked four claims adjoining those of Fred La Rose.

The next play was O'Brian to O'Brien, and then the hulking lumber magnate departed for Cobalt. There he sought out King and purchased the four claims. Perhaps King's alacrity to sell arose from anxiety concerning an impending suit contesting the legality of his staking. Fred La Rose, who filed application to record on the same day as did King, protested the latter's staking on the basis that the fire ranger had not made a bona fide silver discovery, as was then required by the Ontario Department of Mines. The Timmins-McMartin-Dunlap syndicate, which had acquired La Rose's own ground, promptly came forward with the demand that the King claims be awarded them, since their employee, Anson Cartwright, had found silver on the purported King claims. Action was taken into court and lawyers had a Roman holiday. Caught in a situation which was anything but beginner's luck, O'Brien, no doubt, began to rue the impulse that had brought him to Cobalt. But all things have an ending, and so it was with the litigation. After two years of postponements and controversy, the judge allowed O'Brien to retain the claims but awarded a 25 per cent production royalty to the Ontario government. This was later relinquished and, curiously enough, the Timmins group was paid $130,000. The whole affair generated a bitterness which time hardly effaced, but, in any event, O'Brien had a mine destined to become one of the richest in Cobalt. A first carload shipment of ore, taken out in a few weeks, returned $50,000, and the property still continues to produce, its yield being estimated at approximately 40,000,000 ounces of silver. The entire proceeds, until recently when the Sisco purchased the mine from O'Brien employees who were leasing, went to the old man and his five sons.

It was a first bite and it tasted good, lawsuit and all. When Porcupine was discovered O'Brien was on the scene early, optioning the Gillies claims next to the Hollinger. But we have seen how the indignant O'Brien dropped out of the picture when owner Jack Miller refused to grant an extension on a $50,000 payment. Here was a serious mistake, but one which was never repeated. When news of rich silver in Gowganda reached him, O'Brien hastened to the spot and bought the Miller Lake Mine for $200,000 cash, and this, like the O'Brien in Cobalt, was the longest and steadiest producer in the camp.

O'Brien luck, with variations, held in subsequent years. Austin Dumond, a prospector employed by the M. J. O'Brien Company, staked the O'Brien Mine in Cadillac Township, Quebec, and for a time it appeared that the venerable tycoon had hauled in another bonanza at almost no cost. But early hopes were not realized in later development. The ore was rich but patchy, and tonnage possibilities seemed grim. Then, in 1934, a novel event took place. M. J. O'Brien, who made a profession of working alone and secretly, suddenly invited the public to enter partnership with him. In preparation, he had formed the O'Brien Gold Mines, Ltd., a 4,000,000-share company, which allocated 2,000,000 to the M. J. O'Brien Co. (private) for title; 1,250,000 shares were thereupon publicly offered at $1 each.

In Toronto mining circles much merriment greeted the announcement. To those who knew something of the O'Brien organization it appeared evident that the mine was about finished. Otherwise, asked cynics, why would the old fox allow outsiders to participate?

Notwithstanding private remarks, the issue was successfully put over by astute brokers. And in the space of a few months the traditional O'Brien luck, which had somewhat lagged behind events, came to life in an astonishing way. After plodding along with indifferent results, the No. 4 vein blossomed out with the kind of gold only a jeweler knows. The shoot was twenty feet long and a few inches wide, but it was intersected on several different levels. This was enough. The stock, which had been sagging lugubriously, now shot up until it reached the $10 mark and many were the suckers who gleefully sold at enormous profit. O'Brien, it was said, was one of the heaviest buyers.

When he passed away at the ripe age of ninety-six, individual mine financing died with him.

The syndicate idea, so well typified by the Thomson-Chadbourne group, which acquired the Horne claims in Quebec and then went on to build a colossal mining edifice, is a shining example of how several wealthy men, unlike the lone-acting O'Brien, can effectively combine forces. Once having proved ore on the Noranda, they were able to secure substantial funds by issuance of stock purchase rights to shareholders, never once having recourse to the public. This method has its limitations, however, since it requires immediate favorable developments on the property, something which can hardly be expected to repeat often. Even Noranda, a mighty bonanza, had its bad moments, and had there been no Noah Timmins on hand when aid was needed, more orthodox, and even desperate, measures might have been necessary to bring the mine into production.

The syndicate plan has had no more successful exponent than the late David Sloan. A mining engineer, he interested himself in the Bridge River area of British Columbia where the Pioneer Mine, since 1897, had made several attempts to become a steady producer, none of them availing. Sloan's novel ideas were apparently too much for his friends. Instead of the $50,000 he wanted for his syndicate, he was able to raise only $8,000, half of which was his own money. Nothing daunted, he cleaned out an old tunnel leading into the mountain, advanced cautiously and began to pick up odd clusters of ore. This was not very profitable mining, but it was enough for Sloan to keep going and advance closer to his objective. He started a crosscut toward a projected shear zone where he had decided a sizable gold vein might be located. His calculations were only too accurate, for he had not spent more than $4,000 of the original $8,000 before he hit the Pioneer Vein squarely. It was almost too good to be true. From that moment the history of the mine reads like a chapter of the *Arabian Nights*. One pocket containing little more than two tons of ore yielded $200,000 in a hand-picking operation. Another, said to be the richest block of ground ever mined in Canada, provided 5,000 ounces of gold, $190,000, from 900 tons. Sloan's syndicate did exceedingly well. From 1928 to the present, the Pioneer has produced more than $25,000,000 of which $9,301,793 has gone into dividends.

The experience of Noranda and Pioneer is more the exception than the rule. Syndicates are usually most effective when they are limited to hunting for new mines and providing for only preliminary surface work. Such was the Howey Syndicate, which sent prospectors into Red Lake. The Howey Gold Mine Syndicate, later formed by Jack Hammell, had the express purpose of carrying on the development of a promising discovery, and like so many of Hammell's activities was a departure from customary practice. When the more expensive underground stage was imminent, it is to be noted that Hammell enlisted the aid of Dome Mines. Dome failing, Hammell then went to the public. Later, as the need for funds continued to be pressing even after the shaft had been sunk and all the Howey Company's shares had been distributed and sold, W. S. Sherry provided loans of $750,000. In this way, the Howey went through a complete cycle of financing, starting with syndicates and progressing to promotion and then private loans.

No longer does a man hand over a $100 bill, as Jack Miller did with Alec Gillies, and expect a season's prospecting and a mine. Those days are gone forever. Even prospecting, the last refuge of rugged individualism, has become highly organized along with other features of modern society. Things are now done on a scale that befits an age when airplanes are standard transportation and the cost of maintaining fieldmen is heavy. Hammell originated the idea of a syndicate carrying the discovery one step further into the realm of preliminary exploration, dressing the property so that it appears less speculative to hard-boiled venture capital, and at the same time commanding a more attractive price. Fred MacLeod had already done considerable work and spent the money of his Little Long Lac Syndicate in stripping, sampling, and mapping the vein occurrences before approaching Joe Errington. And Errington was pleased with what he saw, as a result of which the MacLeod-Cockshutt became a lucrative producer, the public supplying the bulk of development money.

The Thompson Prospecting Syndicate provided interesting departures from standard practice. In the spring of 1938, eighty-four units were sold at $50 each to supply Fred W. Thompson, the manager, with $4,200 for a season in Yellowknife. As related previously, Thompson discovered gold along the shores of a lake which now bears his name. His syndicate then shared equally with the Burmos and Lahti syndicates in the staking of 97 claims. The Thompson-Lundmark Gold Mines was formed in 1939, the combined syndicates receiving 1,250,000 shares of vendor stock of the 3,500,000 authorized capital. Thereupon 1,000,000 shares were privately sold at 25 cents each, the company obtaining the entire proceeds, for there was no entrepeneur or underwriter whose services required some form of stock or cash consideration. This was novel, particularly as the company had no established list of stockholders; sales were made largely to vendors and their associates and friends. Direct sale of stock to the public has been tried at various times, but with indifferent success. Those wishing to eliminate intermediaries are obliged to advertise freely in the daily press and mining publications, stressing the advantages to the company which receives all the money raised. The amounts necessary are large, however, and sales resistance correspondingly high. Only exceptionally good prospects, such as the Thompson, can take advantage of this undoubtedly superior method of fund raising. The public, whose intelligence has been constantly underrated, reasons that glowing ads are superfluous when a property is really attractive. It knows that reputable mining people can, and do, readily obtain venture capital when the property is really hot. Usually, direct appeals are confined to small prospecting syndicates requiring no more than $25,000.

When the outbreak of war made further financing impractical, Thompson-Lundmark directors underwrote a 500,000-share issue at 35 cents in the face of unlisted market quotations of less than 20 cents. Later the company accepted loans of $750,000 from Consolidated Mining & Smelting and Ventures, Ltd. This was repaid from production before war conditions forced a suspension of operations. As a director, I well remember the satisfaction of stockholders when the Smelters deal was consummated, and then, strangely, the outspoken criticism when the mine so quickly liquidated the loans. Our former distress and financial embarrassment were conveniently forgotten as it was realized that the Thompson was left with only 42 per cent equity in the enterprise. Overlooked was the fact that stockholders were to receive $467,000—the amount they had provided the company before the Smelters agreement was made—from the next production. However, everyone seemed happy in May, 1946, when the capitalization was increased to 4,000,000 shares and the Smelters group accepted 500,000 for a 58 per cent equity. At the same time the company sold 431,500 shares, again privately, for $253,900 in preparation for resumption of operations, leaving 106,349 shares unissued. Thus, in effect, Smelters et al. surrendered a 58 per cent interest for 13 per cent of the issued stock. On the face of it, this appears irrational, but closer inspection reveals decided advantages in the seemingly unbalanced trade. Smelters was immediately relieved of a commitment to advance more money as needed. Second, there was no longer a period of waiting until the Thompson stockholders were reimbursed $467,000; participation was now immediate. And last but not least, the 500,000 shares represented a highly liquid position which could be easily converted on the market into a $400,000 gravy pot by the erstwhile lenders.

The Macassa Mines illustrates further ramifications in mine financing as well as the epic struggle of a determined mine maker. Robert A. Bryce took his engineering degree at the University of Toronto in 1904 and spent the next eight years in Mexico working for various companies. Richer in experience, he returned to Canada in 1912 and established headquarters in Toronto as a mining consultant. He roved throughout the Dominion at a time when mining was beginning to grow and by 1926 decided he was equipped to take part in this great expansion. Kirkland Lake looked especially good to him, specifically the western end beyond the then productive section of the camp. Harry Oakes owned claims here which he had quietly held for years and now Bryce formed the Macassa Gold Mines to take in the ground, Oakes receiving 850,000 shares of vendor stock. The old Elliot Kirkland, a teaser, also was absorbed by the new company and for the same consideration. Thus the 3,500,000-share company parted with 1,700,000 at the outset. Bryce managed to interest Toronto brokers, who disposed of 600,000 shares of treasury stock at 40 cents each, and this, less commissions, provided working capital of approximately $200,000. Attention was immediately given to the Elliot where a small shaft had been sunk in previous years, but Bryce was unable to develop a single consistent ore shoot. As work progressed, funds began to shrink. Driblets of stock were sold privately, among the buyers being Ike Waite, Fred Connell, and the Honorable Thomas Riggs, one-time governor of Alaska.

In 1928, still far from achieving mine stature, Macassa increased its capital to 5,000,000 shares. Bryce decided that the best chance remained in depth and so arranged to drive a long crosscut into his ground from the 2,475-foot level of the adjoining Kirkland Lake Gold Mines. The crash of 1929 came as a blight to the world of capital and Bryce despaired of ever seeing his ambitious plans put into execution. But Watt & Watt, a brokerage firm which had early interested itself in Macassa, happily informed J. H. Hirshhorn of the situation. Joe, a daring speculator, joined forces with Charles Wright, William Hutchinson, and other New Yorkers in purchasing a large block of stock at 15 cents per share. In 1931, therefore, Bryce was able to drive his projected tunnel, and this time he opened a respectable shoot of ore. Additional funds, however, were needed to sink a shaft for operating purposes, necessitating still further sale of stock. This time Joe Hirshhorn supplied a buyer, Case, Pomeroy & Company of New York. Dr. Donald McLaughlin, who since has been appointed president of the hefty Homestake Mine in South Dakota, was sent to examine Macassa. His report being favorable, the late Walter Case purchased sufficient stock to pay for the shaft and a 200-ton mill.

When production commenced in October, 1933, Bryce decided that the adjoining United Kirkland claims should be taken into the fold to protect the extension of Macassa ore on the dip, but in order to achieve this it was imperative to reorganize his company. Accordingly, the capital was reduced from 5,000,000 to 3,000,000 shares, stockholders being allocated one share of Macassa Mines, Ltd., for every two shares of Macassa Gold Mines, Ltd. This done, United Kirkland was then given 110,000 shares for its claims. Fortified against all contingencies, Macassa now went on to exceed the expectations even of Bryce. The first dividend was paid in 1934 and payments have not ceased since that date, the total reaching $7,129,551 at the end of 1945. Absorbed in the larger task of mine making, Bryce neglected to take care of himself. With almost no stock to show for his heroic and protracted efforts, it was no surprise that the directors voted him, in gratitude, an option on 100,000 shares at $1 each.

No other mine in Canada can match the confused and complicated financial meanderings of the Kerr-Addison mine in Larder Lake. Before it emerged from obscurity, this biggest of elephants ran the gamut from A to Z. Since profitable production began in 1938, the history is well known but the earlier period is hazy, and for a very good reason. A complete perusal of the old records would make even a Philadelphia lawyer quail. There are wheels within wheels and spokes which branch in every direction like the limbs of an apple tree. My account here is greatly abridged, but it will serve, I hope, to bring out most of the light and shade in a picture of high and low finance.

The Larder Lake rush of 1906 predated the gold discoveries of Porcupine and Kirkland Lake, the main attraction consisting of narrow high-grade quartz veinlets fingering through a mass of greenish dolomite (mariposite, carbonate). Prominent among the stakings were the Kerr-Addison, Reddick, and Harris-Maxwell mines. The last two dared to construct small stamp mills and attempt to produce gold, but both efforts were dismal failures. By 1910 operations ceased entirely. An interesting commentary on Larder Lake is furnished by an uninhibited newspaperman, A. A. Gard, who wrote in 1909:

> I have been so often asked: "What do you know of Larder Lake?" I have to answer: "I don't know anything and I haven't yet found a man who does." One told about his prospectors finding values running up to $42,000 to the ton. He's now in jail. The Government can stand a whole lot, but $42,000 was the limit, and they brought this hot air artist up to a perpendicular. Think of it! $42,000 in a locality where the few possible mines would be considered excellent if they would produce $3 to the ton. An occasional "mill run" shows a small "brick." The "brick" is taken to some city, put into a window and placarded as something of an everyday affair. But months pass without anything more being heard of "mill runs." Some of the claims may yet prove of value. And well they should in a district where over 7,000 were staked.

But the play was only beginning. The Harris-Maxwell, Kerr-Addison and Reddick properties were absorbed by Goldfields, Ltd., which was organized in 1911 to effect this consolidation. Another try was made to find commercial ore in the tantalizing carbonates. Gold was present and in spots alluringly concentrated, but the overall average value was well below economic grade. The unheard-of sum of $1,000,000 was spent without result, and stockholders vented their dissatisfaction in a series of meetings wherein accusations were hurled at the directors. Nothing could be done about placing more gold in the rocks, but capital changes were possible. And so, despite heated protests, bickerings, charges and countercharges, the company became the unhappy subject of rough financial surgery. And not once, but several times. From the operating table emerged the final emasculation, Canadian Associated Goldfields, Ltd., over the corpses of the Associated Goldfields Mining Company, the Tourenie Mining Company, and the Harris-Maxwell Larder Lake Gold Mining Company.

More stormy weather during the next ten years, but the fundamental deficiency—lack of ore—remained to plague the beleaguered directors. For a time, while the war raged in Europe, stockholders lessened their attacks, but Larder Lake hostilities were resumed with a vengeance when the Germans signed the armistice in France. Respite came unexpectedly, in the person of Jack Costello.

Jack, who had drifted into the area during the boom days, was one of the few prospectors who remained faithful to the old camp. Save for overseas duty in the war, he stayed close to the shores of Larder Lake, working alone and maintaining a saucy cheerfulness throughout the darkest days of Larder's trials. Shortly before his enlistment, he had discovered a gold vein several miles west of the Kerr-Addison, and upon his return to Canada in 1919 resumed work on his ground. Without funds—soldiers' bonuses were unknown in those days—he looked for help and found a partner in Dr. Charles Lucey, a Guelph, Ontario, physician. Lucey, who became an equal partner in Jack's Sphinx claims, was a cousin of Dr. G. MacKay, the guiding head of Associated, a position he had won by shrewd purchases of stock in the various predecessor companies. When Lucey spoke to him about Costello's ground, MacKay was immediately interested, for he realized what everyone familiar with mining knows —there is no situation, however bad, which cannot be cured by ore. His offer of $6,000 for the Sphinx claims was accepted and the sorely pressed Associated Company thereupon had a valid reason for continuing its existence.

The inimitable Jack Costello was not idle. Realizing that his claims were predestined to fall into Associated's hands, he communicated with his friend Sydney Beanland, who was employed as millman and field scout by Porcupine Crown, a subsidiary of Crown Reserve. Beanland and his superior, Harry Stuart, left Porcupine for Larder Lake and there they were apprised of the situation by Costello, who urged that claims next to the Sphinx be staked immediately. This was done and Associated woke up to find itself with an unwelcome neighbor. George Grey, the Associated manager,

Jack Costello

strongly urged MacKay to purchase the Crown Reserve claims, insisting that the development planned would be a travesty otherwise. His recommendation bringing no action, Grey resigned in protest. Then began a spectacle rare in Canadian mining—two shafts being sunk simultaneously within a stone's throw of each other. The production race was easily won by Associated, which was as usual under strong pressure to make a showing with the stockholders.

A mill was constructed and operations, or a facsimile of same, attempted for a short period, but in the end this gesture, as all others the company made, ended ignominiously. On this occasion the denouement of the adventure was bankruptcy. Crown Reserve tried to block out enough ore to justify a mill, but after a minerlike try, it, too, discontinued operations. Jack Costello declared that both companies were washouts and advised a consolidation of property to permit working the Costello Vein as a single unit. He was stonily ignored.

Meanwhile, the tangled affairs of Canadian Associated Goldfields were being scrutinized for the purpose of salvaging something from the wreckage. In 1929, Holders Corporation, Ltd., was formed by the directors of the defunct company as a device to discharge liabilities amounting to more than $600,000. This accomplished nothing. Thereupon, Goldfields Creditors' Syndicate was organized to purchase all assets from the receiver. This was done by pooling the claims of creditors and raising a fund to discharge preferred claims and meet liquidating expenses. Creditors refusing to pool their claims were paid off on the basis of 15 cents on the dollar. Then the stockholders of Canadian Associated Goldfields, who had earned some kind of decoration for receiving the impact of so many reorganizations, were invited to retain their relative position in still one more company, Proprietory Mines, Ltd. The capitalization of Proprietory was 1,000,000 shares of $1 par value, and stock was offered at the modest price of 3 cents. (Proprietory retained title to all the mining property and water power rights owned by the late-lamented Associated.) It is not known how many shareholders availed themselves of this new opportunity, but at the time it seemed inconsequential. Larder Lake was a dog.

Not long after the price of gold was advanced in 1933, Costello's old Sphinx claims, owned by Proprietory, came to life. And Jack's suggestion, made five years previously, was followed. The Canadian Reserve Company was formed to operate the Crown Reserve and Sphinx claims together. Despite enhanced prospects, however, public response to appeals for money was apathetic; baloney was still baloney no matter how it was sliced. For a time it appeared that Canadian Reserve was to die immediately after birth, but unexpected and welcome faces appeared. George Webster, an engineer, sensing possibilities of a mine, interested the McIntyre. McIntyre's subsidiary, the Castle Trethewey Mines, an inactive silver producer, agreed to advance $150,000 with which to settle the indebtedness of the old companies and thus clear the decks for bringing the Costello Vein into 300-ton daily production. All expenditures were to be repaid from operating profit. And so yet one more company was added to the already long list, this one appropriately called the Omega. Castle received 2,000,000 shares, Canadian Reserve 2,000,000, and George Webster 500,000. The old Crown Reserve and Proprietory divided Canadian Reserve vendor stock in the ratio of 163,000 and 2,000,000 shares.

Castle went to work with a will but Omega proved to be a tough nut to crack, even with gold at $35 an ounce. For several years a small operating profit was won. Then, in 1944, its advances only partially repaid, Castle became tired and sold its 2,500,000 shares to Noranda Mines and associated companies for $250,000. Omega has continued to operate since with middling results, but today it is justly famous for providing the crucial link which completed the strange chain of events leading to the miracle of Kerr-Addison. For McIntyre, lured into the camp, began to sniff about the carbonates, scenting big possibilities. A new try, this time the real thing, was rumored. In January, 1936, the *Northern Miner* printed a story headlined "McIntyre May Test Larder Ground."

Webster, who had not wasted any time in the Omega affair, now joined forces with James Rattray, also a mining engineer with long experience in the north, and the two hastened to confer with Dr. MacKay, who held the reins of Proprietory Mines, proposing the formation of the Kerr-Addison Gold Mines, Ltd., a 5,000,000-share company of which 1,000,000 would be assigned to Proprietory for the old Reddick and Kerr-Addison ground. There were difficulties—the details are on file with the Ontario Securities Commission—but in the end the proposition, as outlined, was formally approved at a stockholders' meeting, Rattray and Webster agreeing to purchase a block of Kerr-Addison shares at once. In consideration, they were granted options, at graduated prices, on most of the stock remaining in the company's treasury. This took place in April, 1936, exactly thirty years after the first gold discoveries.

Several companies and friends were invited to participate, among them being Anglo-Huronian, Mining Corporation, International Mining, Harry Seguin, one-time manager of the Imperial Bank of Canada, Fred Connell, and others. At the outset 500,000 shares of Kerr-Addison were purchased at 15 cents each. Months afterward Thayer Lindsley was given a chance to buy stock, but at a somewhat advanced figure. With an initial fund of $75,000, everything was in readiness to sample carefully the dolomite which rose 200 feet above the surrounding bush. It was a large undertaking, for the exposure had been traced on surface for a half mile and averaged well over 400 feet in width. The only satisfactory method to test the occurrence was by large-scale bulk sampling, and for this purpose a small pilot mill was constructed. In charge of the work was the late M. F. Farlie, an able Cobalt operator. First results were inconclusive, and Farlie decided to dewater the old Kerr-Addison shaft and reinvestigate the 175- and 300-foot horizons. This fortunate decision was rewarded by the discovery of two entirely new ore bodies, designated as No. 9 and No. 10, both of them containing several million tons of excellent grade ore. Ironically, it was disclosed that these lenses were located only a short distance north and south of two existing crosscuts which had been driven by early operators. On the Reddick, also, Farlie's work revealed that had the old Associated Company continued the shaft from 86 to 400 feet, the sizable No. 16 ore body would have been hit on the nose. But such is luck in the unpredictable mining industry.

With enormous ore deposits in the carbonates, and subsequently in the lavas also, Kerr-Addison is now a prospective 50,000,000- to 75,000,000-ton gold mine, rivaling anything yet found in the Western Hemisphere. Proving that some of its early stockholders had not even remotely guessed the potentials of their mine, several disposed of shares in the early stages, only to repurchase hurriedly at much higher prices. And they were not alone. Companies like Noranda and Dome bought heavily, as did André Dorfman, the canny head of Anglo-Huronian. Dorfman concentrated his buying in Proprietory Mines, the holding company which retained 1,000,000 shares of Kerr-Addison, and in this he was joined by the ever-active Thayer Lindsley whose Ventures, Ltd., entered the scene late but not too late. Kerr shares advanced to the $15 mark. In this case, the public came into the situation entirely unsolicited. There were no circulars, no advertisements or high-pressure telephone calls and salesmen. The stock sold itself entirely on the basis of mine results. And as for Proprietory, it is doubtful whether any original stockholders who maintained their positions to the end have more than a fractional amount of their aggregate outlays, even with the market at $15 a share.

Thayer Lindsley, without a peer in mining finance, has classified fund raising as follows:

1. Prospecting, staking of claims, and optioning claim groups. (Usually undertaken by individuals and exploration companies.)
2. Development program for the purpose of indicating and

outlining ore reserves. (Undertaken either by large mining groups or by promoters.)

3. Mine preparation, plant, equipment, etc., to place the property into production. (Financed by investment houses or large mining groups.)

He fixes the requirements for each stage as

1. $25,000 to $150,000. Essentially speculative.
2. $500,000 to $1,500,000. This stage is still quite speculative but large capital gains are possible if careful selections are made.
3. $1,000,000 to $5,000,000. Once a mining property has assured ore reserves, it will appeal to investors. Five to six per cent convertible debentures are recommended as a convenient and attractive vehicle at this stage.

There is much food for thought in this brief analysis. The first step, we have seen, is adequately provided for by private grubstaking or syndicates. This, of course, is the riskiest stage of all, but by the same token it holds out the greatest rewards, and for that reason is preferred by speculative minds, such as Lindsley's, or those who cannot afford large losses.

Stage 2 is expensive business, and so the field narrows down considerably. Large sums are needed in addition to a capacity to absorb the slings and arrows of outrageous fortune. This transition is most frequently negotiated by promotion and public division of risks. Another method, now gaining in popularity, is the pooling of resources by the large mining companies. This was done in the Kerr-Addison venture, but is only one of several. Lindsley is an advocate of this plan of "taking slices," as he calls it, not only as a means of reducing risks but also of "spreading bets." Experience has taught the wisdom of dividing $100,000 into five ventures instead of risking all in one throw of the dice. Hollinger, despite its large cash resources, welcomed the participation of the Hanna Company of Cleveland when the Labrador iron development was projected. Not only did this provide a hedge against loss but it also procured a partner well versed in iron mining, a branch of the industry only partially understood in Canada. Ventures, Ltd., joined forces with Macassa in the Amalgamated Kirkland enterprise, and also worked with Nipissing when the Beattie Mine was first optioned. The complete list of such co-operative efforts in Canada is a long one, embracing such powerful organizations as Noranda, Newmont, Dome, McIntyre, Anglo-Huronian, Consolidated Mining & Smelting, International Mining, Coniagas, Mining Corporation, Pioneer, and many others.

On the whole, companies, while long in the habit of themselves grubstaking prospecting parties, have become more forceful in exploration. Mindful of promotional and individual successes of the Hammell and O'Brien type, they now grow bolder and become less exacting in their requirements. In Red Lake they have shown amazing deviation from the ancient attitude of all or nothing. Dome accepted a bare majority position in such a prospect as Campbell Red Lake which was first launched by Toronto brokers.

The Powell and Sylvanite companies together explore the Craibbe-Fletcher claims. Hollinger and Noranda are partners in the Chakuni Red Lake, while Dome has teamed with Noranda in the Robin Red Lake development. Big-company representatives no longer stalk angrily from a conference room when a promoter demands a large interest in a claim group about to enter Stage 2. Nor did Noranda hesitate to buy into Kerr-Addison, at good prices, until its position became a substantial one. Dome, when it brought the Sigma into production, reported to stockholders that it had only 60 per cent interest in one of the major new mines of Quebec. But, to date, this subsidiary has distributed more than $2,000,000 in dividends, and has many years of profitable production ahead. Surely stockholders could do nothing more harmful than vote Dome directors in general, and James G. McCrea, the Sigma midwife and general manager, in particular, a hearty vote of thanks.

The most aggressive and successful of the operating mines to secure outside properties is Noranda. This is due to the brilliant work of Oliver Hall, the chief engineer, manager H. L. Roscoe and the wisdom of experienced directors who are content with slices. The company owns 66 per cent of Waite-Amulet, 46 per cent of Pamour, 55 per cent of Aunor, 64 per cent of La India Mines in Nicaragua, and 12 per cent of Kerr-Addison. It accepted a minority interest in Amalgamated Larder, sharing control with three other mining groups.

There are no permanent company combinations, though some alarm and complaint is expressed by individuals who charge they are being squeezed out of the picture by monopolies. But increasing company participation is a healthy and constructive trend, for it places mining exploration on a sounder, see-it-through basis. The causes for this growing practice, which has reached epidemic proportions, are not hard to find. The hoary adage that half a loaf is better than no bread applies particularly well to mining. And cash assets of companies are large, thanks to a long background of profitable production as compared to a decade or two ago. Then, too, it is realized that mines do not go on forever, and wise managements are seeking to perpetuate themselves in new areas. Also there is the dawning conviction that too much conservatism pays small dividends. Over-cautious company engineers have condemned many prospects which later became producing mines, guided by less circumscribed and more speculative free-lance operators. In the past, the sparrow and pigeon analogy has been drawn, the sparrows being men like Jim Norrie and Jack Hammell who have snatched morsels from under the beaks of waddling overfed pigeons, the latter being the companies. But a change has come. The sparrows are now finding the pigeons far leaner and nimbler in the scramble for food.

The final phase, Stage 3, when the property has been fully explored and requires money for plant construction, is described as the least speculative of all, approaching the respectability of investment. (However, while risks may have been reduced to a minimum, they are still present.) It is here that long-term borrowing has been suggested. Banks have actually advanced funds in exceptional cases where ore is assured, this after the submission of a detailed report by an independent engineer, but the process is so attenuated and the percentage of turndowns so high that few people approach the sacred portals of a bank. Bond issues have more appeal, especially when all or nearly all of the company's stock has been disposed of and a reorganization is to be avoided. A successful issue was made by the Preston East Dome Mine under these circumstances, a property which had long lain idle despite its appealing location next to Dome.

In 1936, Joe Hirshhorn listened to geologist Douglas Wright and was convinced that Preston was a mine. The company was promptly reorganized and supplied with funds by the hard-hitting New Yorker. Drilling, much to the surprise of the mining fraternity, gave excellent ore intersections and underground work outlined substantial tonnages. But most of the stock had already been issued and sold to provide development funds, and a 300-ton mill remained to be built. McIntyre was approached and for a time assumed direction of the work, which disclosed unexpectedly high-grade ore in the porphyry. But Hirshhorn, who was not awed by big names, refused McIntyre's offer to finance the mill. Instead, he came to an agreement with Harry Knight of Draper, Dobie & Company, mining brokers. A $700,000 first-mortgage bond issue, netting Preston $612,000 and bearing 6 per cent interest, was authorized, the bonds being redeemable within five years. Knight received a bonus of 225,000 shares for his underwriting services, and this alone was worth close to $1,000,000 within two years. In any event, the spectacularly high yield of gold in the porphyry, where ore was not supposed to occur, enabled the company to redeem the bonds by January 1, 1940. Two weeks later an initial dividend was paid. At no great sacrifice, Preston stockholders were able to reach production and profit.

A less happy bond issue was one which was sponsored by Jack Hammell, of all people. His Uchi Mine, in the Patricia District of Ontario, seemed, by every yardstick of measurement, to be a sure thing. For once, Hammell listened to high-powered advisers, and agreed to forgo sale of stock in favor of a more imposing bond issue. Accordingly, the company sold $1,000,000 of 6 per cent first-mortgage bonds on July 1, 1941, redeemable on or before December 31, 1946, with the attractive provision of a sinking fund. Buyers were enthusiastic and plentiful. But it seemed that nature was repelled at the idea of a man like Hammell, the personification of speculative courage, having recourse to armchair banking. The mine failed, and the company, after valiant efforts, was forced into bankruptcy three years before the bond issue came due. While the bondholders will recover about a third of their advances, they have learned that the substance, and not the form, of mining securities is all-important. Illusions of safety are dangerous, for the mining industry is primarily speculative and will always remain so.

Bond issues have been usually left to the large companies whose names bespeak security enough. For example, Teck-Hughes, when it undertook the Lamaque development in Quebec, loaned its subsidiary $1,250,000 and received for this 5 per cent bonds maturing within seven years. These were redeemed in full. Then there was the $3,000,000 sale of 7 per cent debentures made by Noranda to Hollinger, with 30,000 shares, now worth $2,000,000, thrown in as a bonus. In 1930 the Hudson Bay Mining & Smelting Company offered its shareholders pro rata rights to purchase $5,000,000 convertible 6 per cent debentures, but it is doubtful whether this issue would have been fully sold without the awesome J. P. Morgan & Company as underwriters.

Altogether, the bond idea has had limited application in Canada, where the mines are predominatingly gold, carrying with them ever-present risks. Large base metal properties, where the occurrences are of such dimensions as to be more surely valued, are better adapted for this superior kind of finance. In one of the few cases where a gold "show" had the earmarks of a bond issue, the Giant Yellowknife, a Lindsley enterprise, increased its capital from 3,000,000 to 4,000,000 shares. Some of the newly created shares were sold to stockholders at $5 each. The same course was followed by Quemont Mines, which added 500,000 shares to its 2,000,000 authorized capital,˜and then gave purchase rights at $15 a share. In both instances the offerings were firmly underwritten by Ventures, Ltd., and Mining Corporation, respectively, the companies taking full advantage of buoyant stock prices—the market was "right." Had conditions been less favorable, it is possible that bond issues might have been tried.

Many people are puzzled by the paucity of English money finding its way into Canadian mining. The English have been unfortunate. Early experiences, save for the Mond Nickel, were unhappy. The various western Ontario fiascos and the Bingo swindle in Manitoba soured the Mother Country, which regarded the brawling Dominion with a jaundiced eye. The English came in too soon, as so many of us did in the various gold rushes. But there is another, and perhaps more important, factor. Conditioned to colonies where large mining concessions were freely granted by a benevolent Foreign Office or local government, most Englishmen, other than the lowly prospectors, decided that Canada was too competitive for their liking. They have been spoiled, too, by the amazing Rand gold fields in Africa, where regularity and size are foregone conclusions. By comparison, the bush country seems like shoddy hunting.

Americans, according to Sidney Norman, an authoritative reporter of Canadian mining, have a $1,000,000,000 investment in the Pre-Cambrian. This is a large sum, but a major portion of it came across the line in the past ten years. Before that time, the multiplicity of camps, the "wild" methods of finance, and the fierce independence of Canadians seemed too much for American companies, accustomed as they were to dominating their respective bailiwicks. Those dipping into Canada were largely miscellaneous operators and speculators, men like Delamar, Denison, Hirshhorn, and Steindler who had no directors' boards to convince. The mighty trusts across the border adhered to their own financial convictions and tried to enforce a take-it-or-leave-it policy for the most part. This brought more lost opportunities than mines. The big fellows were slow in learning that large ore deposits afford room for more than one participant and a portion of the fruit may be safely left for others while satisfying their own voracious appetites. Today younger, better informed, and more progressive executives, aware that the feudal age has indeed passed, never, we hope, to return, are approaching the north with revised ideas. Americans, as should be expected from their proximity and affluence, are steadily coming to Canada and advancing welcome capital to an ever-broadening industry while accepting the customs and rules of a sturdily self-reliant country.

Illustrating an earlier epoch is the story of a Porcupine mine-owner whose property in time waxed into a leading producer of the camp. In New York the management of one of the great mining companies decided that Burke's (not his real name) ground should be purchased. Repeated letters to Porcupine brought no response, and finally an emissary was sent to Canada with instructions to escort the recalcitrant Burke to downtown Manhattan. The mission was faithfully performed with the aid of much good cheer and the incipient mining magnate arrived at the great metropolis. He was a silent, bulky man, proud of his handlebar mustache and completely unaware that celluloid collars were no longer in vogue in Wall Street. His hosts, careful not to mention business, had him installed at their expense in a palatial Waldorf suite and then showered him with every conceivable variety of entertainment. The man from Porcupine received these attentions with unruffled stolidity.

Perplexed, crafty company officials, who wanted the mine almost badly enough to pay its reported value, decided they had better not delay producing the contract for signing. Burke was conducted through the swanky offices, and after usual preliminaries was handed a bulky document, beribboned and bound.

"What in hell's this?" he asked.

Told it was an agreement to purchase the mine and already signed by the company, Burke was requested to read the tome, and if satisfied, affix his name at the end. The bushwhacker grunted unintelligibly, then fingered the neatly typewritten pages. Anxious eyes followed him, more than one watcher wondering whether or not he could read. Burke looked up suddenly. An air of expectancy filled the room; the crucial moment had come.

"Kiss me arse," said Burke.

Consternation! Lawyers snatched at the agreement even while smooth voices assured Burke that all objectionable clauses would be removed. The meeting was hastily adjourned and Burke whiffed back to the Waldorf.

Next morning a revised contract was placed before Burke and once more he gave it the "hasty glance." Then, with an oath, he tossed the paper on the shining table. Pink faces regarded him with astonishment. Was this man able to distinguish the subtleties hidden and woven in the mass of long-winded phrases so painstakingly contrived by high-priced corporation counsel? Burke did not leave them in doubt very long.

"Kiss me arse," he said again, and then, striding toward the door, "I'm leavin' for Toronter tonight!"

The mine was never sold. . . .

CHAPTER XV

Come on, Suckers!

In this fashion, not long ago, a prominent New York daily headlined an article, one of several, warning guileless Americans against the big bad wolves of the north. "Americans losing million a week to brash Canadian gold mine promoters!" cried the aroused reporter. With a wrath worthy of John Brown, he went on to expose the "technical hocus-pocus" contained in the circulars which were flooding the U.S.A. and pointed an accusing finger at slick brokers working their racket out of Toronto, the Queen City.

Such attacks are not new. When the Comstock in Nevada was still young, almost a hundred years ago, puckish Mark Twain coined his imperishable definition, "A mine is a hole in the ground with a liar at the top," and mining, more particularly promotion, has been trying to live down this wisecrack ever since. Times have changed. In Mark Twain's day misinformation was more the rule than the exception. Promotion in the West was as raw as the alkali dust of the desert, nor was it confined to mining. As abuses and enormities continued, regulations and restrictions became necessary, culminating in the passage of the Securities Exchange Act. Americans, willy-nilly, became respectable and, like a woman reformed, burned with fierce virtue. The wave of Canadian mining promotion which rose to unprecedented heights as the war ended evoked storms of criticism and attack. There was no closed season on promoters,

342

and every variety of brickbat was thrown in their direction. In the welter of sound and fury there was much confusion, for the concerted offensive was directed at the effects, and not the causes, of undeniable abuses.

Returning to our New York reporter, this muckraker presents a strong case, perhaps a bit too strong. Or, shall we say, oversimplified? Since his statements are fairly typical of the barrage leveled against the promoter, it might be interesting to analyze a few in the cause of accuracy and fact, making due allowances for the Special Feature of the press which must, perforce, daub people either black or white, and not grayish, as they usually are. No balance sheet should be submitted with only one side of the ledger exposed, unless one has an ax to grind or a tough editor to please. In this case the daily's research department must have been in a hurry to meet a deadline, for it produced an illustration of a shaft and miners posing before an ore bin, with this caption, "Glib promoters capitalize on such legitimate producers as this one." Now, "this one" happens to be an enterprise which turned sour, reorganized so many times that the original stockholders cannot possibly be reimbursed for their initial investment. Trivial mistake? I do not think so, for it is a good commentary on the kind of superficial nonsense that is continually being fed to millions of readers. It is highly questionable, for instance, how the figure of "losing a million a week" was calculated. If statistics are necessary, it would be advisable to quote those which can be verified by standard government publications. Canadian metal mines normally produce at the rate of $1,000,000 each day, of which amount more than 20 per cent goes into dividends. This is not to say that brash promotion causes no loss. Far from it. But among the prolific sucker offerings are certainly as many successes as those which have been derived from other media of finance. It is dangerous to condemn a Canadian mining venture entirely on the grounds of the unbridled language plastered throughout circular letters. Uncertainties and imponderables will ever be present in mining, and respectability, unfortunately, does not necessarily accompany success.

These remarks are not intended as a defense of promotion. On the contrary, the institution will be carefully weighed, justifiable criticism directed at admitted abuses, and corrective and remedial suggestions made—for what they are worth. At the same time, promotion will be defined for what it is and not what it is supposed to be, and its constructive accomplishments set forth. A fair verdict can be rendered only after careful and factual consideration. To castigate promotion without knowing its true relation to Canadian mining is as irrational as offering some crackpots in Congress as proof of a decadent United States.

Webster defines promote in these words: "To contribute to the development, establishment, increase, or influence of; foster; encourage; advance." A promoter is one who "assists by securing capital or otherwise in promoting a financial or commercial enterprise." More specifically, a mining promoter could be described as a conveyer of capital. Unlike an investment banker, who deals with supposedly established enterprises with production and earning records, the promoter starts at scratch, with a muskeg and a quartz vein or two as his only assets. He must, therefore, use various arts of persuasion in order to sell his stock; there are no profit statements to exhibit.

Why, it might be asked here, is a promoter necessary, anyway? Well, he isn't, theoretically, especially now, when there are powerful mining companies on the prowl for desirable properties. They have the requisite money, the technical equipment, and the urge, which logically add up to triumphant mine development. But somewhere along the line the equation has fizzled, for otherwise the promoter could never have come into existence. The companies failed miserably in the beginning. They magnified risks and minimized opportunities. And the public, which at first was inclined to dismiss a prospect which had either been rejected or ignored by the big-money boys, began to revise a too-obvious conclusion when adventurous gentry, with no standing in the industry, began to bring in mines. These men came from all walks of life, storekeepers, a ship captain, prize fighter, farmer, all of them puncturing the myth that a prospect was worthless if it had not fallen into company hands. After Cobalt and Porcupine, the little men who traded in stocks began to realize that mining was different: chances could be overlooked by experts and profitably picked up by amateurs. The promoter, sensitive to the popular pulse, capitalized the situation.

Herein lies the secret of Canadian mining promotion. It was there at the start. The promoter is no interloper or parasite who jumped on the bandwagon and attached himself to an industry begun by others. He was a purveyor of speculative funds when investment houses and directors' boards scorned the Canadian mining field. He has been a vital link in the development of the country. The history of the various mining camps is replete with cases of new discoveries rejected by the best brains in the business and later blown into flourishing life by promoters who were not weighted down with too much schooling and conscience. It is a mistake to think otherwise.

Cobalt was largely a camp of promoters and it produced 400,-000,000 ounces of silver. The Timmins-McMartin-Dunlap combination, Denison, O'Brien, and a few other lone wolves appeared early, long before company denizens were on the scene. Nipissing, shaking off the uncertain touch of the Guggenheims, found its way to the public through promoters Earle, Delamar, and Boyce Thompson and became Cobalt's premier producer. H. H. Lang and associates organized the City of Cobalt Mining Company, acquired mining rights from owners of town lots by judicious stock allocations, and proceeded to bring in an excellent mine. When the Ontario government offered Cobalt Lake for sale in 1906, an Ottawa-Toronto syndicate, headed by D. B. Rochester, purchased the underwater mining rights for $1,000,000, obtained subscriptions of $400,000 in Cobalt Lake stock, and began shipping high-grade silver in 1908. Hudson Bay was peddled at a few cents a share in 1903, and its first dividend in 1905 was in the dollars. Colonel J. Carson formed a syndicate and purchased Kerr Lake for $178,000, promoted working capital, and then nursed Crown Reserve into one of the best mines of the district. Peterson Lake, Coniagas, Silver Queen, Mining Corporation, Foster, Right-Of-Way, Little Nipissing, Cobalt Central, Victoria, Colonial, and other profitable mines were promotions. J. A. Jacobs of Montreal and D. M. Steindler of New York picked a winner in the Kerr Lake Mines and sold a majority interest for several million dollars to the Lewisohn dynasty in New York, one of the few instances of big-company participation. Most of the "smart" money came late, having decided that early pessimism was a mistake.

Cobalt set the fashion for promotion in the camps that followed it. In Porcupine, Noah Timmins staked his future on the Hollinger and won a prize of staggering richness. His one attempt to enlist big-company interests to finance a merger of the McIntyre and part of the Hollinger claims got nowhere, luckily for him. The McIntyre was first taken in hand by Charles Flynn and his brothers who later sold out to A. Freeman, a New York promoter. Later, J. P. Bickell, a stockbroker, completed the job. The Flynns also had much to do with the Vipond, and Dome filtered into the public via Captain Delamar, Ambrose Monell, and Charles Denison. As the camp grew, big capital became interested but most of the choice properties were already in possession of promoters. The Delnite, Aunor, the Pamour, which was an amalgamation of three different promotions, the Paymaster, an outgrowth of the West Dome and United Mineral companies, the Buffalo-Ankerite, Broulan, Goldhawk, Aquarius, Hoyle, and Preston East Dome all must thank a group of miscellaneous entrepreneurs for their being.

The first producer in Kirkland Lake was the Tough-Oakes-Burnside, a promotion. Weldon Young, promoter, formed the Wright-Hargreaves Mine and the Kirkland Lake Gold Mine, through Bob Jowsey and associates, became public property. The Teck-Hughes, after being abandoned by Nipissing, was rescued by Tommy Jones and Charles Denison and the "suckers" allowed to participate in a $40,000,000 dividend payer. While retaining almost half interest in the Lake Shore, Harry Oakes sold stock through the medium of circulars and paid advertisements. Bob Bryce, in his manful struggle to put Macassa over the top, worked with several broker-promoters. The Bidgood, to the east, was promoted by the late Leo Ernhous, and Bob Brown, aided by two brokerage firms which dared to finance what appeared to be a hopeless situation, gave the area its latest producer and dividend payer in the Upper Canada Mines.

After the Noranda, Quebec was almost entirely a province of promoters. The first Waite-Amulet discoveries were "given" to the public, as were also Stadacona, Senator, Wasa Lake, Donalda, McDonald, Pontiac (Anglo-Rouyn), Powell, Marlon, McWatters, Rouyn Merger, Astoria, Wright-Rouyn, Heva Cadillac, Hosco, Normar, and Calder-Bousquet. Aside from the Lindsley-sponsored mines, Lake Dufault and Beattie, the only other property of importance in the immediate district which was acquired by a large company is the Mic-Mac, subsidiary of the U.S. Smelting & Refining Company of Boston. The Waite-Amulet resulted from an amalgamation of two earlier promotions by Noranda. The story of O'Brien, how it was promoted after several years of private management and ownership, has been set forth.

In the Malartic area, Jim Norrie stole the show, the Nesbitt-Thompson Company of Montreal underwriting his various mine-making efforts. The Canadian Malartic was originally a promotion, taken over later by the ubiquitous Ventures, Ltd. The Pandora, West Malartic, Parbec, and East Amphi developments are all promotions.

The Bourlamaque district owes Lamaque and Sigma to large mining organizations, but not before promoters had established the camp. The Sisco Mine probably never would have received attention were it not for Stobie-Furlong, brokers, who supplied the first money by familiar promotion methods. Pierre Beauchemin, in his determination to make a mine out of the Sullivan, worked with promoters, as he did also in the East Sullivan and Louvicourt developments. The Cournor, Perron, Pascalis, Resenor, Aumaque, New Bidlamaque, and many others which constitute the large part of current activities in the area depended upon Toronto promoters for development funds.

We have already seen how the Red Lake area owes its prosperity to the efforts of promoters, without whom the camp would be a ghost town today. Men like Jack Hammell, Sammy Zachs, Charlie Gentles, Joe McDonough, and Bill Cochenour carried on when affairs seemed anything but prosperous. Later, sensing overlooked potentialities of mines, the companies began to buy "positions" from promoters like I. K. Isbell, G. E. Mallen, and Brewis & White.

Little Long Lac is another promoter's triumph. This area was first investigated for iron possibilities almost fifty years ago. It was forgotten until 1909 when A. P. Coleman, geologist of the Ontario Department of Mines, described the geology as favorable for gold deposits. Nothing happened for some time, despite further revealing reports by other government geologists, including that of Percy E. Hopkins, who also had done yeoman work in the Cobalt district. The first actual discovery of gold, as so often happens, is a matter of dispute, the claimants being Bill ("Hardrock") Smith and Tony Oklend. Smith, who represented the Hard Rock Prospecting Syndicate, has on record a letter he sent to Bert Rea in Toronto, dated August 17, 1931, wherein he described a find which later became the Hard Rock Gold Mine. Oklend, a Lithuanian trapper, had spent long years in the area, and is known to have patiently collected a quantity of gold which he used in trading at the local Hudson Bay post. Oklend teamed with Tom Johnson, an experienced prospector who had been poking about the district.

In the summer of 1932 the men found and staked a gold occurrence along the shores of Little Long Lac. Johnson had already been in touch with Percy Hopkins, now a free-lance consultant, and upon making the discovery sent hurried word to his engineer associate in Toronto. Hopkins departed for Little Long Lac immediately, mapped and sampled the veins, then went on to Sudbury where he interviewed Joseph Errington. Errington, who was following developments west of the Johnson claims, agreed to investigate. His engineer, A. A. Barton, was in the area and so he communicated with him, ordering a careful examination of the Johnson-Oklend ground. Hopkins, meanwhile, carried an option in his pocket signed by the two bush partners. They could have made no better choice than trusting their destiny to a man of Hopkins's caliber.

Errington was in Little Long Lac by August, 1932, where he examined the prospect and conferred with Barton. Satisfied that the showing had the makings, Errington, with no one to consult, sat on a log and himself wrote a memo agreeing to make a cash payment of $2,000 within a week and allocate to the prospectors and Hopkins 10 per cent of the Little Long Lac Gold Mines, Ltd., to be formed immediately. With his old associate, General D. M. Hogarth, Errington managed to raise the funds needed for development, and before the end of 1934 a 200-ton mill was treating excellent grade ore. Hopkins, Oklend, and Johnson did well, for the mine, still healthily young, has to date turned out $15,000,000 and has paid almost $4,000,000 in dividends.

Errington's energy had much to do with the upward surge of a camp which for a time appeared to hang in balance. Bill Smith's Hard Rock Mine, promoted by the Rea brothers, became a producer in 1938. In the same year, the MacLeod-Cockshutt Mine made its introductory bow, the public buying generously when Joe Errington and Don Hogarth offered stock for sale. Emboldened by these successes, the Newmont Mining Company of New York led a parade of companies to gain a foothold in Little Long Lac, and while a few properties of merit were acquired, the bulk of gold continues to come from promotional mines.

A high mark of promotion was reached in the saga of the Pickle Crow Mine. Once again we meet the picturesque Jack Hammell, who so eloquently refused to retire after the Flin Flon episode. Jack Macfarlane and H. H. Howell of the N.A.M.E. Company, one of Hammell's earlier promotions, discovered gold at Pickle Lake, a remote section of Ontario's Patricia district, in September, 1928. Not long thereafter Hammell was on the claims, impressed with the high-grade quartz veins in iron formation. It was Indian country, however, completely unknown and untested, and Hammell decided to incorporate the Northern Aerial Canada Golds, Ltd., and provide $100,000 for extensive drilling and shaft work.

Hammell declared the first results completely satisfactory. But the long depression had now begun and it was impossible to convince others that Pickle Crow was a mine. Unable to O.P.M. (his phrase for "Other People's Money") the situation, he dug into his pocket and provided $50,000 as a loan. The development, he decided, must go on. Underground work brightened the picture considerably, and Hammell, realizing that there was little hope in an O.P.M. program, undertook to interview the large companies in quest of a solid moneyed partner. Overlooking no one, he made the rounds of more than a dozen offices, but this time, in contrast to the Flin Flon, he was stymied. He made one final effort, managed to persuade a New York mining group, which had profited handsomely in Canada, to send its engineers into Pickle Crow. He announced himself willing to abide by the findings of the technical men, but the report, to his dismay, was negative. We can see him, pacing the floor of his office, hurling imprecations at New York in general and geologists in particular. In the heat of his failure, he called in his secretary and dictated a letter:

Dear Bill:

Thanks for the report and also for allowing me to have a copy of it, which I am having done.

These boys certainly do not display any vision, courage, or common horse sense. They chopped it off, bottom and both ends. That drill hole stuff is hooey. We all know damn well that we don't expect values in drill holes—it is phenomenal when we get them. These are the best set of values I have ever seen, in drill holes, in the north country, and I don't bar any mine . . . Harry Oakes had three drills go through his main ore body and the best he got was $2.75. M. J. O'Brien lost the Hollinger Mine; he put three drill holes through a $40 section of ore of good widths. . . . It was spotty —sure it was spotty . . . but the spots come often enough to make mines. Mines are made and not found. Why should this vein dip in the harder greenstone? It is much more likely to go down with the contact. And why should it pinch? In my mind it is a hell of a lot more likely to widen. . . . The widest spot on the Lake Shore was 6" . . . Harry Oakes brought the Lake Shore to me when he was down 125 feet and had several hundred feet of drifting done. The best assay on the whole property . . . was 2 foot width of $15 ore. . . .

I had 13 of the greatest geologists and engineers supposed to be in captivity—they all turned the Howey down flat. . . . It discouraged me so much that I went right ahead and made a mine out of it anyway.

I am not sore and I am not disappointed, just sorry. With three groups like yourselves I thought I might get some place. I thought you were different . . . you should be familiar with, and outgrown, the drastic mistakes . . . made in Canada by . . . engineers. They have missed all the good camps here. If it had not been for Harry Oakes, prospector, and Al Wende, hard rock miner, there would have been no Kirkland Lake, because every engineer in the world turned it down. If it had not been for Noah Timmins, there would have been no Porcupine camp. . . . Does this not to you, . . . all engineers, seem a hell of a state of affairs?

Now I am going ahead and make a mine . . . I am not nuts. They laughed . . . at Flin Flon, Howey, and Porcupine Crown, but they all made mines. This is easier . . . sure fire. The worst . . . is enough ore for a 100 ton mill . . . a 200 ton mill. However, that remains to be seen.

I am not asking anything for this property. I am handing it

to you on a platter. All I am asking . . . is prove the property up and pay us back the money which it has cost us. . . . You get all the benefit—we wind up with 1/3 interest . . . you with 2/3rds. Did you ever . . . hear of a deal as good . . . ? I am in $50,000 now and committed to another $100,000. But if you . . . want to see whether your theory . . . or mine is right, I will play ball . . . Take a gambling bet of $50,000 . . . a "white chip" on a working option. If these boys' report is right you don't want any part of the property. But if you take me up . . . take a look at the vein at the 125′ (level). . . . Don't pay any attention to what these boys tell you about pinching out—that is the bunk. . . . Wonder what these boys would have done if they had sampled the Lake Shore . . . down to 125′? . . . probably have taken an elm club and killed Oakes for asking . . . money for it.

If you want to throw in a "white chip" and my theory is right . . . you have a sweet deal. . . . If I am wrong you have only shot a . . . "chip". . . . If something along this line appeals to you, I will come down. . . . Otherwise . . . no use of me wasting your time or my own. . . . Sorry . . . I thought I had finally struck a bunch of live wires and . . . we would go places and do things.

But, as Hammell soon learned, he was wasting his time. Like the Gauls before Caesar, who sought safety in flight, New York presented Hammell with the opportunity to go places and do things alone. And Hammell, as was to be expected, accepted the challenge. It was now O.P.M. or nothing. The firm of H. R. Bain of Toronto was called in and an agreement made for the sale of 1,000,000 shares of Pickle Crow at 50 cents per share, Bain underwriting the issue at something less than the public offering price. The issue was split among several other brokers. Hammell, never niggardly in anything he did, had formed the Pickle Crow Gold Mines, a 3,000,000-share company, and half of this stock was given to the vendor, Northern Aerial Canada Golds, the Hammell company. These shares were placed in escrow for the period ending February 1, 1935, one year from the date of offer, leaving 1,500,000 shares in the treasury. On the circular which Bain distributed to "suckers," Hammell allowed this statement to be printed: "The parent company spent $100,000 and I have spent $115,000 of my own personal funds on the further development of the property and—should Mr. Bain, through any unforeseen reason, be unable to carry this financing to completion, up to the production stage, I hereby guarantee to do so myself. In my opinion this property has the most consistent and best set of gold assays, and the best show, of any gold property in Ontario at the present stage of development."

This was unusual language, and produced the desired results.

Hammell was well known and the public bought stock freely, in time to find itself large shareholders in a veritable bonanza. Even Hammell, never prone to underestimate, was thrilled with Pickle. It never faltered from the earliest moment of production; like Topsy, it "jes' growed." From 1935 to 1945 the mine yielded $22,-092,760 and paid $8,250,000 in dividends. And its future is bright.

Next to Pickle Crow, the Central Patricia Mine, promoted by Fred Connell, who battled adverse conditions for several dreary years, has, after one reorganization and an abortive try at "respectable" money, come through nicely on its own steam, after some remarkably able work on the part of Allan Anderson, the manager. The gold occurrences are lenticular, as contrasted to the vein systems of its distinguished neighbor, but Central Pat has managed to show a production and dividend record of $16,106,675 and $3,975,-000, respectively, to the end of 1945.

A complete recital of other promotions which have rung the bell would be lengthy and perhaps tiresome. I shall touch upon only a few more, such as Ventures, Ltd., which received the lion's share of its initial funds through public sale of stock. The Bralorne, British Columbia's largest gold producer, was promoted, and in the same province Fred M. Wells revived an expiring Cariboo district after it was left for dead by allegedly wiser heads. The Negus Mine in Yellowknife and the Steep Rock iron mine in Western Ontario were promoted by the late Joe Errington. "Brash" promoters have scored heavily throughout Canada.

This brief review, outlining the vital role promotion has played in the development of the north, explains at the same time why it has so wide a public appeal. Attacking the slicker operators, ranting at shysters who are attracted by the prospect of easy money, and thundering at promiscuous chicanery serve a valuable purpose, no doubt, but "liquidation" of mining promotion can come only when the capitalist system itself is thrown into the ash can. As long as mining functions there must be capital, and since the ordinary channels of investment funds are closed to it, the industry is obliged to accept money from any and all sources.

Imagine a prospector walking into a bank and interviewing one of the officers about financing a gold prospect! If the well-groomed vice-president does not swoon, he will escort the presumptuous visitor to the front door, or, if he is husky enough, kick him out bodily. It is an interesting commentary on modern society that banks, which propound learnedly on the gold standard, the foundation of our economy, including banking, are the last people on earth actively to enter the field of gold production. And to those bent on reform who point to other available means of securing capital which await honest mine development, I can only say that they speak with the conviction of ignorance. I wish they themselves would make the rounds of offices in quest of mining money. It is a punishing, dispiriting routine, usually productive of nothing more than tired feet, failing vocal cords, and a desire to quit the business altogether. It is natural for an owner of claims to visit a promoter, who is usually an attentive listener for that is exactly his business.

Some distinctions are necessary. Jack Hammell was more a sponsor than a promoter of Pickle Crow. Bain, a stockbroker, did the actual work of distributing (selling) stock to the public. It is this which is commonly understood as mining promotion. Men like Hammell, Errington, Jim Norrie, and Cochenour pass the ball to the actively selling broker who is the author of the sometimes offensive circulars. He is the man who heads a selling organization which milks telephones in boiler rooms, rings doorbells, and utilizes every device to nail buyers. He makes himself felt in no uncertain way. There is no routine or standard procedure, however. Some operators are adroit. They have carefully built up a following much as does a play producer in New York. Telephone calls or a few letters to associates who have already ventured and won, and the stock issue is completely sold. Later, when, as, and if conditions warrant, the stock can be fed out in a wider radius. Not always are sponsors of the Hammell type necessary, for the promoter, in addition to the voluntary selections which pour into his office, often maintains his own representatives in the bush to seek out likely prospects which have the qualities of a "good promotion." In all cases the attitude is the same: the bona fide promoter insists that he is merely selling a chance to participate in what might prove to be a successful mine. He is a merchandiser of stock, nothing more, so he insists.

What manner of man is he, this unloved broker who brings venture capital and mining prospects together in happy and unhappy marriages? He is no altruist, that he will admit quickly. Nor has he any illusions. He knows that he will be savagely maligned if his stock turns out badly. And so he must be thick skinned. Sensitive people, therefore, cannot be happy promoters. The promoter wastes no sympathy on unfortunate confreres, for he knows they have little for him. He bitterly assails his colleagues, for character assassination is common to his trade. But do not be surprised to see him lunching amiably with one of his supposed enemies whom he blithely enlists as a partner in a deal. At all times this chameleon is called upon to make decisions; his mind must be swift. Self-preservation is his motivating policy always. He conforms to no particular physical type. He is lean, fat, tall, short. He can be a voluble talker, or a silent Joe. He is warm, friendly, a gladhander of the public relations kind, or he can be as cold-blooded and communicative as a fish. He plays hunches, is careless of the truth, and is a master psychologist. Rarely does he venture into the bush. To him, mining properties are merely names, grist for his mill. He passes from one to another blithely, like a bee sucking honey in a field of blossoms.

There is nothing mysterious about his trade. A claim owner either appears voluntarily or is "tied up" by an agent. The agreement is almost a formula, providing for a company of, say, 4,000,-000 shares. Let us call it Moosehorn. The cost of incorporation ranges from $1,000 to $1,500 and is advanced by the broker. The property owner is granted usually 1,000,000 shares of vendor stock, this percentage of the capitalization being the conventional one. (The maximum is 33 1/3, though in special cases as much as one-half has been obtained. The Ontario Securities Commission scrutinizes all such arrangements and has the power, which it sometimes exercises, of modifying the allocation.) In any event, such shares are issued, but not delivered; rather, they are placed in escrow with a bank or trust company, and cannot be released before a stipulated date, and then only by consent of Moosehorn directors and the Securities Commission. Recently, immediate release of 10 per cent has been made mandatory as a result of the insistence of the Ontario Prospectors' Association, a group devoted to furthering the interests of prospectors. The reason for pooling vendor stock is obvious, the promoter obtains an unhampered market situation. No stock will be "thrown" at him when financing operations begin.

It is frequently asked, and understandably, "Why these large capitalizations? Why not a 400,000-share company?" A completely satisfactory answer to this natural query is yet to be found. The pat explanation is that a large number of shares creates a mirage of substance. The average speculator prefers to own 1,000 shares at 20 cents rather than 100 shares which cost him $2 each; he feels he is somehow richer that way. Then, too, there are occasional high-priced mining stocks like Noranda, McIntyre, and Consolidated Mining & Smelting which sell for more than $50 a share. These would be awkward traders at $500. Rather than increase the capital at a later time, when value is firmly established, and split the stock three or four to one as so often happens in the States, Canadian mining finance prefers to start with a plenitude of shares. It is a reversal of process, so to speak. Of course, when issues flounder—and many of them do—penny values appear ridiculous to serious investors. More than once a bright young promoter has tried to reverse the style and introduce more modest capitalizations. By trial and error, however, it has been learned that a 3,000,000-share company is the safest minimum.

Returning to Moosehorn. The broker agrees to buy an initial block of treasury shares. This is a firm commitment. In consideration, he is given options on all, or most, of the remaining shares, at ascending prices. The usual price and time schedule is something on this order:

Date	No. Shares	Price	Net to Company
Contract	500,000 (firm)	5¢	$25,000
3 months	400,000	7½¢	30,000
6 months	400,000	10	40,000
9 months	300,000	15	45,000
1 year	250,000	20	50,000
15 months	250,000	30	75,000
18 months	200,000	40	80,000
21 months	200,000	50	100,000
27 months	200,000	75	150,000
33 months	200,000	$1.00	200,000
36 months	100,000	1.25	125,000
3 years	3,000,000	30.9¢	$920,000

This schedule is worthy of examination. The basic idea is to supply the company with sufficient money to achieve the production stage, if results warrant. Ostensibly, there is enough, for, as we have seen, a million dollars is the average cost of a producing mine in Canada. But it is apparent that the majority of funds will be forthcoming at the tag end of things, when the enterprise is either an assured success or has been already consigned to oblivion. It requires no Einstein to discern that the initial options fall short of the mark. The amounts are far below mine development requirements, and unless good results are swiftly forthcoming, the whole affair will languish and die. It is here that the vendor must assert himself and insist upon higher option prices in the beginning, so that work may be carried on regardless of market conditions. But the broker is equally insistent that there must be a good supply of "cheap" stock for him; otherwise he will have no cushion for further financing. Usually, the vendor's position is weak. His claims are unproved or have been already condemned by examining engineers, and in most cases he accepts what is offered him, hoping that "everything will come out all right." Herein lies the basic weakness of promotion. It is primarily designed to protect the broker rather than the mining property, and if regulation must come this is the starting point. On his side, the promoter will assert, and with some justice, that long chances can be handled in no other way, and higher initial option prices will kill off most ventures before they are fairly started. Nevertheless, a sizable initial development fund will, in the long run, protect the broker as well as speculators, for it gives immediate substance to the enterprise and assures completion of preliminary development.

The agreement signed and the 500,000 shares bought at 5 cents, the broker rolls up his sleeves and is ready to work. At once, the company reimburses him for organization expense. Then he makes a public offering of 500,000 shares at 25 cents per share. Ostensibly, his immediate profit is 20 cents a share—$100,000. Actually, it is something less. There is the considerable expense of printing and mailing thousands of circulars, buying or compiling "sucker" lists, advertising, telephone calls, engineers' reports, legal fees, and so on. Again, he sometimes "wholesales" part of the issue, retaining only part of the "spread" for himself. If he is left with $50,000 he considers the effort a success. Naturally, he does not rush into a deal without first carefully sounding out conditions. He must not venture blindly and then find himself stuck with a deskful of stock certificates; this is disaster. His sense of timing cannot deceive him, for a promoter is soon out of business if he strikes out too often. He is required to bat for .300 if he expects to remain on the team.

With $50,000 on hand, he is now ready to hazard the next step. This requires a rising market price, for he is unable to build up or even maintain his cushion if the stock remains stationary or, worse still, drops.

A horrible thought suggests itself: what is to prevent him from pocketing the $50,000 and blithely ignoring further operations? The answer is—nothing. He can do, and frequently does, this very thing, for there is no compulsion to exercise further options. This kind of operator is known as a hit-and-run artist, and during boom times he is all too prevalent. He has brought much disrepute to the promotional business, but he is guilty of performance only once or twice. The public and fellow brokers soon become aware of his tactics and he finds it impossible to sell stock again. There are losses, and the entire fraternity of promoters is castigated; the guilt is collective.

Brokers of intelligence and integrity—and there are some—prefer to make a stand and support the market, for a time at least. This involves repurchasing whatever stock comes back for sale through the overcounter (wags call it undercounter) market. A portion of sucker stock invariably is fired back at the broker, and unless he demonstrates that there is an honest bid the sale offerings will swell into a deluge. If the market price is lifted without property results or general market conditions justifying the move, pressure to "bang" Moosehorn is immediately felt. On the lookout for short-selling opportunities of this kind are the jackals of the Bay Street jungle. "Short lines" are put out in the confident expectation that the shares can be "covered" (repurchased) later at lower levels.

Some brokers, instead of fighting back, allow the market to sag, even to a point of dipping below their outstanding option prices. Thus they make a virtue of necessity, for they themselves can buy low-priced stock at large and deliver it to clients who purchased at the original offering price. Here again lies a serious weakness, for manifestly the company suffers if options are not exercised, that is, there soon is a dearth of funds on hand for development. But the broker's one thought is to be "short" of stock after the public is "in." With an oversold position he can, if necessary, take down options from the company, or, if it pleases him, make his purchases, as noted, on the open market. Either way there is a profit and he still commands the situation. If he is "long" of stock he has cause for worry, for this means he has been "taking" it, and instead of cash he has paper. This is bad, very bad, and to a broker the situation is compared to that of a man biting a dog. He tries to reverse matters, and once more we find another weak link in the broker-promotional chain. The entire structure is predicated on a rising market, and this, in turn, on satisfactory reports from the north.

It follows as the night the day, therefore, that no chance to paint the lily will be missed. Single assays of $300 per ton and more are flashed to newspapers. The geology is described as "favorable to the deposition of gold." The promoter digs deeply into his bag of clichés and glittering generalities in lieu of positive information. When the Yellowknife boom was at its height, for example, campaign literature featured such an absurdity as "A drill has been ordered and is expected on the property within 60 days" or "John Smith, formerly in the employ of Bluenose Mining Corporation, has been retained as resident manager." To a professional trader, this is the time to sell short. To an amateur, bewilderment comes, for while he knows the status may change for the better, he is beset with doubts and fears, and while he treads water uncertainly the market may weaken.

This is a critical moment. His back to the wall, the broker will try, if he values his standing, to support the stock, at the same time keeping an anxious eye on that $50,000 cushion. As it dwindles, he places more and more pressure on his engineers. News, news! Words fly, resignations are followed by new appointments, but drilling is poor regardless of who points the holes. The fund now diminished to a few thousand dollars, the broker, who almost never wins medals for bravery, pulls the plug. All bids are withdrawn, and the stock takes a perpendicular drop. The fun is over and one more mining casualty is chalked up.

Later the situation may be revived if the area, like Red Lake, becomes hot again. But if several Moosehorn options have been exercised, there is too much stock outstanding to permit continuance under the existing corporate structure. No one will undertake financing with stock "kicking around the street"; he wants to have matters well in hand and not be compelled to spend good money buying up an old mistake. And so reorganization is necessary. A new company, Moosehorn Consolidated, is formed with a capital of 3,000,000 shares, the old company receiving 1,000,000 vendor shares. The original property owners and shareholders of Moosehorn in this way have a reduced equity, the amount of reduction depending upon the outstanding stock at the time of reorganization. A 50 per cent cut is not uncommon. In any event the groundwork has been laid for a new stock-selling campaign. This repetition of effort can go on *ad infinitum*, for hope springs eternal.

There are, of course, refinements in "Operation Moosehorn." The broker may give an "overriding" to his agent, self-appointed or retained. There are individuals constantly drifting about the Canadian mining scene fishing for "sleepers," which are considered good promotional material. They have no intention of themselves providing working capital; their procedure is much simpler. They turn over the enterprise to the broker, before or after they have secured a deal. The commitment, if there is one, is assumed by the broker, who thereupon is assigned all the outstanding options, the agent receiving a cent or two when, as, and if each option is exercised. A smart operator will retain for himself one or two of the later, higher priced options in the event the property becomes a mine. Parasitical? Maybe, but it is all a part of the extensive dragnet that is thrown out in the relentless search for mines, and several have been captured by this technique.

The broker occasionally sells his entire position if the situation looks bright, the buyer being a mining company wishing to catch the bus after missing it at the first station, or a fellow broker who sees, or thinks he sees, overlooked possibilities. Or, if drilling is good, the stock, cleverly handled, can be pushed up sharply, even above the dollar mark when the shorts have guessed wrong and rush to cover. This happened in the case of MacLeod-Cockshutt. Short selling was extensive after the first results from the property were announced. Continuing high-grade core gave impetus to short covering, and this ended in a stampede. At least one brokerage house was forced into bankruptcy as the stock rose above $5 a share, and so for a time the name "MacLeod Caught Short" was bandied about Toronto. Much the same thing happened when Joe Hirshhorn promoted the long ridiculed Preston East Dome. News of ore intersections was greeted with hoots of derision. To the shorts, this was an out-and-out jiggle, and for a while they had a merry time driving the stock down. But Hirshhorn, sure of his information, bought steadily, and when the day of reckoning came, faces of the shorts were very long in Bay Street.

With Moosehorn at $1 a share, the happy broker sells at this figure and buys from the company at 7½ and 10 cents, a far greater spread then he enjoyed at the start. There is no provision in the agreement which forces him to anticipate the higher priced stock, even though this would place the company in large funds. His interest is entirely confined to the market. As far as the broker is concerned, a Moosehorn is merely a receptacle of cheap stock which he can dispose of at an enormous profit.

If events take a sudden turn for the worse, he is not going to be left "holding the bag," as he expresses it. He wants money, not mining securities. If the public continues to buy avidly, well and good. He will then, in due course, reach the expensive options. Herein is another serious deficiency, and even iniquity, in the method. Farseeing men would welcome the rare opportunity of strengthening the company's treasury, so that, come what may, Moosehorn will rest on foundations, and not intentions. If the development ends with a shutdown, funds could then be used for investment purposes or a fling or two at other developments. More than one mining success has been attained in this way.

From my observation, it seems that wise reform should begin here. A broker should be compelled by law to surrender at least one-half of the difference between dollar sales and 10-cent purchases, the beneficiary being the Moosehorn Company. The stockholder would then be getting a run for his money instead of buttering the promoter's bread. At the same time there would be some kind of check on runaway market prices before the value of a property is established by actual development results. No doubt, a requirement of this kind would be very unpopular, but upon reflection the broker himself would recognize that it would afford protection to him. For whether he realizes it or not, the mine, and not promotion, establishes the market eventually, and anything constructively achieved at the property will bolster the Bay Street end.

Exploring further, we find that in the cruder and less-regulated promotional era, the public was completely in the dark regarding the discrepancy between option and market prices. There were vague suspicions, perhaps, but only the broker and his intimates knew that Moosehorn options began at 5 cents. Obviously, there would be great reluctance to buy at 25 cents if this fact was common knowledge. But the Ontario Securities Commission stepped in and made the publication of underwriting and option agreements compulsory. For a time there was gloom on Bay Street, but then the lads discovered a way to overcome this seemingly formidable obstacle. Vendor stock! Why not purchase chunks of it? Surely, the syndicate or prospector would be delighted to obtain cash immediately! Moosehorn, for instance, could take down 500,000 shares at 10 cents or even 15 cents instead of 5 cents, if, at the same time, 500,000 shares were bought from the vendors at 2 cents a share. This would bring the average price somewhat above 5 cents, true, but the difference would be slight. Being a private trade, this transaction would not be broadcast and everyone would be happy. But isn't there a pooling provision attached to vendor stock? Yes, but 10 per cent is immediately released, and then, at a given time, Moosehorn directors can apply to the commission for the release of more. The company has no objection, for it benefits handsomely through higher initial option prices which immediately provide $50,000 or more as against $25,-000. For this reason, perhaps, the commission allows the practice to continue. The broker simply must have his cushion somewhere in the process. If it is taken from him completely, promotion will languish, with consequent deterioration of mining development.

There is justification in the contention that these practices are not healthy. But the essential weaknesses lie more in promoters as men than in promotion itself. Rogues there are in every profession, and promotion has its quota. Brokers, however, are learning that the truly large fortunes in mining are made by accenting the development of meritorious properties rather than in grabbing quick, irresponsible profits. Those who wish to persist in this rugged game, where no quarter is given or asked, are coming to the realization that, like prospecting, promoting a successful mine requires time and patience. One promoter I know has three good mines to his credit in the past ten years. Accidents, perhaps, but his record stands unquestioned and he has far outstripped his colleagues who incline to quickies and so are losing ground fast. It is too much to expect, however, that corrective measures be left to promoters themselves.

When Quemont struck it rich not long after the amazing ore disclosures at Giant Yellowknife and the exciting new developments in Red Lake, the orgy of promotion and speculation from 1943 onward attained unheard-of proportions. There was never anything like it in the history of Canada. Strange faces appeared on Bay Street, many of them American. All available office space was commandeered; telephone wires began to sizzle. Promotions mushroomed daily and the mails groaned with tons of garish literature. Stocks rose and fell, then rose again. Volume of trading reached such heights that the overtaxed facilities of the Exchange necessitated Saturday closings. In 1945 the Toronto Stock Exchange traded only a few thousand shares less than did the New York Exchange, omitting the extensive activity of the "undercounter" market on which no accurate records are kept. Long-distance calls were made to garner buyers in transactions involving as little as $10. There seemed no limit to the extravagances of neophyte promoters who introduced new "wrinkles" to an already overgrown situation. Reaction to this flight from reason was not slow in coming and it took the form of condemning all promotion. Much of the criticism, such as the article quoted early in this chapter, came from the United States and the affair began to assume international importance. Ontario, from which most of the mining promotion stems, decided that the clamor for regulation must be answered. The situation was threatening to get out of hand.

One factor was recognized: more money was being placed in company treasuries than ever before. While admitting the necessity of disciplinary action, politicians moved warily toward a new Securities Act despite growing clamor for swift action. It was realized that an SEC type of law would wreak havoc with one of Canada's leading industries. Practical in respect to most industries, this kind of legislation would make no exceptions for speculative ventures, and those in authority, with commendable caution, declared that the Securities Act contemplated would be designed to smoke out the thieves without burning the entire mining structure. Still a pioneer country, Canada could not afford to commit the fatal error of controling all its citizenry in order to trap the offending few. It was pointed out that the winning of the American West would have been long delayed or largely sabotaged had the the SEC been in operation during the previous century. Fear was expressed, also, that complete removal of promotion would narrow the field of mining development and throw it into the arms of the large companies, few of which, until the past few years, have distinguished themselves in exploration.

The Securities Act of 1945 met with mixed reception. To some, it was too drastic, to others it did not go far enough. The law provided for yearly registration of all brokers, promoters, and stock salesmen, all applications to be reviewed by the commission. Submission of a prospectus was required, without, however, the finely spun procedures which new enterprise has found so exasperating in Washington. The Toronto Stock Exchange, at the same time, stiffened its listing requirements. These steps were entirely justified. But it is to be noted that accent was placed on public information. It was recognized that no statute can take the place of individual judgment, for, in the last analysis, the speculator must himself judge the merits and risks of a mining promotion.

Headed by the Honorable C. P. McTague, the Securities Commission proceeded to demonstrate that it meant business. In the spring of 1946 hardly a week elapsed without one or more security-selling licenses being canceled or refused an applicant, and while this dampened speculative and promotional ardor, public opinion generally applauded this long-needed house cleaning. Bay Street, however, was unhappy; rumors and statements circulated to the effect that few brokerage houses and stock salesmen would remain in business long. McTague, in May, 1946, was under the necessity of scotching these stories. In a carefully prepared statement he disclosed that of 362 houses applying for registration, 324 were accepted. Of 1,068 salesmen applying, 1,001 received licenses. Shortly thereafter he made a public address, in the course of which he urged that the Investment Dealers of Canada emulate the example of similar American associations and take disciplinary action, whenever necessary, among their own membership, warning that unless some such step was followed the inevitable answer would be increased government regulation. Surely, no one can dispute this excellent suggestion.

Until some better means can be found to facilitate the flow of venture capital into Canada's mining areas, present promotional techniques, with some modifications, will probably endure. It is to be hoped that security dealers act upon McTague's advice and obviate the necessity of governmental control. But whatever measures are taken, there is no conceivable formula which can minimize or eliminate the uncertainties and risks inherent to the mining industry, and the promoter, imperfect as he is, has proved by performance that he has served in expediting the wihning of the north.

There are no laws yet devised which create mass intelligence. The speculator is, or should be, qualified to provide his own protection against an irrepressible gambling instinct. Historians, in a later day, will undoubtedly characterize our age as one of too much government, which, like too much work and no play, made Jack a hell of a dull boy!

CHAPTER XVI

Caveat Emptor!

"Some owners prefer to buy shares in mines abounding in metals, rather than to be troubled themselves to search for the veins; These men employ an easier and less uncertain method of increasing their property. Although their hopes in the shares of one or another mine may be frustrated, the buyers of shares should not abandon the rest of the mines, for all the money expended will be recovered with interest from some other mine. They should not buy only high priced shares in those mines producing metals, nor should they buy too many in neighboring mines where metal has not yet been found, lest, should fortune not respond, they may be exhausted by their losses and have nothing with which they may meet their expenses or buy other shares which may replace their losses. This calamity overtakes those who wish to grow suddenly rich from mines, and instead, they become very much poorer than before. So then, in the buying of shares, as in other matters, there should be a certain limit of expenditure which miners should set themselves, lest blinded by the desire for excessive wealth, they throw all their money away. Moreover, a prudent owner, before he buys shares, ought to go to the mine and carefully examine the nature of the vein, for it is very important that he should be on his guard less fraudulent sellers of shares should deceive him. Investors in shares may perhaps become less wealthy, but they are more certain of some gain than those who mine for metals at their own expense, as they are more cautious in trusting to fortune. Neither ought miners to be altogether distrustful of fortune, as we see some are, who as soon as the shares of any mine begin to go up in value, sell them, on which account they seldom obtain even moderate wealth. . . ."

Georgius Agricola (1555)

When asked how he had managed to amass such great wealth one of the Rothschilds replied, "I always sold out too quickly." George Baker, Wall Street tycoon, is reported to have answered the same question in this wise: "I buy but I never sell."

A most ingenious paradox, as Gilbert and Sullivan would say; the road to fortune can split into divergent paths and yet arrive at the same glorious destination. Here is a suggestion of contortion which no rational mind can accept, but experts in speculation and investment have a simple explanation of this phenomenon. In their language, the good baron, certainly an eminent practitioner of the art of speculation, would be a champion of the short-pull method. His no less distinguished confrere would be a worthy exponent of the long-pull school. Under varying circumstances both can prosper.

Wall Street, with typical cynicism, has coined a phrase of its own regarding the business of speculation: "Bulls make money, bears make money, but pigs always lose money." Said Mark Twain: "There are two times in a man's life when he should not speculate; when he can't afford it, and when he can."

True speculation is an occupation rather than a disease. This applies as much to mining as it does to industrials. Contrary to popular belief, there have been, are, and will continue to be successful mining speculators, but they have learned their craft only after long study and application. When asked by government interrogators what his vocation was, Barney Baruch replied from the witness stand, "I am a speculator." Whoever follows hot tips or acts upon "confidential" information will, in the end, find the habit expensive. To be permanent, profit must be earned.

There is more than cupidity and gullibility involved when the proverbial sucker buys a mining stock. The promoter is a shrewd psychologist, particularly the one who trades more on cunning than on honesty. He stresses the romance of faraway places where buried treasure awaits the gallant prospector. Such glamor finds some response in the average man, eager as he is to escape the deadening routine of workshop and office. He is also excited at the illusion of being a participant, even a remote one, in an enterprise which challenges nature in the raw. Purchasing stock in a textile mill or pickle factory, for example, provides no such vicarious thrill. The speculator is filled with hope too; he is made fully aware of the huge fortunes which have been derived from long chances in mining speculation, 1,000-to-1 shots no staid industrial enterprise can hope to equal. And so many a little man follows the prescription which Napoleon made his motto: *Attempto!* I dare!

It is wrong to assume that victims of financial adventurers are confined to widows and orphans. The people who accept representations impossible of fulfillment are found in all walks of life. Sagacious Wall Street operators have been "taken over" as easily as the waiters serving them palatial luncheons at the Bankers' Club.

In New York, not long ago, one of the partners of a large investment house, which specialized in railroad and industrial bond issues, was presented to a mining engineer at a social function. The banker, skilled at brain picking, asked several leading questions about Canadian mining. The answers were brief but pointed; the man, apparently, knew his business.

"Have lunch with me," suggested Reid, using a Wall Street formula for spearing free information—and misinformation. Hunter (not his real name), successful in his profession but somewhat unsophisticated, graciously accepted the invitation. A few days thereafter the men were seated in an exclusive downtown club. The meal was excellent—Reid did such things well—and by the time cigars were lighted, conversation took a direct turn.

"By the way," said Reid, appearing casual, "in the course of your work in Canada you must have met a man named Lund, I'm sure."

"Not L. P. Lund?" Hunter was genuinely amused. Noting this, Reid's manner hardened.

"Yes, that's the chap." He bit into his cigar. "Anything wrong with him?" and for the first time an unfriendly note crept into the suave banker's tone.

"Oh, he may be all right"—Hunter shrugged—"but I just wouldn't care to do business with him, that's all."

"Wait a minute." Reid was brusque. "You can't say a thing like that about anyone unless you have a definite reason."

"I can't, eh?" Hunter's eye suddenly became glinty. "And what makes you think I can't?"

"Excuse me." Reid laughed mirthlessly. "I didn't mean to be rude. But you've cast aspersions at a man and I think, in all fairness, you should explain your statement."

"You put some money into that proposition of his? Is that why you ask about him?"

Reid stared at his cigar an instant; this was not going well, he had slipped badly.

"Well, a little." He almost felt like blushing.

"I see." Hunter grinned. "You've lost it, then."

"How do you know?" shot Hunter.

"I've seen the show, that's why. The district's no damn good. And the fellow's just a plain thief, down here raising money on an impossible situation."

"But there's gold on his claims," insisted Reid, desperate now. "He showed me some of the specimens."

"Sure there's gold," agreed Hunter with unction, "but he's carrying all of it with him, in his pocket. He's shown you more gold than will ever come out of the property."

"You can't condemn a mine like that," insisted Reid. "Lund has several reports and maps which show excellent prospects. I've seen them myself."

"Yes, I know." Hunter tossed his cigar into an ash tray. "You just don't want to hear the truth. That property has been examined by dozens of competent men who have turned in negative reports. Lots of money been spent there, too. But this fellow Lund doesn't mind. He's had a pamphlet printed up with all kinds of fancy assays, maps, and pictures, and he manages to find men who fall for that kind of bilge."

"Pardon me," rejoined the banker icily, "but I don't think you're detached about the matter. When I risk $50,000, I—"

"Fifty thousand!" interrupted Hunter. "Good God, I couldn't raise fifty cents on a show like that!"

"I see no point in continuing the discussion." Reid pushed back his chair.

"Nor do I." Hunter rose to his feet. "You know, Reid, I don't understand you fellows down here. When you float one of your fancy bond issues you retain all kinds of professional advisers who visit plants and study the particular industry. But when it comes to mining, you never think of an engineer to consult before you throw money into a wildcat. Maybe it's because you don't want to pay for that kind of information when your firm doesn't foot the bill."

"Good day!" Reid stalked for the nearest door. . . .

Widows and orphans, take heart! You have distinguished company!

If there were infallible rules which could be applied to mining speculation they would be more popular than the Ten Commandments. But the game is akin to horse racing, where differences of opinion set the odds—in this case, stock prices. Just as the track addict studies nags, so the mining speculator studies mines, or he should if he wishes to remain solvent. The trick is not entirely in placing good bets; retaining one's winnings is equally important. Above all, some carefully thought-out procedure or system must be followed. To those who wish to avoid work and get rich quickly, my counsel is to seek advice elsewhere. I can only show the way to thoughtful speculation and means of avoiding ordinary pitfalls.

Speculations should be resolved at once into their proper categories, each of which involves its own special problems and considerations. There are three broad divisions:

1. New issues, so familiar to recipients of sucker literature.
2. Development prospects engaged in an attempt to broaden ore horizons already indicated in drilling.
3. Producing mines, which may or may not pay dividends.

More than half of Canadian mining speculation falls into the classification of new issues, for here a large increment of capital gain is possible. These stocks offer particular attraction to Canadians, since profit is not taxable unless the speculator makes trading his exclusive profession. Americans also have the itch to buy. Not only does distance lend enchantment to the view, but capital gains are only partially taxed. There are grave dangers, however, and even the most expert speculators are stung. Losses are inevitable, but by no means necessary, and in any event they should provide valuable experience to the discerning speculator. He learns to separate the chaff from the wheat. Circulars and "informational bulletins" provide valuable clues. The prominent note is flamboyant and so is repugnant to many readers, but buried in the welter of paper and ink may be an incipient producer, and those who seek protective education must take the trouble of analysis.

The first check to make is inquiry as to the character of the sponsor. Has he any successes to his record? The answer can be supplied by those familiar with Canada, either through firsthand knowledge or that gained by regular study of various mining publications, notably the *Northern Miner,* which conducts a sizable Question and Answer column. More important, what is the character of the entrepreneur? Has he been involved in any suspect situations? If so, the best policy is to let his issues alone despite an occasional winner which he proudly, and loudly, trumpets. Such men are poor medicine, and in the long run bring nothing but loss and regret to their following. It must be remembered that everyone can sail easily in fair weather, when the great boom is on, but the proof of quality comes only with a demonstration that foul weather can be navigated too. The more unscrupulous a promoter is, the more he is in evidence during a bull market, for then he draws on a wider range of buyers, many of whom are green and greedy for immediate profit. Gains can be made, but it is unnatural to pocket these and desist from further speculation. The appetite is whetted. Profits are risked, then savings, and when the final collapse comes losses can be catastrophic. The first rule, then, strictly forbids playing with a sharp or dishonest operator.

The directors of an enterprise sometimes supply guides in an appraisal of stock offerings. If they are mere names which have no significance in mining, the enterprise becomes nondescript. One or two may be connected with other mining ventures, and these should be immediately checked in a *Canadian Mines Handbook*. When, on the other hand, the board generally consists of experienced and reputable mining men, the speculator can be assured that in most cases they will not lend themselves to any shenanigans. He can be comforted in the thought that money will be spent intelligently and honestly, an asset which words and balance sheets can never supply. Rule Two: Consult the list of directors, since this may determine the character of the enterprise.

The next point of inquiry rests in location of the claims. Are they situated in well-known mining camps or off in the blue where little is known about ore habits? It is unwise to eliminate a property merely because it is far from familiar country, but at the same time the speculator should know that he is betting on an entirely new district where promising surface showings may not be of any consequence. This kind of speculation involves more than the usual risks, but here, again, some approach to safeguards is available. There are few potential mineral areas in Canada which have not been mapped and reported on by government geologists. These publications can be obtained from Ottawa and the Provincial Capitals, or can be consulted at the Public Libraries of large cities. No one is qualified to pass decisive judgment after reading such reports, but there may be significant information which will help formulate intelligent judgment. The reader might be surprised to learn, for example, that many attempts have been made to develop mines in the particular district, all of them failures, due to an underlying granite which cut off and limited ore structures. There are always exceptions, of course, and this try may be different, but many informed speculators are unwilling to be guinea pigs.

As to proven areas, where mines are in active production, indiscriminate speculation can be disastrous, also. Each camp, especially as it grows in age, has certain demonstrated geological features which favor ore deposition. This is not mere guesswork, but cold fact. Usually the ores are found in definite rock types, and so effective exploration is directed toward the investigation of these strata. Such work has been carried on to an extent that the presence of a belt is well defined. A property situated far from the strike of this break must still be regarded as pure wildcat. On Bay Street, they call it being "off the main street." Nor should the speculator be misled by small-scale maps which show provocative proximity to the big mines. A mile or two can be a thousand miles as far as ore is concerned. Indeed, properties can adjoin the Noranda or Hollinger, and be as barren of mineral as the acres of Central Park, for the ore may be "going the other way."

Rule Three: Look to location.

Is the development actually new or is it a "warmed-over potato"? There are many promotions which capitalize on poor memories. Three, five, ten years elapse, and an old property is exhumed for public exhibition. There is no shaft, only ancient drilling records which have been lost in the recesses of time. A fresh drill hole or two, confirming one or two former high-grade sections with convenient skipping of blank areas and lo! the cadaver has come to life. This cannot happen, however, when there is a shaft in existence, proving beyond all doubt that extensive work has already been carried out. And yet the prospect may, for all that, be an attractive one. For, as already noted, reorganizations affect the capital structure and not the ground. As a matter of fact, the methods employed in Canadian promotion engender many incomplete developments which falter more through financial anemia than absence of ore possibilities. While this is unfortunate from many points of view, it does afford the speculator exceptional opportunities. It is doubtful, for example, whether the Kerr-Addison would have been available in 1936 if a competently financed and managed enterprise had existed twenty years before. The drifts that missed ore so narrowly could have been used as diamond drill stations, with flat horizontal holes put out at regular intervals. These would have encountered the ore beyond question. Why wasn't this done? As a matter of fact, the engineer in charge strongly urged this exact program, but the company, overpromoted and underfinanced, worked on such narrow finances that this drilling was never attempted. Instead, the property was shut down.

There are many cases analogous to Kerr-Addison, though on a smaller scale. Lack of money and professional direction, rather than lack of ore possibilities, has been the offender. Well-informed mining men and speculators have grown rich from situations of this kind, and there are enough of them at large to provide material for an interesting and profitable specialty. Many of the Red Lake mines were second and third attempts; the Giant Yellowknife was a repair job. Quemont is another prominent mine which came back from the grave. An account of similar rehabilitations would embrace a surprisingly large percentage of today's dividend payers.

Rule Four, accordingly, is scrutiny for evidence of previous development. Wherever possible, previous histories should be unearthed and evaluated.

In the embryonic stage of a mining venture, we have already noted in some detail how prolific is the promotional literature accompanying it. Most people toss these circulars into the wastebasket, but the serious speculator reads and files them assiduously, for they constitute a mining education in themselves. More than that, they provide many of the answers which less methodical speculators are constantly seeking. For in verbosity the nature of the promoter is revealed. We read, for example: "In offering you the opportunity to participate in the development of one of the outstanding prospects in this great mineralized zone, we believe we are offering you the opportunity to share in the immense profits which this district will eventually and undoubtedly yield." Whoever buys a mining stock on such representations deserves little sympathy when he loses his money and complains to the authorities. There is no information, merely a set of come-on phrases. A more adroit approach, ever more popular, is to tie in the Department of Mines to the property in question. "Maps and surveys prepared by the Ontario Department of Mines definitely record the geology of this area as possessing gold-bearing ore in enormous quantities." This is pure distortion and at once disqualifies the venture from further consideration. All government reports are confined to structural features and a detached, objective description of prospects and mines, if any are in the area.

Another favorite stratagem of a prospectus, so rich in adjectives but vague in facts, is the accentuation of high assays. These are usually from samples of the "grab" variety, that is, a selected chip or fragment of a vein which is taken as an indication, but not a measure, of value. Naturally, the best-looking material is chosen. But the circular cries forth, "samples which have averaged better than $245 per ton." Beware of such representations! Any gold mine which possesses a tonnage of $8 ore is all that anyone in Canada can desire. The African Rand, producer of almost half the world's gold, operates on a $5 to $6 ore. The Quebec field averages $6.40 per ton, which is considerably above that of Matachewan, Ontario. Porcupine averages approximately $8. Kirkland Lake is considered a high-grade camp with $12 to $15 material. The producing mines of Yellowknife treat better than $20 rock, but this is regarded as exceptional. High costs force the development and treatment of high-grade ore which, happily, the camp is blessed with. A few isolated mines, such as the Leitch, also have high-grade ore, but it is to be noted that in such cases the tonnage is comparatively small. Assays can be obtained almost anywhere in auriferous country, but tonnage is another matter. Grab samples are so common as to attract slight attention among the knowing, but to the novice they appear singularly impressive.

It is also fashionable to make half-baked references to geology. This one is almost standard: "Sketch map of the property shows rich vein system and high grade geological formation which is above the average of Yellowknife gold values. All veins pan gold. This, plus the fact that the sediments contact the granites from north and south along the east as well as the western boundaries of the property positively indicates an unusually heavy concentration of gold in this area." Exactly what does the author of this gem mean? It is hard to say. Here, indeed, is technical hocus-pocus which adds up to nothing, but is designed to trap the innocent. If the integrity of the composer of this gibberish is to be measured by his geology, the speculator can safely look elsewhere.

There are many other revealing tidbits which should serve their own warning. The promoter to avoid is one who oozes confidence and ingratiation. He "sincerely believes," and "in his candid opinion," or he "honestly feels," "frankly admits," etc. This language, in a prospectus supposed to convey information, is not only superfluous but clearly attempts to soften the reader for the kill. In the same order are the catch phrases. "Mining is safe," we are told, "the risk is in finding mines." Or, "We remove 99 per cent of the risk from prospecting and 85 per cent of the cost of financing," or, "Invest, don't speculate!" Statements of this nature insult the intelligence. A romantic appeal, also, should leave the cautious heart stony and indifferent. Enjoy the humor but ignore the call of the "prospector facing the perils of the north, this hardy soldier of progress who taps the inexhaustible wealth of the Pre-Cambrian." Above all, reject all entreaties which urge the immediate purchase of stock on the representation that the price "will absolutely be advanced one week from date."

If there is any value in a brochure it is found in the so-called engineer's report. The first precaution is to ascertain the technician's standing in the profession. There are men who lightly trade their signatures for stock options and cash fees, but there are not so many that they cannot be spotted. Reputable engineers are sometimes quoted without their knowledge or consent, but more frequently they are misrepresented by publication of only segments of their conclusions. The entire report should be submitted and not merely excerpts which may depart entirely from the general tenor of the text. Even when the requirement of a complete report is met, the answer can still be No! I quote from one of these masterpieces:

> The level from which the mine is now being worked is on a level with the mill crusher. From this level there is a face of ore exposed to a height of 200 feet. I estimate that for every 1000 feet of depth the mine will yield 4,000,000 tons of ore which at the present price of gold will bring the sum of $9,133,330. I do not know the extent of this immense dike, but it seems that a 1000 ton mill could be operated there for generations without exhausting the ore supply.

No honest engineer would attach his name to this statement. The "ore" is a far cry from commercial grade, and the language arouses a suspicion that this "engineer" received most of his education in the lecture halls and laboratories of promotional offices.

Distinguishing between a market play and a genuine development effort is possible. There are circulars which outline the project simply and with dignity, and while success is far from assured, the speculator has confidence that funds will be expended wisely. That is all he can expect.

Those inclined to gamble should divide the risk by placing funds in several ventures which have successfully passed scrutiny. It is too much to expect that one selection will prove a winner. Judicious spreading of bets, as in horse racing, increases possibilities of capturing a prize.

Rule Five: Dissect the circular or prospectus, and if examination meets various prescribed tests, purchase several, and not one, of the new offerings.

Coming to prospects which are being drilled or already have been successfully drilled, a somewhat different approach is necessary. We are no longer dealing with unproven ground, or mere surface showings. There is now an approximation of the vital third dimension, depth. In this stage, exact valuations are impossible. The prospect may or may not become a valuable mine and the size of the deposit is wide open for guesswork. "Drillers" are most difficult to appraise, and in this situation the speculator is like a man holding a bull by the tail. He does not know whether to hold on or let go. If he guesses what the bull will do he may emerge from the experience with something more than scars to exhibit. The broker, of course, takes full advantage of this uncertainty. It is at this point that markets are made in volume and with wildly fluctuating prices. A driller is the promoter's delight. With the experience of Noranda, Giant, Quemont, and others constantly drummed into his consciousness, the speculator is loath to part with his stock; he may even buy more in the expectation of an eventual competence.

A word here about drilling. In the discussion of mineral deposits, it was pointed out that a drill core of approximately one inch in diameter can be misleading in a positive or negative way. Actual widths, lengths, and grade of a deposit cannot be determined accurately until investigation takes place where the ore must be mined—underground. Surprises of all varieties await the miner. The public, lacking in experience, is often wont to exaggerate the conclusiveness of drilling. To some extent this holds true among technical men also. Those of us who were active in the field twenty years ago will not soon forget the Treadwell-Yukon fiasco. This Sudbury property received 50,000 feet of drilling and was pronounced a wonder mine, having indicated more than one billion dollars in lead-zinc-silver ore. This was not a promoter's statement, moreover. It came from the developer himself, a man heading an American organization which enjoyed well-earned distinction for a remarkable series of mining achievements. Treadwell-Yukon soared from $1 to $25 a share. Then came the rude awakening. Underground, the ore was found to consist of small lenses having limited vertical and horizontal persistence. By a strange fatality, the drills had intersected these on the nose with hardly a blank, thus creating the impression of a single enormous ore body. For a time noble efforts were made to establish some continuity and tonnage, but to no avail. Operations were finally stopped and the shares limped back to where they started—obscurity.

On the other side, however, we have a Pickle Crow. Hammell, remember, was plagued in his financing because the drilling was not positive enough. There were low as well as high assays in the cores. To overcautious minds this type of erratic drilling presented a logical out. And yet the prevailing note of Canadian gold deposition is this very unevenness of values. It is the nature of Canada as contrasted with other countries, like the African Rand, where values are amazingly consistent and regular. How, then, can a speculator apply some rule of appraisal in this difficult drilling stage?

He can do so only if he has some understanding of the districts. Noranda, where huge replacement sulphide ore bodies are known to exist, should yield fairly consistent results, and they have in the case of Quemont. Extremely erratic results there would have been definitely unfavorable. A gold vein, in this same area where the occurrences are proven to be intimately associated with pyrite mineralization, well disseminated throughout the rock, are reasonably expected to provide fairly uniform results. And at Wasa Lake Mines this happened. Such yardsticks, however, are not applicable to an entirely unproven district where comparisons cannot be made. Instead, careful averages are made to approximate the true grade, but problems arise when the gold is found in its native state and concentrated in short ore shoots alternating with completely barren sections. Too much weight should not be attached to a few inordinately high assays, but if there is an abundance of these rich spots, an over-all commercial grade of ore is entirely possible, as proven in other districts where similar deposits are being profitably mined.

It is to be imagined, and rightly so, that brokers take every advantage of the situation when drilling has clicked. Speculators may be uncertain but he is not; this is his big moment. He now directs every effort at his disposal to drive the stock upward, meanwhile "laying off" his inexpensive option shares. He strives for a position which will at once place him in complete safety. Let us eavesdrop in a broker's sanctum just after thrilling news has been flashed down from Atlas Mines, "Hole R 16 encountered 12 feet true width assaying $11.55. Full report in mail follows."

I introduce Gus Miller, one-time minor league baseball player who is today a Bay Street magnate financing seven different mining ventures. Seven is his lucky number, so he is not surprised when Atlas clicks. He is a thin wiry man in his early fifties, partially bald, and with dark eyes that stare fixedly. An old hand, he has a rule which he has never been known to break: "Never get sold on your own stocks." Now that Atlas has reported its first positive drill hole, the thin man swings into action. On a littered desk before him stands a veritable battery of telephones, but as they ring he has the uncanny faculty of picking the right one, no mean accomplishment in this forest of instruments. As we look, he snatches at a receiver with rapierlike quickness, at the same time tucking two others under his armpits; his elbows are prehensile.

"What's Atlas?" His voice is unexpectedly deep and hoarse. "Last quote. It is? Well, make 'er 24 to 26."

He seizes another telephone, bends low and whispers in order to be unheard by unseen interlocutors impatiently awaiting answers at the end of other lines. They are, of course, completely unaware that they rest in Miller's tense armpits.

"Birks offering? Much? Well, take it, dope! Take it. Hafter tell you what to do? Take it and make 'er 30 to 32." And then, talking under his shoulder, "Yup, Gus. 'Lo, Harry. Yes, sir. Real stuff, no malarkey—$12 over 11 feet an' wide open. Sue me if it ain't right. How much? Okay. You bought 10,000 at 30. What? Best I can do." He scribbles on a pad with difficulty, for he is swamped with appending telephones. "S'long. Come back later. . . ." He speaks at his left armpit. "That you, Wes? Yeah, I know. All busy. You still got your Atlas? Well, don't sell. All I can tell you now. Don't sell. . . . 'Lo? That you, Joe? Quote me Atlas. 32 to 4? Make it 4 to 6. Yeah. No, no. Wait a minute. Call it 35 to 9. Right, 36 to 9."

He deftly switches to a new receiver while loud, vain noises issue from telephones in suspense.

" 'Lo, Doc. Get yourself some Atlas. Yeah. Hit big. Fourteen dollars over 12 feet. Sure. How much? Sure, sure. Have to pay 36. All right, all right, 35, but don't you go throwing it back at me. Okay, 5,000." And then, with repressed excitement into his armpit again, "Sorry, Jack. Hold on a minute. Be right with you." He inclines toward a loudspeaker, flipping the switch. "Helen, get me Cole in Montreal!" Back to his armpit. "You there, Jack? Sure. Best I can do is 37." Lights flash on his desk. This is urgent. "Just a minute, Jack. 'Lo, Jim? Who's offering it? Bright? How much? Looks like a short to you? So what? Take it at 34. Call me back." Then, over the loudspeaker in raucous tones, "Mr. Cole of Montreal on the wire." Pausing a moment to gulp down a glass of milk, Gus sputters at a fresh telephone: "Bill? Well, we hit. Sure. Twelve dollars over fourteen feet. Not yet, coming down tonight. Oh, getting started. Lost about 30,000 so far. We're 70,000 short already. Not bad, eh? Well, get busy over there. Send you copy of the report when it comes in. Okay." Returning to the nest of telephones: "Frank? Lissen, seven phones going all at once. Oh, you did, did you! Maybe not that good, boy, but good enough. Yeah. Eleven dollars over fourteen feet or something. Sure it's the real thing. Did I ever steer you wrong? 10,000? That's a lot of stock; she's going up to a buck on this move. You'll haveta pay 40 for it. Best I can do. Hold a minute. Hold a minute." His head darts to a corner of the desk. "Joe, how's it going? Good, good, buying from the north, eh?" Back to Frank now. "Listen, orders coming down from the north. All the miners, everyone's buying. Better grab it. Okay, 10,000 at 40. You'll make enough for that Florida trip."

The day wears on but Gus does not budge from his desk. No corps of smooth-tongued salesmen here. Gus runs his own show. The tide of fortune swings this way and that, but the stock forges ahead steadily. A rumor in the late afternoon begins to circulate. Noranda is reported to be a heavy buyer! Gus sends frantic messages to his key men, "See who's going for that stock." The story is discredited; Atlas is offered in large lots, but Gus, like a cool general under fire, keeps the market orderly and repurchases some of his earlier sales at lower prices. More rumors circulate; a well-known engineer has looked at Atlas and pronounced it an outstanding bet. Fresh demand for the stock has Gus circulating among his telephones like an active minnow. He closes the market at 65 to 67, and rushes to the golf course where more trades, of a private nature, will be made while all Toronto buzzes with the newest drilling sensation.

Atlas, in the course of weeks, becomes the bellwether of mining stocks. Additional drill holes return fair values and substantial widths of ore. The stock is listed on the Exchange and becomes one of the active traders. Many who have sold out too quickly re-enter the market and purchase the stock at $1.50. When the company is fully financed for underground work, a shaft is announced, and frenzied buying moves the quotations above the $3 mark. Atlas is now beyond the wildcat stage.

The enterprise, as anticipated by shrewd observers, begins to slip into something resembling a vacuum. There is no fresh news to maintain the excited tempo of the drive. The hypodermic has been injected too often, and now comes the aftermath. The stock becomes sluggish. It will be months before underground news will be forthcoming and meanwhile opinions, both favorable and unfavorable, are freely expressed. There are doubts about the quality of drilling and the accuracy of the assays, and nothing can be done to dispel them until the shaft has been completed and lateral work is in progress. But while stockholders may be worried, Gus Miller is not. He is sitting on a large cushion, comfortably short of stock. Funds are on hand; neither he nor the company can suffer at this point. When, finally, the shaft has reached the first objective of 500 feet, stations are cut on three levels and crosscuts begin to crawl toward the debated ore zone. The stock acts nervous, is traded in volume again, but this time minus signs are more frequent than the plus. A statement is made; Atlas is in the news again.

> The company reports excellent progress of the 500-foot level where work is now being confined, due to shortage of miners. The crosscut has been driven 96 feet and at the present rate should encounter the ore zone within two weeks.

The two weeks pass without further announcement. A number of stockholders decide to take their cash. Once again prices recede. Gus telephones the mine manager and is informed of an unexpected watercourse encountered on the level. Nothing serious, but several drill rounds have been lost while the damaging cracks in the rock are being cemented. Ore should be hit within another week. Gus immediately circulates word around the Street, big things are about to happen.

The eagerly anticipated intelligence arrives at last: $7.70 ore has been cut across eleven feet and drift headings have been started east and west. To many these results are something of a disappointment; to others, more discerning, there is now more positive likelihood of a mine. The grade, while something less than the drilling average, leaves a fair margin of profit. Providing there is sufficient ore, Atlas will develop into a producer, especially since it is located in Rouyn where mines are in operation. But public sentiment, whipped up to hopes of better things, suffers a pronounced relapse. Atlas is no longer a favorite. Sights, once too high, are drastically lowered. The time has come when paper, pencil, and a bit of simple arithmetic replace mere expectations.

Drilling has indicated an ore shoot 1,200 feet long, 9 feet wide, and $8.50 grade. The length will probably be substantiated, but a safer grade, allowing for dilution caused by unavoidable breaking of waste rock with the ore when actual mining operations are begun, would be $7. A 10-foot width is reasonable to expect on the basis of information to date. This would give Atlas an ore potential of 1,000 tons per foot of depth, since ore of this kind is computed at 12 cubic feet to the ton

$$\frac{(1200 \times 10}{12} = 1000).$$

Costs of, say, $5 per ton, usual in the district, means a profit of $2. With a 500-ton mill, one-half the estimated tonnage per foot of depth, there would be an annual operating profit of $352,000, or 12 cents for each of the 3,000,000 shares issued. The deposit should extend to the 1,000-foot horizon and below—again making comparisons with other Rouyn mines.

Proving that many such computations are being made, Atlas stock gradually stabilizes at around the dollar mark, there to hover for some time until events more conclusively prove the intrinsic value of the property.

Atlas does not actually work out in this fashion, of course. More commonly the drilling is inconclusive or poor and the property is abandoned by Gus Miller, who has undoubtedly unearthed more profitable business elsewhere. And the one-time stock favorite becomes another teaser which may or may not be revived later by surer hands than Miller's. But what of the speculator? How does he fare through all this?

Familiarity with the Canadian scene leads to one inescapable conclusion regarding drillers: they achieve market levels far above those which obtain after the property becomes a producing mine. There are exceptions, but not many. A driller is valued by men like Gus Miller at a time when many factors are unknown. But as more exact appraisal becomes possible as underground work progresses, the stock may be calculated with greater exactness. Therefore, I submit Rule Six, which is preached by many and followed by few, but is none the less a good one: Sell one-half of the stock and retain the balance against future events. Capital is preserved regardless of consequences, and, if a mine results, the speculator has little cause for regret. This combines the wisdom of Agricola, Baron Rothschild, and George Baker.

The producing mine is close to an investment, but not quite. Ore is a wasting asset. It must be replaced faster than it is extracted; otherwise the operation is in peril. Those seeking the comparative safety of mines gravitate toward dividend payers. The real nub of any situation, however, lies in the ore reserves; a dividend may represent partial liquidation in consequence of failing ore. The stockholder, fortunately, has access to annual reports which should, and usually do, contain pertinent information. Possibilities of increased tonnage should be noted, particularly with respect to gold mines which rarely show more than five years' reserves. In this respect, figures can be entirely misleading. The generally erratic and uneven gold distribution in northern ore deposits renders development of ore costly, and most producers, especially the younger ones which are just emerging from the long expensive period of mine making, wisely defer this task until such time as the company is on a sounder financial and physical position. Speculators conditioned to large published ore reserves, such as the Homestake with twenty years' life assured underground, mistakenly conclude that the Canadians overvalue their gold mines. This attitude stems from lack of familiarity with the field.

The first gold mine I ever visited was the mighty Lake Shore in the summer of 1922. It was a humble beginner then, equipped with a mill treating less than 100 tons daily. Bob Coffey, who conducted Robert and me underground, emphasized the unusual regularity of the since famous No. 2 vein. The mine was less than 1,000 feet deep and millfeed was being derived largely from development drifts, that is, openings along the vein which test new ground for ore. So wide was the ore shoot, and rich too, that the mine was literally feeding itself on exploratory work, a phenomenal situation in mining. In the accepted sense of the word, there were no ore reserves of any consequence. A hard-boiled engineer, judging the mine entirely on blocked-out ore, would have turned Lake Shore down cold. As a matter of fact, this is exactly what happened. But to us, unprejudiced by experience in other mining camps, the possibilities of large tonnage seemed extraordinarily good. Robert, months later, conveyed his thoughts to one of his old professors at Harvard, describing Lake Shore as a potential bonanza.

"You are young," he was told. "When you have been out in the field several years you will recognize the impossibility of the conditions you describe. There just cannot be a Canadian gold mine as good as Lake Shore."

Nor were attempts to interest smart money any more effective. The north was still young; the aftermath of war had retarded and obscured the rise of gold mining. And for some unaccountable reason, few engineers considered a trip to Kirkland Lake worth while. But later, when Lake Shore was treating 2,500 tons of ore daily, and in a single year paid $12,000,000 in dividends, the once-scorned "Jewel Box of America" was the subject of learned dissertations and articles. And, to date, the property has mined 12,000,000 tons and is still going strong. This was a lesson in mine valuation we could never learn in college.

All the senior gold mines started life as infants, an elemental fact which is often overlooked. The initial tonnages milled in Porcupine were small, but they grew enormously. McIntyre's 100 tons daily expanded to 2,500 tons, and ore reserves, negligible at first, now stand at 4,000,000 tons, this after treating more than 16,000,000 since 1912. The Hollinger, though more ore was in evidence, began to produce even more modestly. Starting with a two-ton stamp mill, it is now handling 5,000 tons each day, and despite extraction of 44,300,000 tons since 1912, this proud leader has current ore reserves of 8,000,000 tons. Dome, too, increased from 300 to 1,750 tons daily, and has a 3,000,000-ton reserve after producing 14,778,000 tons in the past thirty-five years.

And, speaking of Dome, it was just twenty years ago that a standard Wall Street publication warned that the company was short of ore and dividends must be considered as a final liquidation of a once-splendid enterprise. Faint hope was held out for the Howey Mine, then under option to Dome, but when the management relinquished the option and withdrew from Red Lake, Dome, by every rule and precedent, should have passed into the limbo of forgotten things. But the expert on mine valuation was confounded and Dome dispensed with the services of an undertaker. Circumstances beyond the vision of a mere mortal—the imponderables—completely altered the situation. The increased gold price, the acquisition of the Schumacker and Sigma properties, and a parent mine in Porcupine which responded to intelligent exploration enabled Dome to distribute $53,000,000 in dividends, $27 per share, since the requiem was sounded, and the stock has risen 500 per cent in value during that time. The mine, too, is in better shape now than at any other moment in its long and lucrative history.

I also recall the ridicule heaped upon Albert Wende in Kirkland Lake when he decided to construct a mill at the Wright-Hargreaves Mine. Production began in 1922, and one year later town gossips described the venture as Wende's Folly and the "mill without a mine." Notwithstanding, Wende became something of a prophet: Kirkland Lake proved to be the kind of camp that heaped reward upon courage. More than 6,000,000 tons of ore have been developed and treated at the mill to date, and a production exceeding $100,000,000, with a dividend record of $43,000,000, is a record which not many gold mines can hope to equal anywhere. Here, as in so many other cases, conventional valuation formulas missed the target completely.

As might be expected, such experiences have added to the complexities of the situation. The effects of Porcupine and Kirkland Lake have actually been harmful, causing operators and speculators alike to regard every prospect as an incipient big elephant. But in my own time I have witnessed the gradual emergence of sanity from immodest expectations. The Canadian mining world has come to realize that all gold mines need not be Hollingers or Lake Shores to be profitable. And so today there is a healthier and more balanced attitude throughout the industry—contentedness with a 100-ton producer which offers reasonable hope of expansion with fewer failures arising from overpowering ambition to emulate the seniors.

These remarks apply to gold mines exclusively. When we confront base metals, estimates must be revised, for large tonnages are first necessary before the staggering capital outlays can be justified. Hudson Bay Mining & Smelting had almost 20,000,000 tons of ore in sight before production began. Noranda, however, was the exception that proved the rule. With only 1,000,000 tons initially, the company dared to equip for production, and this step accounted for the extremely speculative quality of the venture in its early stages. On the plus side there was the conviction that large sulphide ore bodies in the Pre-Cambrian could be expected to repeat, Sudbury, Ontario, being a healthy precedent to follow. Noranda ventured and won. After mining 27,000,000 tons of ore since 1927, the Horne still has more than 20,000,000 in reserve, with ore expectations by no means exhausted.

Ore, then, makes the mine, and the mine, in turn, sets the value of the stock. Rule Seven: Look to ore reserves but do not neglect ore expectations. Read annual reports greedily and do not become complacent through prosperity.

There are minor, but still important, factors which I shall only mention here. Production, like freedom, is not only a goal to attain, but it must be fought for and maintained. There are enemies to guard against, dilution which reduces ore grade, metallurgical problems which might appear unexpectedly with changing ore character in depth. Imponderables cannot be anticipated but they should be regarded as possibilities. Surface caving and filling of the Beattie Mine with several million tons of mud and debris cut heavily into profit. Two years of effort and expense went into clearing of the underground workings, necessitating heavy loans, cessation of dividends, and an increase in capitalization. Mines also suffer from water coming in to force suspension of work and installation of new and costly pumping equipment. Or there are geological changes, such as faults, which may cut off ore entirely or require long exploration work to solve. A good speculator must be on his toes continually.

The mature and seasoned speculator should be a man conversant with world affairs, especially today when metals are creatures of price and currency controls. Mining does not live in an ivory tower. It is a vital part of everyday life, inextricably interwoven with the affairs of men. To be well informed is to be well armed against the contingencies of an uncertain future. Worldliness, in addition to making better people, makes better speculators.

It is fashionable among certain elements of our complex society to describe promotion and speculation as parasitical and destructive. "Fellow travelers" are as tireless in their attacks as their vocal cords are indestructible. The vital necessity of venture capital to a speculative industry is overlooked, nay, it is castigated as proof of a decadent social system rapidly consuming itself with greed and rapine. Sincere or designing, these zealots wholeheartedly advocate state socialism, with production for use and not for profit. Mines, they contend, should be developed and operated by the people through their government.

I do not intend to propound a defense of capitalism; others are far better equipped for the task. But the reader may be curious to know where I stand on the issue of state operation of mines. At the risk of sneering abuse, I will say that, while I am aware of the iniquities and shortcomings that beset private enterprise, our form of society is far more effective in productiveness than the collectivism forced upon other less fortunate countries. Cruelty, stupidity, and ruthlessness are confined to no one creed or social-political philosophy, but to the individual there must, or should, be compensations, such as a semblance of liberty and free expression, and, above all, human dignity. This I did not find in Russia. And since I am writing of mining, I may say that I did find a shocking inefficiency in Russia's mining operations and organizations such as would never be tolerated in Canada or the United States. Interestingly enough, the Kremlin, after a study of American methods, instigated a bonus system for ore discovery and metal production, an appeal to private gain which is an admission of the state's inadequacies and a complete surrender to individualism. Apologists are quick to point out that this is in the nature of a temporary truce while Russia strives for pure communism, but to me such explanations are rather hollow.

The fact remains that Russia's mineral production, despite all palliatives and "liquidations," has lagged woefully behind the country's undoubted large potentialities. Canada stands out in welcome contrast, its mining industry reaching new heights of achievement yearly. And in elevating itself to a great and enviable position, truly a model for the rest of the world to follow, Canada is indebted to promotion and speculation which are possible only in a society of free men.

With this digression, I present the reader to a man who never received any technical training, and yet has amassed a fortune in "penny" stocks. He is calm, almost shy, as he sits and faces me, belying his incredible record of speculative acumen.

"It's work, hard work," he confesses. "Yes, sir. I visit the properties if I can; if not, I send up a geologist. Costs money, but it's cheap in the end. However"—and he smiles—"I make the decisions. I read mining publications and subscribe to Jim Eakins' Mining Evaluation Service in Noranda. What I want is the facts. Engineers know too much, like doctors who recognize symptoms of all the diseases. Me, I just need to know enough. The ore's the thing, every time. Brokers can rig stock prices but what keeps 'em up is ore, or a good chance of finding it. Booms are fine; they give money to wildcats and make work possible. But there must be results; they can't be manufactured. I rarely buy during a boom. That's the time to get out, I say. I believe in taking positions in dull times when most people are not interested."

I ask if he holds stocks for any length of time.

"You bet I do," he replies warmly. "When there's ore. Keep coming back to that, ore. No one can steal it from you when it's in the ground. Oh, I've taken my duckings now and again, especially when I was green at the game, but I've learned to stick with values. And I'm not above visiting company offices and chatting with the boys. That tells me a lot. If they're fly-by-nighters, I sell or stay out; I don't like that kind to spend my money. Once or twice I've lost by passing up such situations, but I believe I've saved money in the long run by this policy. In the long run," he repeats. "That's mining. Time, time, you've got to be patient. That's the trouble with most people, they want fast profits. Well, they find 'em, all right, but the losses are just as quick, maybe quicker."

"How about diversification?"

"The only method," he answers immediately. "I always spread my shots. I take a certain percentage of wildcat stuff along with development properties and producers. Remember, you only need a single good one to beat the game. And I take my chances on backing men too. Don't go overboard, though, because time changes people. They might become greedy and with greed comes bad judgment."

"And the little fellows, with a hundred or two, who cannot afford to send engineers for reports. How about them?" I ask.

"Oh," he chuckled, "they come in only during the booms. Speculation is just like a sweepstakes to them. Sure, they lose, but some of 'em win, and if they stay at it long enough they'll learn the ropes. It's tips that do the great harm. Myself, I never listen to that stuff; I figure that rumors are spread for a purpose. Nor do I give out any information. Used to, but found I lost friends that way. If they win, they're smart and I'm forgotten. If they lose, I'm a heel who profited at their expense. So I mind my own business. I'm learning all the time too, and that's what makes speculation so stimulating. For instance, I keep in touch with depth operations and note how they affect costs. And I've been careful about trends too. Inflation is bad for gold mines, what with more expensive labor and supplies while the price of gold remains the same. Deflation time is gold time for me. And then I never hold a stock unless I consider it's still worth buying. You see, I don't trade on market psychology; it leaves you at the mercy of other people. It's easy to figure when a stock is cheap, but that's a small part of the game. You must know when it's too high, and there's the nub of speculation, knowing when to sell."

And how, I ask, can that moment be determined?

"Instinct, I would say." His eyebrows arched. "Can't tell what it is exactly, part hunch and part experience. I try not to be too hungry, for that sort of thing, I've found, defeats a man. You just can't buy at the bottom of the curve and sell at the top. Somewhere in between the two extremes is all anyone can expect. There are so many things to watch—outside exploration, which makes an old company young, changes of management, new finds. I read everything I can lay my hands on; you can't go wrong in Canada where there's so much about mining being published. Sure, I've had my losses, but who hasn't? That's life, my boy. You accept the gains and place the mistakes on the experience side of the ledger. But, win or lose, speculation is far more sensible than gambling at cards or on horses. The money, or some part of it, is put to some useful purpose."

And regulation by a Securities Commission. Does he approve?

"Well," he drawls, "a certain amount is necessary, but the danger is it may go too far. The greatest protection a man can find is within himself. To my mind, education in mining is wiser than all the legislation in the world. If a speculator can't learn the fundamentals of the industry he ought to pay others trained in the business. Regulation or not, speculation will always be necessary. Without it, mining would wither away. Regardless of individual ups and downs, speculation directs capital to the proper place, where everything comes from and goes to in the end—the ground."

Johnny Dillon Again

The coral waxes, the palm tree grows, but man departs.
Old Tahitian proverb

We paused at the shaft while the shift boss telephoned the hoistman at surface. Overhead cold water dripped, splashed gently on our hard-boiled hats. The smell of carbide bit into our nostrils with sharp comfort, and the muffled roar of distant rock drills gave life to the semidarkness. It was good to be underground again.

" 'Bout fifteen minutes?" asked Johnny.

"Yup, 'bout that." The wet, brown tailor-made cigarette danced jerkily about the lips of the shift boss as he spoke. "Loadin' steel on the second."

"Okay, Jim." Johnny turned to me, wiping his glistening neck with a grimy hand. "C'mon, laddie, rest your weary arse, as ole Klondike Jess'd say." He let himself down gently on a pile of creosoted stulls, then produced the inevitable cigar.

"Have one?" he offered.

Smiling in negation, I waved my pipe.

"Ole Sherlock Holmes hisself." He removed his hat and grinned. It was the same old golden smile, but a shade more wrinkled now. The miner's hat had pressed deeply into his forehead, leaving an angry red line. He was becoming quite bald, I saw, but the twinkle in his eye was as bright as ever. He rubbed his chin lazily.

"Some show, ain't it?"

Yes, Johnny, quite a show. You've come a long way from that happy afternoon in Jimmy Green's Hotel when you argued about cabbages and straight time.

"Yeah, she's all right, all right." He sucked at the big cigar until it glowed like a beacon. "Twelve hun'red feet in good ore on the fift' level an' seven nice drill holes below us."

Under the lake too, I reminded him.

"Yes, sir," he agreed quickly. " 'At's the place to look for 'em, where the country's low. Funny how we all of us use' to go after the outcrops when most o' the mines is under swamps an' lakes. Took time to learn, but guess I been lucky, jest like Harry Oakes."

Not entirely, Johnny; you worked for years, don't forget, when lesser men found reason enough to quit the bush.

"Sure, I worked hard. But so has a lot o' the boys, an' they ain't found so much." He drew in his breath lugubriously. "S'pose I oughter be gettin' a big kick outer this"—and he waved a hand toward the obscurity of the level heading. "Been dreamin' all my life, I have, about gettin' a mine, an' now as I have it . . . well, I dunno, it jest ain't what I thought it'd be. You understan'?"

Yes, I think I do, Johnny. The gold is in the seeking, and only those like you, who are fortunate enough to gain a mine, are overcome with the helplessness of disillusionment. And that is why men continue to seek, for in the search, and not in discovery, is there any fulfillment. It explains so much, Johnny—the quick dissipation of fortunes, the extravagances of many mine finders and prospectors when they strike pay dirt, as though they are eager to lose everything in order to return to the bush, their only true love.

"You put it good, real good," and he nodded several times. "But," he added with conviction, "I ain't throwin' anythin' away at my time o' life. No, sir. Too old for that, an' there's my fam'ly, remember. But what you say has a lot o' trut', on'y there's somethin' to this business o' diggin' up a mine. It ain't the money, exac'ly; it's more in the satisfaction you get, bein' a real part o' the big picture, makin' Canader the country she is. You must admit that, laddie."

I do, I do, indeed.

"Awright." He slapped my back affectionately. "Now you an' Bob go out an' find your own mine. You're about due, I'd say. An' forget all about this here diss'lution, dislocation, or whatever you call it. Jest let yourself have the feel o' walkin' over your own property."

Disillusion, Johnny. But shall we do a bit of reckoning? You've been at the game since Cobalt in 1904, roaming the bush and watching mines spring up all round you. So it's been a cool matter of forty-two years before you captured a prize and earned the right to travel along drifts and ride the cage of your own mine. A few more years for us, then, I venture to say?

"Sound discouraged." Johnny spat toward the shaft. "Don't go gettin' the crud, d'ya hear? You lads keep punchin' and you'll hit Lady Luck right on the kisser. I know, I see it happen. They's mines all over this country, but it takes stout lads to find an' make 'em. Me, I done my bit awready, an' so has Bob Jowsey, Jack Hammell, an' the rest o' the ole-timers. Now it's up to you gaffers to take over the job, or elset where in hell will Canader be, tell me?" He swung his shoulders belligerently. "I'm gonna talk to you like a Dutch uncle. You ferget that there philosophy of yourn an' get busy. They's plenty to do, plenty. You ain't a Canadian, sure, I know, but you been up here long enough to be one of us. An' do I have to tell you we'd go to pot in Canader if it wassen for minin'? Sure, it's growed but it hasta grow faster yet if we expec' to keep up with the world."

Johnny waxed enthusiastic as he sketched a deft and comprehensive summary of Canadian mining. Mining furnished the incentive to push back frontiers, and this expansion allowed the "weak sisters" to come north.

"Sure, them city people stick to shops an' offices forever if we diden show 'em the way to better life in the north. But Gawd knows we need more up here an' the way to get 'em is to encourage minin'. If them damn fools in Ottawa had any sense they'd lead the way instead of havin' us on their tails all the time, beggin' for roads an' the like. They should cut down on the taxes too, an' we'll find 'em more stuff they can tax so they'd have more in the end, an' all the time we'd be goin' places faster. Why, the gover'ment takes more outer this country than it puts in. Now, that ain't fair and it ain't smart. They're bitin' off their own noses. We've proved the north kin be settled, haven' we? Lookit the cities, Timmins, Kirkland, Yellowknife, this place; us fellers made 'em possible. This ain't like the American West you talk about. Them lads reached the coast an' sat down when they was nothin' left for 'em to do. We're different; they's still a healthy chunk o' north left. You listenin'?"

I am, and very attentively too.

He lit a fresh cigar and continued to expound his considerable views. He now turned to the liberality of mining laws, which made no distinctions of nationality in eligibility to stake claims.

"That's somethin'. Not like them bloody Limeys." Johnny was on his favorite subject now. "Not them. They must have concessions for themselves, gobblin' up whole countries like Africa an' Asia with fences to keep ev'ryone elset out. They're gentlemen, y'see, an' the rest of us is roughnecks. Well, sir, damn hogs would better describe 'em. They haven' pulled their tricks in Canader, neither. An' they never will. We give ev'ryone the same chances, an' 'at's a novelty these days when monkeys all over the world is yellin' for their own gover'ment so's they can keep foreigners out."

The shift boss interrupted.

"Surface says it'll be another few minutes before that steel is loaded."

"No hurry," Johnny reassured him as he settled back comfortably. "We kin wait. Now," to me, "what was I shootin' off about, annyway?"

When I reminded him, he pointed out the inconsistency between the mining policy, which welcomed all comers, and the rigid immigration laws, which excluded them save for a pitifully small quota.

"We should open the doors wide, that's what." He banged his fist against a stull. "I'm Catholic, but I can't see this idee of the French in Kebec teamin' up with them Tories who carries on like Canader's goin' to be invaded. Hell, they's all kinds o' room an' we need all the workers we kin get. What is it, eleven million in Canader?"

When I informed him the population was nearer twelve million, he became sarcastic.

"Twelve, is it! Ain't that somethin'? Shoulden we be happy now, to have as many people as Czechoslovakia an' fifty times the space! Hell, man, we should have somethin' near the States. How did you Americans get where you are, if not by lettin' them poor devils in Europe have a chance? Sure, let 'em come, the good ones annyway, who appreciate what we give 'em an' wants to work. You agree?"

Yes, I agree. In a sick and dispirited world, Canada could offer hope and comfort, situated as it is with more than 3,500,000 square miles of land, most of it untenanted. There are selfish reasons, too, for lowering the iron gates; with a larger population Canada would not be dependent on continued large exports, certainly a dangerous dependence in these times of international stress. Greater domestic consumption to absorb a growing productiveness could take place within national boundaries and no one's toes would be stepped upon.

"You shoulda been a politician," said Johnny admiringly. "Annyway, them's my sentiments too. What I can't get through my noodle is this; in a war we'll do annythin', build armies an' navies an' send food we need ourselves to them poor starvin' English who always has their hands out, an' pour all our metals into the common pot, an' all the rest. You know. Take that Canol Projec', f'r instance. They spent millions, built 'er in record time, and now what? Jest read the other day they'll let 'er grow into bush again. Now that don't make sense to me. If that's one good thing comin' outer this war, I say, keep 'er. It's somethin' to be proud of, for it helps to produce an' not tear down."

I have underestimated you, Johnny, and owe you an apology. But at the same time, you should remember that human chemistry has never been satisfactorily analyzed. Man is a suspicious animal; he prefers the hard to the easy, rational way of doing things.

"Gettin' deep again." Johnny shook his head disapprovingly. "People jest don't use the brains God give 'em. Now, if I was runnin' the show (how I wish you were, Johnny!), mining'd come first in Canader. Not because I'm in the business, neither, but because 'at's where the future is. Sure! We fellers has made this country what it is an' without almos' no help, too. But the job's gettin' big, too big for bushwhackers. The lads sittin' at them fancy conference tables an' spoutin' about the gold standard, trade, an' all that high-soundin' talk, now they done a hell of a lot to make them things possible, diden they? Like hell they did! Laddie, we're carryin' all them stuffed shirts on our backs like the Ole Man o' the Sea, an' no tumpline, either! An' if we ask for a spot o' help to lighten the load, all we get is more talkin' by them baboons. Pah!" He spat in anger. "We should be havin' roads without the beggin' an' whinin', power dams, decent metal prices an' so fort'. If the fatheads down below don't wise up an' stop snipin' at the golden goose, well, sir, there won't be no golden eggs much longer. Canader will lose the big chance an' become jest about as important as one o' them Balkan countries, up Dung Creek without a paddle."

Strong words, Johnny.

"So what?" He grinned, and even in the half-light I caught the gleam of gold. "I'm talkin' to a frien', ain't I? Not goin' to report me to teacher, are you?" he taunted.

I promised to be discreet.

"You're a good lad," he said with sudden sobriety. "Y'know, I kinder hate to step outer the picture jest when people outside is beginnin' to realize we have a nice little minin' country here. I sure would like to stick aroun' an' see the fun, doncher know?"

You'll be here, seeing the fun, for a long while yet.

"Not too sure." A weary note crept into his voice. "Gettin' old, laddie, gettin' old. The ticker ain't what it used to be. The doc says I hafter take 'er easy, an' so I'm fattenin' up like a hog. Can't move aroun' like in the early days." His eye brightened. "You knew me then. Don't hafter tell you I could hoist a pack with the best Gawd-damn men in the north, an' without usin' no tumpline, either. Yeah, sure. But I've slowed down to a walk. I ain't kiddin' meself." He toyed with the ashes of his cigar thoughtfully.

Before I could protest, a sudden rush of cold air from the shaft, accompanied by a warning rattle of cable, announced that the cage was fast approaching the level. Without a word Johnny and I rose and stretched our cramped limbs. Johnny yawned prodigiously, then said:

"We had a nice bull session, laddie, the best."

"Here she comes!" sang the shift boss.

The wet, glittering cage, exuding a tangy odor of carbide, dropped into view abruptly and we stepped toward the gate. Waiting for the springy cable to cease motion until the cage floor steadied flush with the level, the cageman, whistling a lively air, opened the gate bar to admit us. Dutifully, we extinguished our lights and reached for the handrail above. Outside, his fingers on the signal cord, the shift boss called forth sharply:

"Surface, Johnny!"

"Surface!" repeated Johnny, and the signal grunted briefly, like a hoarse telegraph key. We hurtled upward instantly, the cage grazing wooden shaft rails at quick, rattling intervals. Levels sped by us, mere blurs of light, and presently the warm glow of sunlight was in our eyes.

"Nice, wassen it?" said Johnny, as we walked from the shaft house and unscrewed our lamps to rid them of water and dump the remaining carbide on a screen receptacle. "Always enjoy goin' down 'at hole."

I stopped to scan the countryside that spread below us. Head-frames stood out in prominent relief, and in the background, hanging lazily above the settlement like a huge comforter, rose the umbrella-shaped smoke of the Noranda smelter. The adjoining cities of Rouyn and Noranda huddled together along the lake shore and pushed growing tendrils of life into the back country where occasional patches of green and brown denoted farms and pasturelands, grimly won from an inhospitable bush by ever-toiling habitants. Cutting in from the west, so far away as to seem a toy, a long train pushed over a winding roadbed, emitting faint nostalgic whistles while it moved closer to home. The landscape was depressingly bare, shaved by constant timbering and further depleted by fire. Dirty groups of birch stumps, leaning at weird angles or fallen into heaps, were all that remained of a once-lush forest. Even the lake seemed melancholy in its sparse reflections.

Johnny lounged beside me.

"Quite a sight, ain't it?" he observed. "You'd hardly know the ole place." He laughed shortly. "Wonder what Klondike Jess, an' Slim Hallowell, an' the rest o' the gang'd think? S'pose they wooden like 'er much."

I nodded agreement.

"Yeah, she's sober an' quiet nowadays. Too towned."

But this is progress, Johnny, I reminded him; the march of civilization about which you were so eloquent.

"Yeah, that's right." He scratched his head in a gesture of doubt. "It's jest what we all wanted to see, smoke, choo-choo trains an' all. But even so, I think . . . I'd like to say . . ."—and his voice trailed incoherently.

Shall I speak for you, Johnny, and articulate what you feel so keenly? Yes? This, then; the advance we all herald, the onward step, but leads us into a world where we find ourselves strangers, with only the slightest of threads holding us to the familiar security of the past. That is why, when you gaze at this bleak panorama, your thoughts tumble back to Klondike, Slim, and those you used to know, for they are symbols of a time when your feet trod surer ground. It is the secret, too, of deep northern friendships and accounts for the special sadness when one of our number passes, for we then have brought home to us how closer we are to the day when we shall stand alone, with nothing but weakening memories. This, Johnny, is the price of our pioneering, and it has been paid by an army of good men before us.

Johnny only nodded, and we were silent for a long period, each of us wrapped in thoughts of his own.

The harsh honking of a car, as from another planet, roused us.

"Our taxi," said Johnny heavily. "It's here." He made an effort, held up his watch with something of his accustomed verve. "On the dot, an' that's somethin' in Kebec. C'mon, laddie, before you have me weepin' on your shoulder. I'm gonna buy you a real meal at the hotel."

Johnny tried to be noisily jocular and cheerful during lunch, but the usual braggadocio and tartness were conspicuously absent. The snow-white linen, the excellent menu, and the efficient, deferential waitress had a peculiar effect of unreality on us both, immersed as we were in recollections of the rough, early days. We hardly exchanged a word, and yet, more than ever, there was warm understanding and communication between us.

"Good food, Johnny," I ventured finally.

"Yeah, the chuck's tops here. Wait till you try some o' the beefsteak, though. Best medicine in the world." But my friend lacked his old vigor in speaking of victuals.

We completed the meal in silence.

In the lobby we parted, Johnny to confer with his engineers about mill plans and I, still deep in a mood of retrospection, to visit Rouyn town. As I skirted Osisko's shore, I thought of a morning I watched a moose luxuriating among the lily pads not far from Gamble's Point. Since that time, the banks of the lake have been manicured into an attractive park by the diligent Noranda management. Flowering shrubs, rock gardens, and benches dotted the way. A French couple, gurgling endearments, stopped to eye me curiously as I slowly strolled toward the large hospital at the turn of the path. Behind, where the old Lake Fortune winter road once made its sodden entrance into town, now loomed the race track and recreation grounds, deserted and silent. Autos whizzed by, driven by gay, careless youngsters delighting in the novelty of paved roads. And then, with a start, I realized that Rouyn was before me.

The older community, in striking contrast to the subdued atmosphere of Noranda, exuded noisy bustle and warmth. Beer parlors gave forth heavy smells and juke-box strains, while hurrying residents streamed in and out of shops. Lively neighbors gossiped from open windows, unmindful of their numerous progeny frolicking shrilly in the muddy streets. Cinema marquees were ablaze with Greer Garson's newest interpretation of middle-class nobility, and store display windows fought for attention with sparkling jewelry and resplendent women's wear. Overcome with the strangeness of it all, I halted before a barbershop and gazed about me.

No more Jimmy Green's Hotel. In its stead rose an ugly stucco office building decorated with "avocat" and "dentiste" shingles. The site of Klondike Jessie's cabin of joy was completely obscured by a church towering over the settlement, and adjoining it was the inevitable parochial school. All traces of the post office, once so important to our existence, were effaced, torn down to make way for a squat brick structure, the pride of Rouyn. (Mrs. Dumulon, I have been told, still reigns over the letterboxes. A widow, now, she remains one of the few links to the forgotten past.) Landmarks were not easy to distinguish in the confusion of new construction, but here and there I discovered a few and they were like unexpected friends.

George Watts, the strong-arm boy of Rouyn, once lorded it over his fellows here. And there is Vimy Ridge, if you can recognize the slight elevation among the muck of crowded houses, Vimy, so well named after that never-to-be-forgotten local battle on a Do-minion Day almost twenty-five years ago, when Ken McPhadyen, bloody but victorious, crawled into daylight with the precious Tricolor in his hand. Bill Gamble's poolroom has disappeared, but I identify the spot where it used to be and half expect to see the rotund, jovial proprietor appear from round the corner any moment, "The Prisoner's Song" on his lips. And I can also see "Long Aggie," queen of the sporting girls, stepping from her cabin to muse upon the pristine beauty of a yet-unsullied lake. Behind her is the Rain-bow Kid, hitching his trousers and grinning sheepishly. I think of the time we carried poor drunken Finnegan to his shack while Bill Broach, the pilot, remained by the lake before his engineless air-plane and roundly cursed his erring mechanic. Slim Hallowell, as ready to smile as he was to deal a hand of poker, used to call stakes where sulks that blackened row of shanties, and Archie McCaffery, who loved his native Huntsville so well but vainly, cut capers on the ice in front of Ferguson's Store. Enjoying the performance and smiling hugely is boyish Joe Tower. Jimmy Green, his braces dan-gling, hangs a new and garish sign above his threshold while his brother nods in wonder at his own handiwork. Hallooing from the lake as his canoe nears the shore, Bud Mallory is bursting to tell us fresh news of the outside. Again I see the lights of sputtering Coleman lamps through carelessly open doors and hear the muffled shouts of simple, childish men, in from the bush and happy with their Rouyn town. A parade of ghostly old-timers streams through my vision even as pedestrians elbow me in unashamed eagerness to reach their homes.

Gone, all gone, swallowed by the ravages of time. A wave of sadness comes over me, and there are tears in my eyes as I find myself poignantly longing to see old faces again.

Glossary

Alligator. Stern-wheel steamboat which negotiates land as well as water.
Amalgamation. Recovery of gold from crushed ore by use of mercury.
Andesite. Lava-flow rock type. Also called "greenstone."
Assay. Determination of metallic content of ore, expressed in dollar or percentage value.
Auriferous. Containing gold.
Bannock. Large sourdough pancake used as bread substitute.
Base metals. Other than those of precious variety.
Bay Street. Toronto's financial community.
Belt. Regional surface zone along which mines and prospects occur.
Blanketing. Staking but not recording claims.
Blaze. Cutting long thin section of a tree on both sides as a marker.
Bleb. Small round or elongated inclusions.
Blind pig. Illicit distillery.
Blister. Copper as a smelter product before it is refined.
Boiler room. Office from which telephone calls are made to solicit stock sales.
Bonanza. Rich ore body.
Break. Local shear zone within which mines are found.
Breakup. Spring thaw.
Brecciated. Fragmental rock, often a sign of favorable ore conditions.
Bring in. Develop a mine from prospect stage.
Brûlée. Windfall of dead trees and brush. Also called "slash."
Brunton. Hand compass, named after inventor.
Bucket. Cylindrical steel receptacle used in mine shaft, or winze, before permanent cage is installed.
Bull quartz. Quartz without mineral.
Bullfit bag. Small knapsack.
Bush. The forest.
Bushed. Mental state brought on by protracted stay in woods.
Cache. Hiding place in bush for storing supplies, dynamite, etc.
Calling the market. Quotations of stock on the bid and asked sides when broker is first establishing a new issue.
Carbonate. Rocks high in carbon dioxide, such as limestone, dolomite, etc.
Casing. Steel pipe enclosing diamond drill rods.
Chlorite. Highly altered rock, differing in composition and appearance from original state.

393

Cleanup. Collection of gold in a recovery mill at a given period.

Commercial (ore). Mineralized material currently profitable at prevailing metal prices (see "Economic").

Concentrate. Enriched ore after removal of waste in beneficiation mill.

Concentrator. Milling plant which reduces ore to concentrates.

Conglomerate. Rock consisting of cemented fragments of other rocks.

Crock. Bottle of whisky.

Crosscut. Underground mine passage driven at right angles to ore zone.

Crud. Rush of fear across the heart.

Cursing in work. False affidavit of assessment work on mining claims.

Deadheads. Logs forced into bottom of waterway during timber drives.

Dog. Slang for hopeless property or mining stock.

Doodlebug. Slang for geophysical prospecting device.

Double jacking. Rock drilling by hand performed by two men, one holding the steel bit and the other swinging sledge hammer (see "Single jacking").

Dressing. Developing claims to take them out of "wildcat" class.

Driller. Property being diamond drilled as compared to one undergoing underground development.

Dump. Accumulation of excavated rock at a mine, which may be ore or waste. Term also applied to mill tailings.

Economic (ore). Profitable (see "Commercial").

Eiderdown. Sleeping bag used in cold weather.

Elbow grease. Paddling canoe.

Face. Extremity of underground mine passage.

Fault. A displacement in rock strata, breaking the continuity.

Feed. Ore "fed" to mill.

Ferrous. Containing iron.

Fire! Cry warning that dynamite charge has been fused.

Flux. Mineral used to precipitate smelting process.

Fly dope. Insect repellent containing oil.

Footwall. The underside of vein or lens in relation to dip of ore deposit.

Free gold. Occurrence of gold in its native state (see "Native").

Freezeup. The descent of winter when waterways are frozen.

Fuse. Casing prepared with combustible materials by which dynamite is detonated. "Fusing" is term applied to lighting fuse. Also called "spitting."

Gangue. Waste. Rock associated with ore but having no mineral content or value.

Glory hole. Large open-pit excavation.

Gophering. Digging small holes to locate or extract ore.

Gossan. Oxidized outcrop, rich in iron, having reddish-brown color.

Greenstone. Generalized name given to Pre-Cambrian lavas.

Grubstake. Financing a prospector for an interest in his claim acquisitions.

Handsteel. Short steel bits used in surface rock work largely.

Hangingwall. Upper side of vein or lense in relation to dip of ore deposit.

Headframe. Gallows over shaft to which cable for hoisting cage is attached.

Heading. Underground passage in mine, drift or crosscut, being driven toward a definite objective.

Heads. Material taken from ore in treatment plant and containing the valuable metallic constituents. Opposite of "Tails" (which see).

High grade. Very rich ore, specimen stuff worthy of museums.

High-grading. Purloining high-grade ore which is easily concealed and carried.

Horizon. A zone. Used in a relative sense, as "upper," "lower," etc.

Horse. Large segment of barren rock caught in an ore body.

Hudson Baying. Traveling in a canoe as passenger while others paddle.

Hummingbirds. Mosquitoes.

Hungry. Barren of mineral or geological indications of ore.

Inclusion. Small or large fragment of another rock enclosed in an igneous rock.

Jiggle. Stimulated activity in stock, induced by broker-promoter.

Jump (a claim). Staking or otherwise trying to acquire claims already staked or owned by others.

Jumper. Sled with wooden runners used in summer hauling.

Jumping-off place. Point on railroad nearest prospector's bush objective.

Keewatin. Pre-Cambrian rocks other than the prevalent granites.

Kick. Assay with metal values. Also a geophysical "indication" of ore.

Kicker. Outboard motor.

Kicking out. Wholesale dumping of stock by broker-promoter.

Labrador tea. Shrub growing in barren lands and muskegs.

Laying off. Selling stock to public by promoter after he has exercised low-priced options from mining company.

Level. Underground horizontal mine passage. Levels are cut at regular intervals of 100 feet or more apart.

Long clear. Salt pork.

Loon dung. Silt on lake and river bottoms.

Making a market. Calling stock quotations, purchasing and selling, etc.

Matte. Furnace product derived from ores or concentrates, later refined into final metals by electrolysis.

Mill. Reducing plant where ore is concentrated and/or metals recovered.

Mine. Site of operations where ores and/or metals are excavated.

Mining camp. District wherein mines and developing prospects are located.

Moose pasture. Derisive term applied to mining country which is largely muskeg.

Muck. Rock or ore broken in process of mining. Also used to denote confusion and litter.

Mucker. Man who shovels muck into mine cars. The lowliest underground job.

Mucking. Removing muck. Slang term to denote the act of cleaning up.

Muskeg. Swamp with heavy vegetation.

Native (metal). Occurring as an element. Only a few metals are found in this state, notably gold, silver, platinum, and copper (see "Free Gold").

Nonferrous. Base metals, other than iron.

Ore. Mineral compound containing one or more of the metals that can be extracted and sold at a profit.

Ore shoot. Section of vein or lens within which commercial ore values occur.

Outcrop. Surface exposure of rock or ore.

Outlier. Ore or favorable geology distant from main ore zone of a district.

Outside. The large world of cities beyond the bush.

Overburden. Glacial or alluvial debris deposited upon old surface.

Overriding. Sum added to option prices as payment to agent.

Peneplain. Eroded land areas, close to or at sea level.

Pitchblende. Common ore of uranium and radium.

Portage. Trail between waterways.

Precious (metal). Gold, silver, and platinum. Also called "noble."

Prospect. Nonproducing mining property under development or considered worthy of such attention.

Prove up. Establish economic value of a property.

Pulling the plug. Withdrawal of market support in a given stock by the once-interested broker-promoter.

Raise. Mine passage driven upward.

Rake. Direction of ore below surface. Also called "plunge."

Riding. Voting district.

Rigging. Bidding up the price of a stock to create illusion of favorable property results (see "Jiggle").

Rush. Stampede of prospectors into a new discovery area.

Rutting the dog. Loafing or soldiering on a job.

Shoot (ore). See "Ore shoot."

Showing. Surface occurrence of mineral.

Sleeper. Old property, abandoned, which later is successfully revived.

Slimes. Finely crushed ore in moistened condition. A mill product.

Sporting girl. Prostitute.

Squaw man. White man who marries Indian squaw. Commonly designates any married man.

Stake (n.). A fortune, or a claim post.

Stake (v.). To cut lines in bush by blazing trees, marking posts in prescribed rectangles to designate mining claims.

Steal down. Paying for continuing shaft sinking by finding ore in progress.

Steel. The railroad. Also, drill steel used in various mining and rock-cutting tools.

Stoneboat. Jumper (which see).

Stope. Locus of ore excavation. Extraction process takes many forms, and stoping is a highly developed art.

Strike. A discovery. Also the horizontal direction of rock bedding or ore deposit.

Strip. To remove soil and vegetation covering mineral deposit.

Stull. Timber used to brace the walls of mine openings.

Sump. Reservoir below lowest mine level where water gathers and is pumped to surface.

Tailings. Reject from concentrator, which contains little or no mineral.

Tails. Portion of tailings containing some mineral which cannot be economically removed. This is constantly assayed as it leaves the treatment plant so that recovery can be known and controlled at all times.

Teaser. Prospect with values but no defined ore shoots.

Ticket. Slang. The cost of a mining property or enterprise.

Tight (rock). Without evidence of shearing or mineralization.

Towned. Citified. Used derisively by the prospector.

Track. Railroad. Word used in the same sense as "Steel" (which see).

Tumpline. Wide leather strap attached to packsacks and fitted to reach over carrier's head and rest against his forehead.

Value. Containing some metal as measured by assay.

Wildcat. Mining claim with little or no visible mineral.

Wildcatting. Staking claims for quick sale.

Windfall. "Brûlée" (which see).

Winter road. Stumped right-of-way cut in heart of bush between waterways, passage for vehicles only over high snows of winter.

Winze. Interior mine shaft.

Index

AKLAVIK

THE YUKON

DAWSON

JUNEAU

Coppermine

URANIUM

Fort Norman

MACKENZIE RIVER

Great Bear Lake

YELLOWKNIFE

BARREN LANDS

GREAT SLAVE LAKE

Slave River

URANIUM ATHABASKA

CHU

FLIN FLON

EDMONTON

CALGARY

BRIDGE RIVER

KIMBERLY

VANCOUVER

TRAIL

WINN

250 MILES

SCALE-500 MILES